DEBATING HEALTH CARE ETHICS

FIRST EDITION

DORAN SMOLKIN

Kwantlen Polytechnic University

WARREN BOURGEOIS

Kwantlen Polytechnic University

PATRICK FINDLER

Kwantlen Polytechnic University

McGraw-Hill Ryerson

Connect. Learn. Succeed.

The McGraw-Hill Companies

McGraw-Hill Ryerson
Connect. Learn. Succeed.

Debating Health Care Ethics
First Edition

ISBN-13: 978-0-07-083540-5
ISBN-10: 0-07-083540-3

1 2 3 4 5 6 7 8 9 0 TCP 1 9 8 7 6 5 4 3 2 1 0

Printed and bound in Canada.

Vice-President and Editor-in-Chief: *Joanna Cotton*
Publisher: *Cara Yarzab*
Sponsoring Editor: *Lisa Rahn*
Marketing Manager: *Michele Peach*
Developmental Editors: *Suzanne Simpson Millar and Melanie Berthier*
Supervising Editor: *Kara Stahl*
Editorial Associate: *Marina Seguin*
Copy Editor: *Cy Strom*
Production Coordinator: *Lena Keating*
Cover and Interior Design: *Greg Devitt Design*
Cover Image Credit: *© Odilon Dimier/PhotoAlto Agency RF Collections/Getty Images*
Page Layout: *Laserwords Private Limited*
Printer: *Transcontinental Printing Group*

Library and Archives Canada Cataloguing-in-Publication Data

Smolkin, Doran
    Debating health care ethics/written by Doran Smolkin, Warren Bourgeois, Patrick Findler.
Includes bibliographical references and index.
ISBN 978-0-07-083540-5
    1. Medical ethics—Canada—Textbooks. I. Bourgeois, Warren, 1947-
II. Findler, Patrick III. Title.

R724.S575 2009   174.20971   C2009-902888-3

DEDICATIONS

For Julie.—Doran Smolkin

I dedicate this work to my wife, a compassionate and wise physician and hospital president, whose unflagging efforts on behalf of patients are an inspiration, to my mother for her constant faith in me, and to my sons who keep me focused on making this world a better place.—Warren Bourgeois

For Cara, my wife and best friend, and our children, Cashel and Reese, who always amaze and inspire.—Patrick Findler

ABOUT THE AUTHORS

Doran Smolkin, Ph.D., earned his B.A. at the University of British Columbia, and his M.A. and Ph.D. at the University of Illinois at Chicago. Doran was an Assistant Professor at Kansas State University from 1992 to 1996. Since 1996, he has been a member of the Philosophy Department at Kwantlen Polytechnic University. Doran also teaches regularly in the Philosophy Department at the University of British Columbia. Doran enjoys working with students and he has received several awards in recognition of teaching excellence. His research interests are in moral and political philosophy, with article publications on the nature of trust, the nature of our obligations to future generations, and the ethical obligations of physicians to treat patients with HIV. In addition to his current research in health care ethics, Doran is working on the question of forgiveness. When not doing philosophy, Doran loves to spend time with his wife and kids, and to run in the trails near his home with his two dogs.

Warren Bourgeois, Ph.D., received his B.A. at the University of Toronto and his doctorate at the University of California, Irvine. He has taught at the University of Salzburg, Austria, the University of California, San Diego, and the University of British Columbia. At Kwantlen Polytechnic University he helped develop policies on academic freedom and on research ethics. He chaired the Research Ethics Board through its challenging first five years of development. Among his published writings is the book *Persons: What Philosophers Say about You,* released in its second edition by Wilfrid Laurier University Press in 2003. Since 1977 he has been a director of the BC Civil Liberties Association. He has helped to found and has served on two hospital ethics committees.

Patrick Findler, Ph.D., received his Ph.D., with a specialization in ethics, from the University of California, Davis, in 2001. Patrick joined the Philosophy Department at Kwantlen Polytechnic University in 2002, and has served on Kwantlen's Research Ethics Board for the past several years. Patrick also regularly teaches courses for the Philosophy Departments at the University of British Columbia and Capilano University. His teaching and research interests are in ethics (theoretical and applied) and metaphysics. Current projects include papers addressing both foundational and substantive questions in ethics. In addition to philosophy, Patrick's main interests are his family and bicycles (mountain and road).

CONTENTS IN BRIEF

CONTENTS

PREFACE

Debating Health Care Ethics addresses both traditional and cutting-edge topics in health care ethics, with a special emphasis on issues of particular concern to Canadians. Many textbooks display the results of debates in ethics. This textbook shows *how* the debates are done.

Debating Health Care Ethics provides the tools to examine issues critically and debate topics intelligently. This text provides students with background information about philosophical methods and ethical theories, and then shows how to defend these positions using these theories and methods.

Dramatized case studies on issues followed by a three-way debate by the textbook authors form the major thrust of this book. Positions emerge, are defended, and sometimes are revised or rejected in response to objections. Rather than confronting students with only the complex outcome of long discussion and thought, the text demonstrates *how* philosophical ethics is done.

Students need the tools to examine critically and to debate intelligently various topics in health care ethics. The textbook's structure reflects that goal, beginning with a chapter on **philosophical arguments and methods.** This first chapter serves as a brief introduction for students new to philosophy or as a refresher for more seasoned students.

The second chapter provides a very readable, yet in-depth introduction to the strengths and weakness of major **normative ethical theories.** Understanding the theories can be challenging, so the text attempts to make this material very accessible. At the same time, the book does not gloss over the fact that every ethical theory is the object of serious debate: the authors present some of the most difficult objections confronting each ethical theory, and they suggest ways in which defenders of these theories may respond to these criticisms. In sum, the introduction to normative ethical theory aims to be clear and informative, and to give a sense of where the strengths and weaknesses of each theory are thought to lie, while avoiding the appearance that ethics is just a game of setting up views and knocking them down.

The third chapter, **our philosophical approaches,** briefly explains the particular ethical positions of the three debaters—the authors of this text. In this chapter, we present and defend our own particular brand of three of the ethical theories discussed in Chapter 2: Deontological Pluralism, Contractarianism, and Virtue Ethics. After reading this chapter, students will understand how each of the text authors will approach various ethical issues.

After laying the foundation for argumentation and theory, Chapters 4 through 10 examine important ethical issues in health care. Each of these chapters begins with a brief drama—dialogues among, for example, the patient, family members, and health care providers—which introduces a particular set of moral problems. These dramas will engage readers while bringing certain ethical issues in health care to light. In the debates following the dramas, a philosophical discussion takes place: facts are clarified; questions for debate are identified; and arguments are advanced and critically examined.

The debate format has the advantage of demonstrating to students how philosophy is done. Students see a wide array of ethical theories applied to specific questions; they see arguments from a variety of perspectives carefully developed, criticized, and reformulated; they see how consensus can sometimes be reached, and they see how thoughtful disagreement can remain.

In addition to chapters on philosophical methods, normative ethical theory, and the authors' favoured philosophical approaches, the following ethical issues are examined in this text:

Euthanasia: A drama discussing the film *Million Dollar Baby* motivates this debate on the moral permissibility of voluntary and non-voluntary active euthanasia.

Autonomy and the Right to Refuse Treatment: A drama concerning an elderly patient who insists on being discharged from the hospital even though she is at high risk of choking leads to a philosophical discussion of the concepts of competence, autonomy, and valid consent.

Abortion: A woman named Deb discovers that the fetus she is carrying has Down's syndrome. She has to decide whether to continue with the pregnancy when that means she will lose her family-run business and possibly her marriage. This leads to a debate about the moral permissibility of abortion, in general, and in Deb's case, in particular.

C-Section by Choice: A woman requests a Caesarean section for non-medical reasons. Her physician refuses, but she finds another who is willing to grant her request, even though vaginal delivery is recommended in her case. This leads to a debate about the moral permissibility of Caesarean section for non-medical reasons. What, in general, are the moral obligations of parents to avoid needless risks to themselves, their children, and others?

Two-Tier Health Care: The case of two young hockey players who both need MRIs motivates a discussion on the justice of allowing private MRI in addition to the public health care system's provision of MRI. Under what conditions, if any, is a two-tier health care system just?

Mircroallocation of Scarce Resources: A small-town emergency department must cope with a horrible car accident. There are not enough staff and resources to treat all the patients who need care. This prompts a debate on the morally justified rules for triaging patients in emergency situations

Alternative Medications and Professional Relationships: A woman who received a diagnosis of cancer rejects the standard medical therapy and opts for an unproven alternative therapy. She finds a doctor who is willing to administer this unproven therapy, even though he thinks the standard therapy is a better option. This leads to a debate over how much discretion physicians should have to administer unproven therapies.

Debating Health Care Ethics also includes a number of **pedagogical tools:**

- *Up for Discussion* **questions** encourage readers to participate in the debate in various ways.
- **Definition sidebars** demystify some concepts.
- **Background and Theory sidebars** connect the discussion to everything from current events to great thinkers of the past.
- **Technique sidebars** point out helpful strategies for presenting and critically examining arguments.
- **Key terms** are **bolded** in each chapter and are defined in an end-of-text **Glossary.**

RECOMMENDATIONS FOR USING THIS TEXTBOOK

There are various pathways through this book that an instructor may wish to consider. We recommend that all introductory students read the first chapter to gain some acquaintance with techniques of argument. Ideally, students will then work through the second chapter on ethical theories, and the third chapter where each author's approach to ethics is explained, prior to turning to the debate chapters 4–10. The debate chapters are self-contained and can be read in any order. In a one-semester course, however, especially for students in health professions not used to ethical theory, it may be advisable to skip over Chapter 2 initially. As questions arise, the instructor in such a course may wish to use Chapter 2 as a reference text for students wanting more detail concerning theory.

The debate format of the book lends itself to novel and productive exercises. For example, when assigning a topic in health care ethics, instructors may ask students to write their own debates, using the text as a model. For many students, beginning with a conversation rather than formal prose also has the advantage of being less intimidating and can be more productive of ideas. It helps students produce, in an elementary form, the positions, arguments, objections, and replies that can form the basis of a more formal academic paper. This sort of exercise also avoids the copying and pasting of poorly understood passages from the Internet or other sources. After the instructor returns comments to students on their debates, the instructor may want to ask students to turn their debates into polished position papers.

Another sort of assignment that has worked well when using this material in medical ethics courses is to have students answer specific questions about the drama and debate. For example, on the issue of abortion, the instructor may ask the following questions:

1. Do you think it was morally permissible for Deb to obtain an abortion? Why or why not?
2. Consider an objection to your reasoning.

3. Explain why that objection fails.
4. Consider an argument discussed in the text which you think fails, even though it leads to a similar (or even to the same) conclusion as your favoured argument.
5. Explain why that argument fails.
6. Explain what you take to be the strongest argument for the opposite conclusion to yours.
7. Explain why you think that argument is unsound.
8. What was your view about the permissibility of Deb's abortion immediately after reading the drama, before reading the debate? At that point, what reasons did you have for your view? Has your view or have the reasons for your view changed, and if so, why?

The advantage of using these focused questions is that it requires students to state their own views and arguments; to think critically about their own arguments; to consider other arguments and why they think those arguments fail; and to reflect about how their views and reasons have changed as a result of debate. It is also a relatively straightforward matter to have students transform their answers to these questions into a polished academic paper.

STUDENT RESOURCES

Visit the text's *Online Learning Centre* at **www.mcgrawhill.ca/olc/smolkin** to access the following helpful learning and study tools:

- Leading philosophical articles relevant to the debates in the textbook.
- Four more cases to debate: Removal of Life Support; Mental Health and Confidentiality; Superbugs and the Public's Right to Know; The Ethics of Human Cloning.
- Explanations of how leading ethical theories would approach the above-mentioned cases, as well as relevant background information.
- A mini debate on whether active euthanasia should be legalized.
- References for students to engage in further research.
- Codes of ethics.
- A glossary including new terms used in the *Online Learning Centre* and an annotated bibliography.
- Links to other relevant websites.

INSTRUCTOR RESOURCES

The Online Learning Centre for *Debating Health Care Ethics* at **www.mcgrawhill.ca/olc/smolkin** features learning and study tools, as well as a password-protected Instructor's Site with downloadable supplements, including the complete *Instructor's Manual*.

The *Instructor's Manual* contains:

- Sample syllabi.
- Extended chapter information for discussion.
- Teaching suggestions.
- A case reporting form which the authors use to interact with their students and to increase the relevance of the text to students' lives.

ACKNOWLEDGEMENTS

I want to thank Patrick and Warren for their tireless work on this project. The book could not have been written without them. They have my respect and admiration both as first-rate philosophers and, more importantly, as fine human beings. On a more personal note, I am most grateful to my best friend and wife, Julie, for her love, wisdom, constant support and encouragement. I want to thank my children Mischa, Andy, Kayti, and Elie for their love and encouragement; for making me think and smile and play; and for demonstrating that the future is bright and full of hope. Last, but never least, I am indebted to my mom and dad who have always been there for me.—*Doran Smolkin*

I am grateful to my patient family who saw me through the years of debates, writing, and revision that led to this text. My students and colleagues, too, deserve thanks for their enthusiastic questioning of our positions. Of course my co-authors deserve much gratitude for their persistence, dedication, and insight. I wrote the dramas. They do not reflect the tastes or style of Patrick or Doran, but I am grateful for their comments and those of my nursing students. I must also thank physicians and nurses who looked at these cases with an eye to verisimilitude. Their comments helped to bring the cases presented more in line with reality. Any lack of verisimilitude must, however, be laid at my doorstep.—*Warren Bourgeois*

I am most grateful to my wife, Cara, for her limitless patience, understanding, and support. Our children, Cashel and Reese, deserve special thanks too for their patience, but also for their curiosity and insight, which provide constant reminders of the excitement and value of philosophy. Finally, I would like to thank my colleagues and co-authors, Doran and Warren, for their hard work, perseverance, and friendship.—*Patrick Findler*

Collaboration among three authors brings various challenges to a project. Invariably, disagreements surface, compromise is required, and each author ends up taking on certain roles and responsibilities. There are also great advantages in co-authoring a book. Different points of view make for more interesting reading, arguments are improved because of helpful suggestions made by one's co-authors, and the workload is shared. In our case, there is no doubt that our book is much stronger because it had three authors who each made different, though equally important, intellectual contributions.

We wish to thank Kwantlen Polytechnic University for the Minor Research Grants that gave us much-needed time to do revisions, and the numerous reviewers of this book for their helpful suggestions. We are also grateful to the editorial team at McGraw-Hill Ryerson for their encouragement and support. Special thanks are owed to our sponsoring editor, Lisa Rahn, our developmental editors, Suzanne Simpson Millar and Melanie Berthier, our supervising editor, Kara Stahl, and to our copy editor, Cy Strom.

Lastly, we owe a debt of gratitude to the following reviewers:

Eva Beattie, *St. Clair College*

Leslie Burkholder, *University of British Columbia*

Carolyn Ells, *McGill University*

Ken Ferguson, *University of Ottawa*

Kenneth Kirkwood, *University of Western Ontario*

Arthur Schafer, *University of Manitoba*

Karen Shirley, *Camosun College*

Edrie Sobstyl, *Douglas College*

Jeremy Snyder, *Simon Fraser University*

Duff R. Waring, *York University*

Brian Wetstein, *University of Guelph*

ARGUMENTS AND METHODOLOGY

INTRODUCTION

We should accept philosophical views in general, and moral views in particular, on the basis of the arguments offered in their support. It is therefore crucial to understand what an argument is, and how to evaluate an argument. In this chapter, we explain the kinds of arguments philosophers give, the features of good and bad arguments, and some common tools and methods that will aid in the evaluation of arguments.

LEARNING OBJECTIVES

After completing this chapter, you should be able to:

- Distinguish deductive from inductive arguments
- Define deductive validity and soundness
- Explain inductive strength and weakness
- Describe common fallacies when constructing and evaluating arguments
- Recognize the role of moral principles when constructing moral arguments
- Understand the nature and purpose of thought experiments
- Construct counterexamples to test philosophical analyses and claims

ARGUMENTS

What Is an Argument?

An **argument** is simply a set of at least two claims. One of these is the conclusion, and any other claims are premises. The **conclusion** is the claim that one is trying to prove, and the **premises** are the reasons offered in support of the conclusion. To illustrate, consider the following example:

(1) It is always wrong to kill an innocent person.
(2) Abortion is the killing of an innocent person.
(3) Therefore, abortion is wrong.

The conclusion of this argument is the claim that abortion is wrong. The other two claims are the premises, or supporting reasons. Arguments must have at least one premise, but there is no upper limit to the number of premises an argument can have.

Sometimes the arguments given in support of a position are clearly and explicitly stated. Other times, however, the arguments may be buried in difficult and lengthy passages. In these cases, it will take work to spot the conclusion and supporting premises. Often, certain terms are present that can help you to piece together an author's argument. Philosophers call these terms **premise indicators** and **conclusion indicators.**

Premise indicators include the terms *for, because, since,* and *given that.* Here are a few examples to illustrate how these terms are used in the context of an argument.

> *Because* active euthanasia involves the intentional killing of a person, it is always wrong.
> You should not deceive others, *for* this is disrespectful.
> *Since* abortion is murder, it is wrong.

The following terms are conclusion indicators: *therefore, thus, hence, so,* and *consequently.* Again, here are examples to show how some of these terms are used to signal the conclusion of an argument.

> Active euthanasia involves the intentional killing of a person. *Therefore,* it is always wrong.
> Deceiving others is disrespectful, *so* you should not deceive others.
> Abortion is murder; *thus* it is wrong.

In some instances, arguments may be given without the use of premise or conclusion indicators. Determining the structure of an argument in such cases can be tricky. You have to ask yourself what *role* each sentence is playing in the passage. If a particular sentence expresses the point the author is trying to prove, then it is the author's conclusion. If a sentence is given as support for some other claim, then it is a premise. Still other sentences in the passage may not play a direct role in the argument, and these would be neither the premises nor the conclusion.

Upon finding a passage in a text that contains an argument, it is often helpful to rewrite it in what is known as **standard form.** In standard form, each premise is numbered and stated on its own line, and then the conclusion is stated last. Usually, the conclusion is separated from the premises by a horizontal line, with the premises above the line and the conclusion below it. To illustrate, consider the following argument:

> Abortion is morally permissible, for it is morally permissible for women to make their own decisions when it comes to controlling their own bodies, and abortion is a decision that involves women and their own bodies.

We can rewrite the argument in standard form as follows:

(1) It is morally permissible for women to make their own decisions when it comes to controlling their own bodies.
(2) Abortion is a decision that involves a woman and her own body.
_____
(3) Therefore, abortion is morally permissible.

There are numerous advantages in writing out an argument in standard form—not the least of which is that it makes the argument clearer and thus easier to evaluate.

Evaluating Arguments

The point of providing an argument in support of a view is typically to show that the view is correct and to persuade others to accept it.[1] Good arguments—ones we should accept—have two features. First, all of the premises are true. And second, the premises logically support the conclusion. Thus, when evaluating arguments, we need to ask two basic questions. First, are all of the premises true? Second, do the premises support the conclusion? If the answer to *both* of these questions is "yes," then the argument is a good one and we have good reason to accept its conclusion. If, however, the answer to *either* question (or both) is "no," then the argument is bad and we do not have good reason to accept its conclusion. Notice, then, that an argument might fail for one of two reasons: it might have a false premise, or it might have premises that do not support the conclusion. (Of course, an argument might have both of these problems.)

It is important to recognize that whether the premises are true, and whether the premises support the conclusion, are logically distinct issues. Consider the following example:

(1) All patients have cancer.
(2) All cancer patients have appendicitis.
_____
(3) Therefore, all patients have appendicitis.

_____
[1] Arguments can, of course, have different purposes. For example, in science, arguments can be used to deduce predictions from general principles and observations.

This, of course, is a bad argument. What makes it bad is not that the premises fail to support the conclusion. In this example, the premises very strongly support the conclusion. If the premises were true, the conclusion would have to be true.[2] The problem with this argument is that the premises are not true. Now consider an argument with the opposite problem:

(1) Some Canadians have cancer.
(2) Some Americans have arthritis.
(3) Therefore, a broken leg is painful.

This, too, is a bad argument. But what makes this argument bad is not that the premises are false. Rather, the problem with this argument is that the premises do not logically support the conclusion. Acceptance of the premises does not give us any reason to accept the conclusion. Even though the premises are true, the conclusion still *could be* false. It is important, then, not to assume that the conclusion of an argument is true simply because the premises are true. The premises must also logically support the conclusion.

Deductive Arguments: Validity and Soundness

A **deductive argument** is an argument where the truth of the premises is intended to *guarantee* the truth of the conclusion. For example, the following is likely offered as a deductive argument:

(1) It is seriously immoral to deprive an individual of a future of value.
(2) Abortion, in standard cases, deprives the fetus of a future of value.
(3) Therefore, in standard cases, abortion is seriously immoral.

When evaluating deductive arguments, there are certain technical terms that philosophers commonly use. In particular, philosophers use the terms **valid** and **sound** to refer to properties that deductive arguments can have or lack. A deductively valid argument (or for simplicity's sake, a valid argument) is an argument with the following feature: It is *impossible* for all of the premises to be true and the conclusion false. Put a little differently, *if* all of the premises are true, the conclusion must be true. To illustrate, let's return to an example considered earlier:

(1) All patients have cancer.
(2) All cancer patients have appendicitis.
(3) Therefore, all patients have appendicitis.

Here's another example:

(1) No Canadian is an American
(2) Wayne Gretzky is a Canadian.
(3) Therefore, Wayne Gretzky is not an American.

---

[2] Arguments that have this feature are said to be *valid*. We discuss the concept of validity in the following section.

Notice that in each of these examples, *if* the premises were true, the conclusion would have to be true. The truth of the premises *logically guarantees* the truth of the conclusion. Hence, these are valid arguments.

It is very important to note that valid arguments need not have true premises. In saying that an argument is valid, we are not claiming that the premises are true. We are claiming, rather, that the premises, *if true,* guarantee that the conclusion is true. In other words, to say that an argument is valid is to say something about the *logical relationship* between the argument's premises and its conclusion: the relationship is such that if the premises are true, then the conclusion must be true. Deductive arguments that do not have this property are said to be **invalid.**

UP FOR DISCUSSION

Can a valid argument have false premises and a true conclusion? Explain your answer using an example.

A sound argument is a valid argument with all true premises. A virtue of sound arguments is that they always have true conclusions.[3] Notice that this is guaranteed by the definition of a sound argument. Here is a simple example of a sound argument:

(1) If mercy killing was illegal in Canada in 1993, then Robert Latimer broke the law when he committed the mercy killing of his daughter, Tracy.
(2) Mercy killing was illegal in Canada in 1993.
(3) Therefore, Robert Latimer broke the law when he committed the mercy killing of his daughter, Tracy.

This is a valid argument: if the premises are true, the conclusion must be true. The premises, moreover, are in fact true. Hence, this argument is sound.

An **unsound** argument is a deductive argument that is either invalid or has at least one false premise. Unsound arguments are therefore bad arguments. They are bad because if an argument is unsound, it has failed to establish the truth of its conclusion. Note, however, that this is not to say that the conclusions of unsound arguments must be false. To illustrate, here is an example of an unsound argument with a true conclusion:

(1) Everyone who goes to a private clinic is terminally ill.
(2) Some Canadians go to private clinics.
(3) Therefore, some Canadians are terminally ill.

Here we have an unsound argument with a true conclusion. The argument is unsound because premise (1) is false. Thus, when we claim that an argument is unsound, we are not saying that its conclusion is false. Rather, we are saying that its conclusion should not be accepted on the basis of this argument. Either the argument is invalid, so the premises do not logically support the conclusion, or at least one premise is false, so the argument does not necessarily lead us to the truth.

---

[3] Notice, however, that not all sound arguments are informative or useful. Circular arguments, for instance, may be sound, but not informative or useful. Here's an example of a sound circular argument: Cancer is sometimes fatal. Therefore, cancer is sometimes fatal.

Inductive Arguments

Not all arguments are intended to be deductive arguments. In some arguments, the premises, if true, may not be intended to *guarantee* the truth of the conclusion. Instead, the premises provided may be intended to demonstrate only that the conclusion is *probably* true. In that case, the argument is **inductive.** Here is an example of this kind of argument:

(1) Most healthy pregnancies at 24 weeks result in successful births.
(2) Tina has a healthy pregnancy at 24 weeks.
(3) Therefore, Tina's pregnancy will result in a successful birth.

Now, the fact that healthy pregnancies at 24 weeks generally result in successful births does not guarantee or conclusively prove that Tina's pregnancy will result in a successful birth. That is, it is *possible* that the conclusion is false, even if the premises are true. However, if the premises of the argument are true, they certainly do provide some support for the conclusion. This support is not, however, the kind of support we talked about earlier when we looked at valid arguments. The premises just make the conclusion more probable.

When it comes to evaluating inductive arguments, philosophers do not use the terms *valid/invalid* and *sound/unsound;* instead, they speak of inductive arguments as being either **strong** or **weak.** A strong inductive argument is an argument which is not deductive, and where the premises, if true, make the conclusion probably true. The more support provided by the premises of an inductive argument, the stronger the argument. Here is an example of an inductively strong argument:

(1) Dr. Badesh will see 100 flu sufferers this year.
(2) Dr. Badesh has treated 99 flu sufferers this year with antibiotics.
(3) Therefore, Dr. Badesh will treat all of the flu sufferers he sees this year with antibiotics.

This is a strong inductive argument, because if the premises are true, it is likely that the conclusion is true.[4]

An inductive argument is weak when the premises, if true, provide little support for the conclusion. Here is an example of an inductively weak argument:

(1) Dr. Badesh will see 100 flu sufferers this year.
(2) Dr. Badesh has treated 1 flu sufferer this year with antibiotics.
(3) Therefore, Dr. Badesh will treat all of the flu sufferers he sees this year with antibiotics.

---

[4] When we say this is a strong argument, we do so against typical background assumptions like these: Dr. Badesh is not likely to suddenly change his treatment preferences, and one case of the flu is much like the others. Of course there might be an unexpected difference in case number 100, but the very fact that a difference is unexpected attests to our thinking the argument is strong. The argument could be much stronger if we made all the background assumptions explicit.

What makes this an inductively weak argument, of course, is that the premises, if true, do not make the conclusion probable or likely to be true. In this instance, the argument commits the familiar error of generalizing from a single case. As the saying goes, one swallow does not make a summer. We should not infer conclusions from too little evidence.

Moral Arguments

What we call a **moral argument** is an argument in support of a **substantive moral claim**—that is, a claim about the moral status of acts, policies, persons, and so forth. The following, for instance, are examples of substantive moral claims: Euthanasia is morally permissible; progressive taxation is unjust; an unrepentant serial murderer is evil. In the next chapter, we examine several influential normative ethical theories. One of the principal aims of these theories, we shall see, is to provide correct, general principles that tell us what makes actions (policies, and so forth) right and wrong, and persons good and bad. As we'll now explain, these principles can play an important role in arguing for substantive moral conclusions.

Consider the following simple argument:

(1) Active euthanasia minimizes overall suffering.
(2) Therefore, active euthanasia is morally right.

Notice that this argument is invalid: the premise, if true, does not guarantee the truth of the conclusion. Although active euthanasia may well minimize overall suffering, it does not logically follow that it is right. But now consider the following moral principle:

Any act that minimizes overall suffering is morally right.

This principle tells us that minimizing overall suffering is a "right-making" feature of actions; any action that has this feature is morally right. With this principle in hand, we can now construct a deductively valid argument for our conclusion:

(1) *Any act that minimizes overall suffering is morally right.*
(2) Active euthanasia minimizes overall suffering.
(3) Therefore, active euthanasia is morally right.

Notice the structure of this argument. Premise (1) tells us that any act that has a certain property is morally right. Premise (2) tells us that a particular act has this property. We can therefore validly conclude that the act in question is morally right. In this way, moral principles can be combined with relevant factual premises to construct deductively valid arguments in support of substantive moral claims.

Although we have been focusing on the role of moral principles in the construction of deductively valid moral arguments, it is worth noting that our comments about the interplay between moral principles and relevant factual claims apply also in the case of inductive arguments. Consider, for example, the following argument:

(1) Usually, but not always, acts of dishonesty are wrong.
(2) By withholding relevant information, Dr. Badesh acted dishonestly toward his patient.

(3) Therefore, it was wrong for Dr. Badesh to withhold relevant information from his patient.

This argument is inductive. The premises, if true, are not intended to guarantee that the conclusion is true. Rather, the premises provided are intended only to make the conclusion probably true. Still, the omission of either the moral principle or the relevant factual claim would significantly weaken the argument.

In summary, the general moral principles provided by normative ethical theories can play an important role in arguing for substantive moral claims. As explained above, the moral principles, when combined with relevant factual claims, can be used to construct deductively valid or inductively strong arguments for substantive moral views. We critically examine the moral principles offered by leading normative ethical theories in the next chapter. First, however, we consider some useful methods for evaluating moral principles in particular, and philosophical claims in general. We also consider common fallacies to avoid when constructing and evaluating arguments.

UP FOR DISCUSSION

Consider the following argument: Homosexuality is unnatural; therefore, homosexuality is wrong. What is the missing premise?

PHILOSOPHICAL METHODOLOGY— COUNTEREXAMPLES AND THOUGHT EXPERIMENTS

We mentioned earlier that philosophical views should be accepted or rejected on the basis of the arguments offered in their support. If you disagree with an author's position on some issue, then you must believe that the author's argument for that view is unsound or weak. So you must believe either that the premises fail to adequately support the conclusion or that at least one premise is false. Let's now consider methods employed by philosophers to show that a philosophical claim is false, or that the premises do not adequately support the conclusion.

To evaluate or test philosophical claims and arguments, philosophers often employ *counterexamples* and *thought experiments*. A **counterexample** is just that—an example that counters a given claim or argument. A **thought experiment** is a kind of mental experiment one performs through an exercise of imagination. Thought experiments are a very useful way to generate counterexamples. To illustrate these methods, let's return to an argument discussed earlier:

(1) Any act that minimizes overall suffering is morally right.
(2) Active euthanasia minimizes overall suffering.
(3) Therefore, active euthanasia is morally right.

We noted earlier that this argument is valid. If you disagree with the conclusion, you must therefore show that at least one of the premises of this argument is false.[5] The first premise expresses the moral principle that any act that minimizes overall suffering is morally right. But is that true? A good way to test this claim is to see whether we can find a counterexample to it. That is, we want to see whether can find an instance of an act that minimizes overall suffering yet is not right. Engaging in a thought experiment will help us to discover possible counterexamples. The task here is to see if we can *imagine* a situation in which an act that minimizes overall suffering is not right. With a little thought, it seems that we can in fact imagine many such situations. The following paragraph presents one example.[6]

Suppose a boy from the neighbourhood knocks on my door one Saturday morning and offers to mow my lawn for $20. My lawn needs mowing, and I'm too busy to take care of it myself, so I agree. An hour later the boy knocks on my door again to collect his money. I inspect the lawn and see that he has done a very nice job. As I reach for my wallet to pay the boy, it occurs to me that I could minimize overall suffering by donating the $20 I promised to pay him to a local charity. Let's suppose that I'm right: breaking my promise to pay the boy and donating the money to a local charity really would minimize overall suffering. In that case, premise (1) implies that breaking my promise is the morally right thing to do. But our common-sense moral beliefs suggest that this is not the right thing to do. And so we seem to have a counterexample to (1); we have an example of an action that minimizes overall suffering, yet does not appear to be morally right.

This counterexample provides us with good reason for thinking that (1) is false, and that the above argument is

UP FOR DISCUSSION

Can you think of another counterexample to the claim that "any act that minimizes suffering is morally right"?

---

[5] One could attack this argument by criticizing either premise (1) or (2). Since our present concern is to explain how to test philosophical claims in general, and moral principles in particular, we focus our attention on criticizing premise (1), and the moral principle that it contains. Premise (2) does not contain a moral claim. It simply says that active euthanasia minimizes overall suffering. Whether this is in fact true is an empirical matter, and can be evaluated through ordinary empirical methods.

[6] This example is based on an objection raised by Will Kymlicka in his *Contemporary Political Philosophy: An Introduction,* 2nd ed. (Oxford: Oxford University Press, 2006), 24.

therefore unsound. But remember, it doesn't follow from this that the conclusion of the argument—that active euthanasia is permissible—is false.

One might wonder why this counterexample provides good reason for thinking that the moral principle in question is false. After all, we seem to have done little more than show that the moral principle in question conflicts with what you and I happen to *believe* is the right thing to do in the example described. Perhaps, though, the principle is correct, and it is our belief about what's right that is mistaken. The more general question here is how the use of counterexamples can show that any moral principle or theory is false, if the counterexamples are simply based on our commonsense moral beliefs. There is a great deal to be said about this topic that we cannot address here. We shall have to limit ourselves to a brief discussion of the concept of **reflective equilibrium.** This will help to shed some light on the legitimacy of thought experiments and counterexamples when evaluating moral principles and theories.

Reflective equilibrium, in the context of moral philosophy, is the end point of a process of moral deliberation that involves going back and forth between moral principles and what they imply about specific cases. The ultimate goal of this process is to attain a state of coherence or consistency between the moral principles we accept and our considered moral beliefs. We have achieved reflective equilibrium when we have achieved this state of consistency. The basic process goes like this. If a principle or theory has implications that conflict with our moral beliefs, and we have a high degree of confidence in our moral beliefs, then we may reject or revise the principle until we find one that matches our beliefs. However, if a principle conflicts with our moral beliefs, but we lack confidence in these beliefs, then we may want to revise or reject our beliefs to achieve a state of consistency.

To illustrate, let's return to the principle considered above: *Any act that minimizes overall suffering is morally right.* We want to know whether this principle is correct and deserves our acceptance. So we then consider what this principle implies in specific cases. We saw earlier that this principle implies that it would be morally right to refuse to pay the boy who mowed your lawn and to give the money to a charity instead, for this would minimize overall suffering. Upon reflection, however, most of us believe that it would be wrong to give the money to the charity if that meant breaking the promise to pay the boy. That is our considered belief or judgment about this case. Since we have a high degree of confidence in this judgment—more confidence that this judgment is correct than that the principle is correct—we should revise or reject the principle in question, and seek another that is consistent with our judgment. If we lacked confidence in this judgment, however, then we might want to seek consistency by revising or rejecting the judgment. The goal, again, is to attain a consistent fit between our moral principles and moral judgments about cases. And the fact that the moral principles we accept are in equilibrium with our considered moral judgments confers justification on both the principles and the beliefs.[7]

One final point about thought experiments is in order before we turn our attention to fallacies. Thought experiments often involve unusual and unrealistic situations. But it is important to see the relevance of these examples. The force of the counterexample described does not depend on whether the imagined example would ever actually happen, or whether it involves a situation we might actually find ourselves in. The only constraint is that the imagined situation is one that is logically (or conceptually) possible. Notice that (1) asserts that *any* act that minimizes overall suffering is morally right. Given this, it is perfectly legitimate to test this claim by imagining situations that may or may not be very realistic. It is very important to bear this point in mind as you read the debates, for you'll sometimes encounter strange counterexamples and thought experiments that are used to test the authors' (and others') moral views.

> **TECHNIQUE**
>
> As a matter of argumentative strategy, it is sometimes wise to make your counterexamples as realistic as possible. People are sometimes distracted and confused by fanciful fictional counterexamples, and thus fail to see their relevance.

COMMON FALLACIES

A **fallacy** is a mistake in reasoning. There are many different kinds of fallacies, but we focus here only on a few of the more common errors in reasoning. We begin with some fallacies that occur in developing arguments, and then turn to some fallacies involving the misuse of language, and finally consider some mistakes in reasoning that occur when people criticize arguments.[8]

Circularity (a.k.a. Begging the Question)

A **circular argument** is one in which the truth of the conclusion is presupposed by one or more premises.[9] The most blatant form of circularity occurs when

---

[7] The method of testing moral principles against our considered beliefs is one that is both common and widely accepted among moral philosophers. We recognize, however, that there is some controversy about this method and about "coherence" accounts of justification, but discussion of this controversy is well beyond the scope of this book. For an excellent discussion of reflective equilibrium, see the *Stanford Encyclopedia of Philosophy,* http://plato.stanford.edu/entries/reflective-equilibrium/.

[8] For a more thorough discussion of fallacies, see the entry on fallacies in the *Internet Encyclopedia of Philosophy,* http://www.iep.utm.edu/f/fallacy.htm.

[9] An argument like "It is raining; therefore, it is raining," is clearly circular. Note that it nonetheless fits our earlier definition of an argument: "An argument is simply a set of at least two claims. One of these is the conclusion, and any other claims are premises." There is no requirement in the definition that the premises all be distinct from the conclusion. In fact, circular arguments, though rarely useful, are even valid, for it is not possible for their premises to be true while the conclusion is false.

THEORY

It is rather difficult to state the problem of circularity in precise terms, because all valid arguments are circular in the sense that the conclusion is logically "contained" in the premises. Yet we certainly don't want to say that all valid arguments are fallacious. So why is circularity a problem in some cases, but not others? To answer this question, it may help to consider a common reason for giving an argument. The point is often to convince others that your conclusion is correct. It will not help to convince others that your conclusion is correct, however, if you appeal to the conclusion to help establish it. Circularity is a problem, then, when the conclusion you are arguing for appears as one of your premises, or is offered as a reason for accepting one of your premises, and you intend to convince someone of the conclusion.

the conclusion you are arguing for appears as a premise in your argument. Consider, for instance, the following argument:

(1) Abortion is wrong.
(2) Therefore, abortion is wrong.

There are, however, less obvious cases of circularity, as illustrated by this example:

(1) Abortion is murder.
(2) Therefore, abortion is wrong.

This second example is simply a disguised version of the conclusion, for "murder" simply means "wrongful killing." To make this point explicit, the argument could be more clearly expressed as follows:

(1) Abortion is wrong.
(2) Abortion is killing.
(3) Therefore, abortion is wrong.

The circle in the argument is now apparent. The problem with the circle is that we would not accept the premises of this argument unless we already accepted the conclusion. So if you are in doubt whether abortion is wrong, this argument will do little to persuade you that it is wrong. Although circular arguments are generally uninformative and unpersuasive, notice that they are valid and may be sound.

UP FOR DISCUSSION

Is the following argument guilty of circularity? Explain your answer.

(1) The Bible is the inerrant word of God.
(2) The Bible says that God exists.
(3) Therefore, God exists.

False Dilemma

Presenting fewer options than are actually available when arguing for a view is known as the **false dilemma** fallacy. When attempting to garner support for his "war on terror," for instance, former US President George W. Bush (in)famously claimed: "Every nation, in every region, now has a decision to make. Either you are with us, or you are with the terrorists."[10] Faced with just these two options, there is little choice except to side with the United States. However, President Bush is guilty of presenting a false dilemma. There were (and are), in fact, a number of positions nations can take aside from supporting President Bush's "war on terror" or the terrorists themselves.

---

[10] As reported by CNN, 6 November 2001, http://archives.cnn.com/2001/US/11/06/gen.attack.on.terror/ (accessed 10 May 2009).

Equivocation

There are a host of fallacies involving the manipulation of language in order to attempt to support a conclusion. We will consider two of the more common of these, beginning with the fallacy of **equivocation.**

An example of the fallacy or equivocation is the following:

(1) All humans have a right to life.
(2) My appendix is human.
(3) Therefore, my appendix has a right to life.

This argument is clearly invalid. The problem is that the word *human* is ambiguous—that is, it has more than one meaning. It can mean a biological classification (membership in the species *Homo sapiens*), and it can refer to having moral status. Once this is realized, the fallacy of equivocation becomes apparent. The term *human* is most clearly used to refer to moral status in the first premise, and to biological status in the second premise. Once this is noted, we can rewrite the argument without the ambiguous term, and the invalidity of the argument reveals itself.

(1) It is wrong to kill those with moral status.
(2) My appendix is biologically human.
(3) Therefore, it is wrong to kill my appendix.

Now that the premises are clarified, we see that even if they are true, they fail to prove the conclusion. As critical thinkers who are searching for the truth, we need to try to spot equivocation. And we need to try to avoid falling into the trap of committing this mistake when developing our own arguments.

Appeal to Emotion

Another fallacy involving the misuse of language is the **appeal to emotion** in order to argue for some claim. Claiming that euthanasia and abortion ought to be opposed because they're murderous would be an instance of using inflammatory language in order to make one's point. Of course, such claims not only beg the question, but they also are often advanced so as to get the reader or listener to accept the conclusion without having to think carefully about the issues involved.

Straw Man

The **straw man** fallacy is the fallacy of misrepresenting your opponent's argument so that it is easily shown to be unsound or weak. The fallacy is so named because a straw man argument is easily blown down. Suppose, for instance, that a philosopher offers the following argument in support of euthanasia:

(1) If competent, seriously disabled adults express a preference to die, then they should be permitted to die.
(2) Some competent, seriously disabled adults do in fact express a preference to die.
(3) Therefore, some competent, seriously disabled adults should be permitted to die.

Now, suppose a critic objects as follows: "My opponent is claiming that we should euthanize all disabled persons, since all disabled persons desire to die. But it is not true that all disabled people want to die. So my opponent's argument is clearly unsound." This critic would be guilty of the straw man fallacy, since he has misrepresented his opponent's view to make it easier to refute. His opponent's actual position is much more subtle and less easily refuted than the argument attributed to him.

Ad Hominem

Ad hominem is a Latin expression that means "against the man." One commits the ***ad hominem*** fallacy when one tries to refute an argument by attacking the one who offered the argument. For example, suppose that a leader of an evangelical church presented the following argument in support of his "pro-life" position on abortion:

(1) All human lives are sacred.
(2) Fetuses are human.
(3) Therefore, fetuses' lives are sacred.

Now, imagine that a critic objects as follows: "We can safely reject this argument, since it is being advocated by a religious extremist who believes all sorts of crazy things!" This critic would be guilty of committing the *ad hominem* fallacy, since he attempts to refute his opponent's argument by attacking his opponent. The only way to show that an argument fails is to show that there is a problem with the argument itself.

CONCLUSION

There are, of course, many other fallacies that we cannot explain here. What counts as a fallacy depends, moreover, on the context in which an argument is offered and the intentions of the person offering it. A full discussion would be very complex. The general point is that moral philosophy—indeed, philosophy in general—is first and foremost a matter of searching for the truth through the careful use of reason. We want to discover the truth by fairly and carefully considering the arguments on all sides of an issue. Doing philosophy therefore requires a sense of fairness, as well as a sharp, critical, and open mind. We want to arrive at the truth, but we should accept a claim as true only if we are reasonably confident that it is supported by a good argument.

Review Questions

1. What are the two features of a good argument?
2. What is a valid argument?
3. Construct your own example of a valid argument.
4. What is a sound argument?
5. What is an inductive argument?
6. What makes an inductive argument strong?
7. What is a moral argument?
8. What is a counterexample?
9. Describe an example that counters the following claim: Killing human beings is always wrong.
10. What is reflective equilibrium?
11. Explain the fallacy of circularity.
12. Explain the straw man fallacy.
13. Explain the fallacy of equivocation.
14. Explain the fallacy of appeal to emotion.
15. Explain the *ad hominem* fallacy.
16. Explain the false dilemma fallacy.

WWW.MCGRAWHILL.CA/OLC/SMOLKIN

CHAPTER 2

PHILOSOPHICAL ETHICS: AN INTRODUCTION

INTRODUCTION

This book explores some key issues in health care ethics. Health care ethics is a topic within the broader field of normative ethics. Normative ethics is concerned, in large part, with general theoretical questions such as what makes acts morally right or wrong; what states of affairs are desirable or undesirable; what constitutes a good life for the person who leads it; which character traits are virtuous and which are vicious; and, most generally, how one ought to live. Philosophers have developed a number of normative ethical theories in an effort to address these questions. The principal goal of this chapter is to introduce students to some of the most important and influential ethical theories, and to explain their major strengths and weaknesses. A grasp of these ethical theories is helpful, if not essential, for thinking about moral problems that arise in health care.

LEARNING OBJECTIVES

After completing this chapter, you should be able to:

- Distinguish between metaethics, normative ethics, and descriptive ethics
- Explain ethical relativism and its problems
- Define classical act utilitarianism, explain objections to it, and utilitarian responses to those objections
- Describe Kant's distinction between an action's having moral worth and an action's being morally right
- Understand and apply the universal law version and the humanity version of Kant's categorical imperative
- Outline the main strengths and weaknesses of Kant's moral theory
- Describe W. D. Ross's distinction between *prima facie* duties and duties, all things considered
- Explain Ross's moral theory, and explain its strengths and weaknesses
- Define what justifies moral rules according to social contract theory
- Explain why John Rawls's theory of justice is called *justice as fairness*
- Outline the strengths and weaknesses of Rawls's theory, and of social contract theories in general
- Recognize how virtue ethics differs from other approaches to ethics
- Describe Aristotle's concept of moral virtue and his doctrine of the mean
- Identify the strengths and weaknesses of virtue ethics
- Explain the ethics of care, and how it differs from other normative ethical theories
- Point out the strengths and weaknesses of the ethics of care

THREE TYPES OF ETHICAL INQUIRY

We begin by explaining **normative ethics** and distinguishing it from **descriptive ethics** and **metaethics.**[1] As suggested above, normative ethics addresses general theoretical questions about what sorts of things matter, morally speaking. When

---

[1] Some philosophers distinguish between the meanings of the terms *ethics* and *morality*. However, for the sake of simplicity, we use these terms interchangeably.

considering whether an act is right or wrong, for example, should we look only at its consequences? Or are other things important—for example, a person's motives? But normative ethics is also concerned with practical or applied issues. Here the concern is to try to resolve concrete moral problems, such as whether mercy killing is sometimes morally permissible, whether cloning is immoral, and what obligations people have to non-human animals and the environment. What is distinctive about normative ethics is that it is *prescriptive:* it is concerned with what ought to be, not with what is the case. Thus, to say that **health care ethics** is an area of inquiry within normative ethics, or more narrowly, within **practical ethics,** is to say that it is concerned with how one ought to act, the character traits one ought to develop, the policies that ought to be adopted, and so forth, when dealing with ethical problems that arise in and around the practice of health.[2]

It is helpful to distinguish normative ethics from descriptive ethics. Descriptive ethics is concerned with the examination of a given population's beliefs about a particular moral issue. For example, we might ask: "What percentage of the Canadian population believes that mercy killing is sometimes morally acceptable?" Descriptive ethics seeks to describe what is the case; for instance, it seeks to describe what people actually believe about particular moral issues. Descriptive ethics also is concerned with questions of why people believe what they believe about ethics, and how they come to hold their particular moral beliefs and attitudes. Comparisons between different cultures' moral beliefs, and questions of what people in the past have believed about various ethical issues, are also questions that belong to descriptive ethics. So, while descriptive ethics is a rich and interesting area of inquiry, it is an area that properly belongs to the social sciences: careful empirical investigation is the key to doing descriptive ethics well.

But since normative ethics is essentially prescriptive, it differs importantly from descriptive ethics. Thus, for example, in doing health care ethics we want to know what Canadians (or people, in general) *should* think about the moral acceptability of mercy killing, and we are much less concerned about what people happen to think. Here there is the recognition that people's actual moral beliefs and society's laws, policies, and professional ethical codes can be mistaken (recall that prevailing moral beliefs, and many of society's laws and policies, used to favour whites over non-whites, men over women, and so forth), and we attempt to move toward moral beliefs, laws, policies and ethical codes that are justified.[3]

---

[2] Philosophers sometimes carve up the moral terrain differently than we have done here. For these philosophers, normative ethics is described as focusing only on the kinds of general theoretical questions outlined above, while practical or applied ethics is described as a separate area of inquiry that focuses on specific moral problems. We prefer to describe practical/applied ethics as a branch of normative ethics in order to emphasize the normative (prescriptive) focus of practical/applied ethics.

[3] Of course, those who work in normative ethics may be concerned with descriptive matters like the content of established ethical codes of conduct, insofar as some may argue that people ought to act in accordance with these ethical codes. In these cases, however, what is being examined is the acceptability of the normative claim that people ought to follow established ethical codes.

While descriptive ethics requires careful empirical study, the key to doing normative ethics well is good reasoning.[4] That is, normative ethics is a matter of rational investigation. To be sure, this requires an awareness of the relevant facts, but it also requires the defence of various moral principles and careful argumentation from these moral principles and the relevant facts to conclusions about what ought to be done.

One of the most important steps in arguing for one's position in normative ethics is to begin by clearly identifying the facts of the case, and then clearly defining the key concepts one is investigating. For instance, if we want to determine whether mercy killing is always morally wrong, we will need to determine first what "mercy killing" involves. Does the person have to be suffering in order for it to be a case of *mercy* killing? Is it mercy *killing* to remove a breathing tube from a moribund patient, or to withhold food or hydration, or does *killing* require more direct measures, like a bullet to the head or an injection of potassium chloride? Does mercy killing require the intent to kill, or is it also mercy killing when one merely foresees that a certain treatment may lead to death, as when one administers large doses of morphine to a patient intending to relieve distress but foreseeing (not intending) that this could result in the patient's demise? Obviously, defining the concept one is debating can be a tricky matter, but it is terribly important to get it as clear as one can so that one knows exactly what one is investigating.

Also, when thinking about issues in normative ethics, it is very important to clarify relevant facts. For instance, on the topic of mercy killing, we will presumably need to know whether it can be safely practised: Can we actually determine when a patient's life is no longer worth living, and that a patient who consents to mercy killing is freely consenting and not merely consenting out of depression? We may also want to consider what the likely effect on the physician-patient relationship will be if mercy killing is accepted (or rejected) as morally permissible. Identifying which considerations are relevant for a given moral issue and determining where the facts lie are difficult matters, yet they are crucial if one is to make correct moral judgments.

Finally, once the relevant facts are identified and key terms defined, the next step is to consider whether the act in question is supported (or opposed) by moral principles or moral considerations that we are willing to accept after careful reflection. For instance, we might propose the moral principle that a person should be free to do what she chooses provided that she does not violate others' rights, and provided that she is competent to make her own decisions. We might then argue that mercy killing can be freely chosen by competent persons without violating anyone's rights, and therefore, mercy killing is morally acceptable in these situations. Alternatively, we might put forward the moral principle that it is morally wrong to intentionally kill innocent persons, and since mercy killing involves killing innocent people, it is morally

---

[4] For a more detailed discussion of sound philosophical reasoning, see Chapter 1.

wrong. We then need to examine each of these arguments, and any others that can be brought to bear on this topic, to see whether they are (deductively) sound or (inductively) strong. There is no mechanical method for determining whether a given argument is sound or strong; instead, we have to carefully examine each premise (both the factual claims and the moral principles) and consider whether it is true or vulnerable to criticism. We also have to consider the logical structure of the argument to determine whether the premises, taken together, actually support the conclusion. If a flaw can be identified either in one (or more) of the premises, or in the logic of the argument, then we ought to reject the argument as rationally unpersuasive.

The process of developing, examining, and revising arguments is at the heart of normative ethics, health care ethics, and indeed, all substantive areas of philosophy—it requires creativity, a sharp critical mind, and a sense of fairness. The goal is to find the best arguments on a particular topic and to understand why rival arguments fail. On occasion, on truly difficult issues, one may be unable to tell which argument is best—they may all appear problematic, or there may be opposing arguments that look equally good. In such cases, the appropriate thing to do is to admit that one does not know what to think. Even in hard cases such as these, the investigation itself can be fruitful: for at a minimum, one will better understand the debate around a moral issue—the arguments pro and con, their strengths and their weaknesses—and why the issue is so difficult.

Finally, normative ethics should also be distinguished from metaethics. Metaethics concerns the rational investigation into the nature of morality. Here, the focus is on questions *about* morality, rather than questions *within* morality, such as "Are moral judgments capable of being true or false?" and "What are the meanings of moral terms?" For instance, one might ask, "What does it mean to say that something is morally wrong or that something is morally right?" Is this merely a report about the speaker's feelings, or an expression of emotion, or is it a statement that can be objectively true or false?[5] Metaethics is a rich area of philosophical research. However, because this is a book on health care ethics, not metaethics, we won't be able to explore these issues in depth here.[6]

One of the main purposes of this book, then, is to suggest a number of solutions to some problems that arise in health care ethics by reasoning about them. This will involve clarifying relevant facts; defining key terms; identifying,

---

[5] The notion of objectivity is notoriously difficult to define, and the term gets used in strikingly different ways. By saying that a statement is objectively true, we mean (roughly) that the statement is true independently of what people think or prefer about the statement. Thus, a statement like "The earth orbits around the sun" is objectively true, because it is true regardless of whether people happen to believe it or prefer it to be true. Likewise, to say that the moral claim "Putting people's lives at risk for no good reason is morally wrong" is objectively true is to say that it is true regardless of whether people think that it is true or prefer it to be true.

[6] Readers interested in metaethics would do well to begin by consulting Geoff Sayre-McCord's excellent entry in the *Stanford Encyclopedia of Philosophy,* http://plato.stanford.edu/entries/metaethics/.

explaining, and defending relevant moral principles and values; and then drawing conclusions about these moral problems. In reading this book, you will see how arguments are formed, criticized, reformulated, and debated again. You will see how there can be progress in ethical debate, and how informed and intelligent disagreement sometimes remains. We hope that you will join our debates, reflect on the merits of the arguments presented here, and develop your own arguments for your views on these issues. Thus, in addition to attempting to shed light on some difficult problems in health care ethics, this text aims to improve its readers' critical reasoning skills and to prompt readers to develop their own arguments on these topics. We believe that such a process is intellectually exciting and rewarding. Thus we also hope that in reading this book you will see how challenging these problems are and how stimulating it can be to think philosophically about these problems.

SKEPTICAL CONCERNS: ETHICAL RELATIVISM

Before we explore questions in health care ethics, and normative ethics generally, it is important to address and allay some of the skepticism about the entire enterprise of moral philosophy. There is a long and important minority point of view in the history of philosophy that claims there is no **objective truth** in ethics. Instead, it is suggested that right and wrong are simply relative to a given individual or group. For instance, some may suggest that morality is nothing but a set of conventions that serve the interests of the ruling class; or, perhaps, that right and wrong are merely culturally shared attitudes; or that right and wrong are just a way for an individual to communicate her particular beliefs or feelings about an issue—for example, if a person says something is wrong, it just means she does not like it, and if she says something is right, it just means she likes it. Although each of the above views represents a slightly different understanding of the nature of morality, they share in common a general skepticism about morality: specifically, they deny that there can be objective truths in ethics. That is, they deny the existence of ethical claims that are true independently of whether some particular group or individual believes or feels that they are true. Let's call this basket of views **moral** or **ethical relativism.**[7]

Because this is not a text in metaethics, we cannot do justice to the issues raised by ethical relativism. However, a serious difficulty with this point of view is worth mentioning, namely, that there are dramatic costs to believing in ethical

---

[7] Sometimes philosophers refer to the view that right and wrong are based on the culture or have some other group basis as ethical relativism, and the view that right and wrong are based on the individual as ethical subjectivism. We will refer to both such views as ethical relativism. What they share in common is a skepticism about objective truths in ethics, and a belief that moral truths are *relative*—either to individuals or collections of individuals (cultures).

relativism. One such cost is that ethical relativism conflicts with the widely held commonsense belief that people or groups can be mistaken in their moral judgments. Most of us believe that some of our past moral judgments have been mistaken. Likewise, it seems clear that some previous prevailing moral beliefs in our culture have also been wrong. And, if we are honest with ourselves, most of us would admit that some of our present moral beliefs, and some of our culture's present prevailing moral beliefs, could also be wrong. However, if one is an ethical relativist, it is impossible to believe these things. This is because in order to believe in the fallibility of one's own or one's culture's moral judgments, one would have to believe what the relativist denies, namely, that there is some standard of right and wrong that is not based on what the individual or culture happens to think. Once it is pointed out that ethical relativism implies that an individual's or group's moral beliefs can never be mistaken, ethical relativism loses much of its appeal. For few are prepared to say that their own moral beliefs, much less the moral beliefs of their culture, are incapable of error.

Moreover, because the relativist denies that there are standards of right and wrong that are independent of what individuals or cultures happen to think, the relativist is in the uncomfortable position of being unable to view one person's or group's moral views as objectively better than another's. The individual relativist must be willing to say something like, "Gandhi and Hitler had different moral beliefs, but neither Gandhi's nor Hitler's moral beliefs were objectively better or worse than the other's." Similarly, the cultural relativist must be willing to say that Nazi Germany had its moral beliefs regarding the proper treatment of Jews, Canada has its moral beliefs regarding the proper treatment of Jews, and neither Nazi Germany's nor Canada's moral beliefs in this matter are objectively better or worse. But given that few people really believe that, objectively speaking, Hitler's moral beliefs were as good as Gandhi's or Nazi Germany's were as good as Canada's, few should be willing to accept ethical relativism.

These concerns with ethical relativism directly apply to issues in health care ethics. For there is a long history in medicine of doing dreadful things. For example, consider the Tuskegee syphilis experiments carried on in the United States by the US Public Health Service for forty years:

> The Public Health Service, working with the Tuskegee Institute, began the study in 1932. Nearly 400 poor black men with syphilis from Macon County, Ala., were enrolled in the study. They were never told they had syphilis, nor were they ever treated for it. According to the Centers for Disease Control, the men were told they were being treated for "bad blood," a local term used to describe several illnesses, including syphilis, anemia and fatigue.
>
> For participating in the study, the men were given free medical exams, free meals and free burial insurance.

> At the start of the study, there was no proven treatment for syphilis. But even after penicillin became a standard cure for the disease in 1947, the medicine was withheld from the men. The Tuskegee scientists wanted to continue to study how the disease spreads and kills. The experiment lasted four decades, until public health workers leaked the story to the media.
>
> By then, dozens of the men had died, and many wives and children had been infected.[8]

Now, if one were truly a relativist about ethical matters, one would be in the odd position of saying that if the culture of 1930s, 40s, and 50s approved of such experiments, and if the experimenters felt that what they were doing was right, then they in fact did nothing wrong when they did it. On the other hand, if one thinks that these experimenters were doing something extremely immoral, say, because they violated the basic human rights of the participants, or because they deliberately caused great suffering to the innocent without their consent, or because they caused great distrust of the medical establishment, or because they exploited the most vulnerable in society, then it appears that one has straightforward reasons for criticizing such experiments. But it is hard to see how one can appeal to such reasons and believe that these experimenters were wronging these patients unless one thinks that there are objective moral standards.

Given these evident problems with ethical relativism, one might wonder why anyone would be tempted to embrace it in the first place. We will consider two of the principal arguments that have led people to embrace ethical relativism. One argument is motivated by a desire to be tolerant of other cultures' values and ways of life, and to avoid the kind of cultural imperialism and ethnocentrism that has characterized so much of European and North American history. Notice this, however: this motivation for ethical relativism stems from the belief that cultural imperialism is wrong and that respect for cultural differences is right. But if that is the case, then those who argue in this manner are being inconsistent. They are simultaneously saying (1) that there is no objective right or wrong in ethics, *and* (2) that cultural imperialism is objectively wrong and respect for differences is objectively right. It is evident that something has gone seriously wrong with this line of thought. Indeed, if one wants to defend the belief that cultural imperialism is morally wrong, it seems that one is best served by embracing ethical objectivism rather than by opposing it.[9]

Another argument that has led some to embrace ethical relativism is a general puzzlement about how ethical claims could possibly be objectively true. Many argue that, unlike the claim that tables and chairs exist, or that water

---

[8] Alex Chadwick, "Remembering Tuskegee: Syphilis Study Still Provokes Disbelief, Sadness," *Morning Edition,* NPR, 25 July 2002, http://www.npr.org/programs/morning/features/2002/jul/tuskegee/ (accessed 11 May 2009).

[9] This point is forcefully made by Bernard Williams, *Morality: An Introduction to Ethics* (New York: Harper Torchbooks, 1972).

boils at 100 degrees Celsius, moral claims are not subject to empirical verification. Instead, they say that moral claims seem closer to judgments of taste, or preferences. (For, surely, if someone says something is wrong, they'd prefer it not to be done.) And it is quite reasonable to regard judgments of taste as mere expressions or reports of personal preferences. Thus, one might wonder how moral claims could be objectively true or false.

It is certainly true that judgments about right and wrong seem very different from empirically verifiable judgments such as "the earth is not flat." But it may be a mistake to immediately conclude from this that moral judgments must be expressions or reports of mere preferences or feelings. After all, certain propositions like "There is no greatest number" may not be empirically verifiable, but that does not lead us to conclude that this statement is not objectively true. Thus, it seems that there are ways for judgments to be known to be true or false even if they are not empirically verifiable. Further still, it seems far-fetched to say that moral judgments are similar to reports or expressions of feelings or preferences. Statements like "Vanilla is better than chocolate" seem very different in kind from statements like "Abortion is wrong." For one thing, we tend to think that the former statement needs no justification, while the latter statement requires defence. And indeed, that might be, in part, the sense in which moral judgments are objective—they require rational justification.

NORMATIVE ETHICAL THEORY

A principal concern of normative ethics is its focus on the development and defence of normative ethical theories, which include general moral principles (or approaches) that can be used to determine such things as what acts are right or wrong, what rules are justified and unjustified, and what character traits are virtuous and vicious. While there is no consensus about which normative ethical theory is correct, there are certain leading candidates that have been particularly influential. The following sections present an explanation and preliminary critical examination of these leading theories. We explain each theory and then present some of the most important objections to it. Sometimes, possible replies to these objections are suggested. A very important point to keep in mind is that this overview is intended as an *introduction* to the topic of normative ethical theory. Its aim is to build your critical understanding of normative ethical theories, to help you see their various strengths and weaknesses, while at the same time providing you with some background information that can help inform your thinking about the cases in health care ethics explored later in the text. Our aim is not to tell you what to think, nor is it to pronounce final judgments on any ethical theory. In other words, our aim is to present the beginnings of a conversation, not the final word.

In Chapter 3, each author will present and defend his favoured approach to ethics. This will give you an indication of how ethical theories continue to be developed and defended. In subsequent chapters, as we take up particular issues in health care ethics, you may find the approach of one author or another particularly helpful. However, you may also find it helpful to appeal to some of the other ethical theories discussed below.

CLASSICAL ACT UTILITARIANISM

Perhaps the most influential normative ethical theory of the last 150 years is what is sometimes referred to as **classical act utilitarianism.**[10] Utilitarianism takes many forms, but in its classical formulation, as articulated by Jeremy Bentham and John Stuart Mill, it may be defined as the view that right actions, laws, and policies promote the greatest amount of pleasure, or the least amount of pain, for all concerned.[11] It is helpful to see that utilitarianism is composed of three distinct ideas:

- **Consequentialism:** The right act is entirely determined by its consequences; the right act promotes the most good or the least bad.
- **Hedonism:** The sole ultimate good is pleasure and the sole ultimate bad is pain.
- **Equal consideration:** No one's good is to be counted as more important than anyone else's.

Putting these three ideas together we get, of course, utilitarianism. Right acts promote the most good (pleasure) and the least bad (pain), where everyone's pleasure and pain is given equal consideration.

To better understand this theory, it will be helpful to make a few points about each of these aspects of utilitarianism. Consequentialism is perhaps utilitarianism's most distinctive component. It is the idea that *only* consequences matter in the evaluation of the rightness or wrongness of actions, and that the right act, in any given circumstance, is the one that does the *most good,* or the *least bad.* Thus, for instance, if one has to decide whether or not mercy killing is morally right, the only relevant issue is whether or not the act of mercy killing will (all things considered) do more good (or less bad) than any other alternative. If a particular act of mercy killing will do more good (or less bad) than any other alternative, then it is what ought to be done; however, if some alternative, say palliative care, would in some circumstance do more good than mercy killing, then, in that situation, palliative care would be right and mercy killing would be wrong. So, in theory at least, this aspect of utilitarianism is strikingly simple: consequences are the sole determinant of right action, and an act that fails to produce the best consequences is the wrong thing to do.

A second thing to note about the consequentialist aspect of utilitarianism is that it is a **situational ethic;** that is, whether an act is right or wrong depends on

---

[10] For brevity's sake, classical act utilitarianism will be referred to simply as utilitarianism.

[11] Although utilitarianism is intended to apply to the evaluation of actions, laws, and policies, for the sake of simplicity, we will refer to it as a theory of right action.

the particular situation. Unlike an ethical theory that claims, for instance, that mercy killing is always wrong, utilitarianism looks at the specific situation to determine whether the act is required or forbidden. If, in a particular case, mercy killing will do the most good, then in that case it is morally required. If, in another situation, mercy killing won't do the most good—say, because it will spread fear in the community, or because the person would have recovered—then in that case it is morally forbidden. Thus, unlike supporters of some other ethical theories, the utilitarian holds that what is right or wrong depends on the situation.

A third thing to note about utilitarianism, stemming largely from its acceptance of consequentialism, is its radical implications. That is, it is a theory that frequently challenges commonsense moral beliefs and tries to revise them—to make them more rational and humane. Again, the case of mercy killing will illustrate this point nicely. A principal belief found in many cultures is that it is always wrong to intentionally kill (innocent) human beings. For many, this seems to be a bedrock moral rule, and it seems to imply that mercy killing is always morally wrong since it involves the intentional killing of an innocent human being. But utilitarianism invites us to consider *why* this rule is so important.

Presumably, a major justification for this rule against killing innocent human beings is that it promotes good consequences. By having such a rule, we are able to live, and to live without fear of murder—and that promotes much pleasure and avoids much pain for all of us. That is why the rule against killing innocents is a good rule. However, the utilitarian then points out, there are (rare) situations where killing innocents may actually produce the best consequences—for instance, in cases where the person is suffering terribly and has no hope for recovery, where he begs for death and is joined in that plea by his family who can no longer stand to see him suffer. In such a case, producing the most good may well require that the person be painlessly killed. If that is so, the utilitarian will encourage us to revise our traditional moral beliefs about the wrongness of killing, and to allow for killing innocents in some special circumstances. Thus, it is fair to describe utilitarianism as a radical theory, insofar as it often challenges traditional moral beliefs.

Another ingredient of utilitarianism is its view of what is to count as a good outcome. Classical utilitarians are hedonists: they view pleasure as the sole *ultimate* good (and pain as the sole *ultimate* bad). Other things—like health, income, freedom, and friends—can be good as a means insofar as they tend to lead to pleasure and to diminish pain, but they are not good in themselves. These things are **instrumentally good,** while pleasure is **intrinsically good**—it is valuable for its own sake, and not as a means to anything else. As hedonists are likely to argue, people vary greatly in their sources of pleasure—some like dancing, others like singing, others like reading, and so forth—but all people agree that what they want, ultimately, is to avoid pain and to get pleasure.[12] Further, people can explain why they like to sing or to dance or to read—it gives them pleasure; but they cannot explain why they want pleasure or want to avoid pain—they just

---

[12] Even the masochist seeks pleasure, though the means to this pleasure happens to be pain!

do, since it is an ultimate end.[13] For these utilitarians, then, good consequences are understood as consequences which produce more net pleasure than pain, and right acts produce the greatest amount of pleasure and the least pain.[14]

Lastly, utilitarians believe that everyone's good (pleasure) counts and that it counts as much as everyone else's: the well-being of men and women, whites and non-whites, citizens and non-citizens, and so forth, is equally important. Thus, against a history of moral exclusiveness, utilitarians embrace the idea of impartiality. In assessing the morality of actions, one is to count the effects of one's actions on others equally important as the effects of one's actions on oneself and on one's loved ones. Thus, for example, according to utilitarianism, it would be wrong to do an act that promoted a little bit of good (pleasure) for oneself or for one's friend if an alternative action would promote a greater amount of good (pleasure) for someone else.[15]

To repeat, then, utilitarians claim that the right thing to do in any situation is to promote the most good or the least bad. Good is defined as pleasure, and bad is defined as pain. And everyone's pleasure and pain matters and matters equally. Therefore, one is to do the action that would maximize pleasure or minimize pain for all concerned.

Objections to Utilitarianism

Despite the attractiveness of this theory, many philosophers find utilitarianism to be unacceptable. Some reject utilitarianism because of its consequentialist approach to moral problems; others reject the classical theory's acceptance of hedonism; while still others reject utilitarianism because of its insistence on strict impartiality.[16] In what follows, some important objections to each part of the theory will be explained.

---

[13] See John Stuart Mill, *Utilitarianism* (1861), ed. George Sher (Indianapolis: Hackett Publishing, 1979), chap. 2.

[14] One way to think of hedonism is that it is a view of well-being. In other words, it is a view about what makes a person's life better or worse. According to hedonism, the life with the most well-being is the life which contains, on balance, the greatest amount of pleasure and the least pain. Once hedonism is understood as a theory of well-being, we can again see why utilitarianism is such a tempting idea: it views morality as the attempt to bring about the greatest amount of well-being. Such an idea is, at least on its face, very compelling.

[15] Another radical aspect of utilitarianism is how it regards non-human animals. Many moral theories view moral rules and moral protections as applying only to human beings, or only to rational beings. But utilitarianism takes into consideration the good of everyone affected by an action, and insofar as many non-human animals have a good of their own, utilitarians argue that their interests also need to be taken into account when evaluating whether an act is right or wrong. Thus, for instance, painful experiments on non-human animals raise profound moral concerns for utilitarians. That is not to say that all such experimentation is wrong (remember, it is not an absolutist ethical theory!), but rather that such experimentation needs to be justified by showing that it is necessary to promote the greatest good. If no such justification is possible, the experimentation is immoral, according to utilitarianism.

[16] Of course, some philosophers think that utilitarianism—either in its initial formulation, or suitably modified—can withstand these objections.

Against Consequentialism

Perhaps the most common, and powerful, objection to utilitarianism is the idea that it is too simple. While it can plausibly be maintained that producing good consequences and preventing bad consequences is one morally significant factor, it is hard to believe that it is the *only* morally relevant consideration. Many believe, for instance, that the moral rightness or wrongness of an act also depends on such things as whether or not the act is truthful or deceitful, a case of promise keeping or promise breaking, a case of violating someone's rights or respecting those rights. For example, it is a widely shared common-sense moral belief that it is at least sometimes wrong to violate an innocent person's rights, even if that will produce the best consequences.

To illustrate, suppose a person is dying and refuses to be an organ donor, even though her organs are needed to save another person's life. Suppose also, that after much discussion, the nurse caring for the patient tells her to sign a form stating her refusal to be an organ donor. In fact, though, the form is really an authorization *for* organ donation. The patient signs the form, falsely believing it is protecting her wish not to donate her organs. The patient then dies, the needed organs are harvested, and a transplant takes place which saves the life of someone else who otherwise would have died. Everything is done with great care, and no one ever finds out about the clever deceit. In this case, the best consequences were produced—a person who would otherwise have died is saved, and no one, not even the organ donor, suffers any pain as a result. Yet, it seems quite clear to most of us that the nurse did the wrong thing in deceiving her patient. If this is our reaction, then it looks as though utilitarianism sometimes gives the intuitively unacceptable answer. Utilitarianism says the nurse did the right thing, but common sense strongly suggests otherwise.[17]

Another common criticism of utilitarianism's reliance on consequentialism concerns our frequent inability to know the long-term consequences of our actions. Utilitarianism claims that the right act produces the most good, but, the critic urges, often we do not know what act will produce the most good. Therefore, utilitarianism often will not be useful. Take, for instance, the decision whether or not to set up safe injection sites and to distribute clean needles to heroin addicts. Some say that such a decision will prevent the spread of disease, help reduce violent crime, and give addicts access to social services that will improve their lives. Others say that providing safe injection sites and clean needles will just make things worse by making it easier for addicts to stay hooked on heroin, and that this in turn will have negative consequences for others in terms of crime, health care costs, and so forth. Thus, the seemingly

---

[17] Notice here that a counterexample is being used to criticize consequentialism. Consequentialism is at odds with people's deeply held convictions about what is right, since it implies what moral common sense strongly denies—namely, that it is right for the nurse to lie to the dying patient in this case. Insofar as philosophers are searching for moral principles which can explain and justify our deeply held moral convictions, consequentialism appears to be in trouble.

simple utilitarian idea that we should do the act that will produce the greatest good turns out to be a view that is strikingly difficult to apply, given the complexities of the real world. Now, strictly speaking, this objection does not show that utilitarianism is false, but it does show that the theory is not useful in these sorts of cases.

Against Hedonism

Another criticism of utilitarianism focuses not on its principle of right action (consequentialism), but rather on its view of good results. As explained above, early utilitarians tended to be hedonists. Hedonism is the view that the sole ultimate good is pleasure and the sole ultimate bad is pain. Thus, the right thing to do according to these utilitarians is the act that produces the most pleasure or the least pain. But many argue that hedonism is a flawed theory of the good. This is because *it seems that pleasure is not always good, and that some things are ultimately good besides pleasure.*

Pleasures that we may not want to count as good and worth promoting would presumably include pleasures obtained by violating the rights of others, or pleasures that a virtuous person would not find to be good. Think of a Peeping Tom who gets pleasure from secretly spying on young boys in a locker room, or think of the pleasures that a sadist might experience when watching a newscast about a group of people who died in a tsunami. Surely, we would not want to call these pleasures good, or claim that the pleasures the Peeping Tom and the sadist experience help to justify their actions.

Further, we might regard other things as ultimately good besides pleasure. Knowledge, beauty, creativity, and meaningful relationships often produce pleasure for an individual and for others, but even if they do not, we might want to say that a life is still good for having these things. If you believe that a life with less pleasure but more creativity can be a better life for the person who leads it than a life of more pleasure and very little creativity, then you must not be a hedonist.

To see that pleasure is not the only good, it might help to consider a thought experiment made famous by Robert Nozick.[18] Consider *the experience machine:* scientists have developed a machine that can give a person the experience of anything he or she desires. The way it works is that the patient lies down on a bed, or sits in a chair, and is given a drug that immediately makes the patient forget that he or she is about to go into an experience machine. Doctors then hook the patient's brain up to a computer that has the ability to simulate any experience or feeling the patient desires. If the patient wants to be skiing, or going out for a romantic evening, or winning the lottery, or doing well on a Philosophy test, the machine lets the patient experience all these things. As a result, the patient is pleased, maximally so. The machine can even cause the patient to experience frustration, if later that will lead to super-intense pleasures.

---

[18] Robert Nozick, *Anarchy, State, and Utopia* (New York: Basic Books, 1974), 42–45.

Now, suppose a person could enter this machine for his or her entire life. (No need to worry about the patient's body—he or she could be kept alive indefinitely by inserting a feeding tube.) Suppose, by hypothesis, that life in such a machine would be much more pleasurable than the life any other person has ever lived. It would follow, according to hedonism, that the person who lived his or her life in an experience machine was living the best life ever. But, the critic argues, such a life is not best, and so hedonism must be false. Although this life contains a great amount of pleasure, it is severely lacking in other goods—for instance, it is a life full of false beliefs, full of inactivity, and utterly devoid of meaningful relationships and accomplishments. While the experience machine thought experiment does not reveal what is important in a good life, it does demonstrate that a good life consists in more than merely having a lot of pleasurable experiences. Other things are important, too. And if this is right, then the utilitarian, who is committed to the view that the right act produces the most good for all concerned, needs to revise her theory of what is to count as good. Hedonism, the idea that pleasure (and the absence of pain) is the sole ultimate good, seems false.

Problems with Equal Consideration

Finally, critics often reject utilitarianism because of two related factors: because of its inability to recognize the importance of special relationships, and because it is too demanding. In our daily life, we often put our own interests and the interests of our friends and family ahead of the greater interests of strangers. For instance, often we choose to stay home and read a book to our children, or to go out for dinner and a movie with our friends or loved ones, or to help out a friend who is in need. Indeed, it seems that being a good spouse, parent, sibling, or friend requires that we show special concern for those people who stand in those relationships to us. But, if utilitarianism is correct, and we are supposed to treat everyone's good with equal concern, then it seems that it would be morally wrong to do these kinds of things. We could no longer justify helping a friend who is in need simply because he is our friend; instead, we would have to do whichever act promoted the most good with everyone's interests given equal weight.

In addition to making it seemingly impossible to have special relationships, it seems that utilitarianism is too demanding in another sense. Many of us enjoy things like going to the movies, or to the theatre, or to concerts or sporting events. Also, many of us hope to buy a nice car and a comfortable home, and to take the occasional luxury vacation. But, if utilitarianism is correct, all of this would be seriously immoral. Going to a concert, for instance, will likely produce a certain amount of pleasure for you, but surely more good could be accomplished in the world if, instead, you gave the money to UNICEF or some other worthy cause, and then donated your time to volunteer at a local charity. Indeed, since going to concerts or out for dinner will never, or almost never, produce the most good, they are always, or almost always, going to be morally wrong to do. Generalizing this point, given the tremendous amount of suffering in the world, it seems that it would be wrong according to utilitarianism to acquire any luxury goods, or to take any fancy vacations, or even to take the extra time to just hang out with friends and family, since these choices would not maximize utility.

But such an implication strikes many people as absurd. They believe that morality requires that you do not violate other people's rights, so you should refrain from things like stealing, lying, and doing acts of violence, and that sometimes you should help others who are in need, but that you are not morally required always to treat everyone's interests as if they are as important as your own. To think otherwise is to make it impossible for a person to lead a normal life. Thus, while an earlier objection to utilitarianism's commitment to consequentialism was that it requires us to do things that intuitively seem to be wrong (like lie, violate rights, and break promises in order to promote the greater good), this objection points to the concern that utilitarianism is *too demanding*. It seems to require that we sacrifice too much of our own lives in order to satisfy some of the unmet needs of others.

Utilitarian Responses

Faced with such objections, many are convinced that utilitarianism is hopelessly flawed, and that a different normative ethical theory is needed. But some continue to defend utilitarianism. Confronted with these objections, the utilitarian has several replies available.

Most, although not all, contemporary utilitarians acknowledge that hedonism is flawed. Instead, they appeal to a different theory of the good. Here is a brief indication of what non-hedonistic utilitarianism may look like. Some may argue that what is good is the satisfaction of people's preferences, and so the right thing to do is to maximize preference satisfaction for all concerned.[19] Others argue that what is good is the satisfaction of "informed preferences"—preferences, for example, that one would have if one were free of cognitive impairments and prejudices, and knew all relevant information—and so the right thing to do is to maximize the satisfaction of informed preferences for all concerned.[20] Still other utilitarians opt for a list of objective goods—say, knowledge, beauty, friendship, pleasure—and say that right acts best promote these goods.[21] What these views share is the perception that hedonism is a flawed account of the good; instead, they opt for another account of good consequences.[22]

---

[19] For a defence of preference utilitarianism, see Peter Singer, *Practical Ethics*, 2nd ed. (Cambridge: Cambridge University Press, 1999).

[20] James Griffin, *Well-Being: Its Meaning, Measurement, and Moral Importance* (Oxford: Oxford University Press, 1988), Part 1.

[21] For a defence of ideal or objective list utilitarianism, see David O. Brink, *Moral Realism and the Foundations of Ethics* (Cambridge: Cambridge University Press, 1989).

[22] An excellent account of various theories of well-being can be found in Griffin, *Well-Being: Its Meaning, Measurement, and Moral Importance*. For a recent spirited defence of hedonism, see Fred Feldman, *Pleasure and the Good Life: Concerning the Nature, Varieties, and Plausibility of Hedonism* (New York: Oxford University Press, 2004).

While utilitarians commonly abandon hedonism in the face of serious criticism, their replies to the objections against consequentialism and to the doctrine of equal consideration tend to be more varied.

One common utilitarian response is to say that many of the objections are based on highly fanciful situations that would never occur in real life. When this is realized, they argue, people do not find utilitarianism to be at odds with moral common sense. For instance, in real life, violating people's rights, as in the organ donor case, will not have the best net consequences. The reason for this is that the nurse who tricked the patient will likely get caught, and will be punished. Further, her act will then cause great suffering to countless others who worry that their dying wishes will not be respected. Further still, many will no longer offer to give their organs because they will distrust the system. As a result, even more people will not get the organs they need. Thus, in real life, despite initial appearances, a nurse should not deceive her patient in such a case, and utilitarian ends would be well served by respecting the patient's dying wishes.

Similarly, a utilitarian may argue that the critic exaggerates the objection that utilitarianism is too demanding. Utilitarianism may not, in fact, require that you give every moment of your day to helping others, that you choose a career that is best for humanity, and that you never take a weekend off, since such a life would not in the end do the most good. Realistically, most people who tried to lead such a life would exhaust themselves and crumble psychologically; as a result, in the end they would not be particularly useful to anyone and would themselves be unhappy. Instead, it might be argued that the best way for most people to maximize the good is to choose a fulfilling career, to foster meaningful relationships, to get enough sleep and take the occasional vacation, and to take some time to help others (probably more than we customarily do). Thus, the utilitarian would argue that utilitarianism is not at odds (or is not too much at odds) with moral common sense, and is quite compatible with leading a "normal" life, for that is the best way for most of us to maximize good results in the world.

It is unclear, however, how persuasive these utilitarian responses are to the theory's critics. Perhaps the utilitarian is correct to point out that *almost* always the most good will come from keeping promises, respecting rights, and being honest. But surely there are some real-life cases where violating rights and the like are at odds with commonsense morality and yet will do the most good. Thus, it seems somewhat of an exaggeration to say that utilitarianism is never at odds with commonsense moral judgments. Likewise, it seems highly doubtful that living a lifestyle of conventional North American prosperity will produce the greatest good. Many, for instance, think nothing about buying an expensive new car or a new wardrobe or going to see a professional sports match, but it is extremely unlikely that such acts would do as much good as volunteering at a homeless shelter, donating money to help people in impoverished countries, and so forth. An honest assessment of utilitarianism therefore suggests that it is sometimes at odds with commonsense moral attitudes—it *does* allow for some rights violations, and it *is* very demanding.

In the light of this, other utilitarians acknowledge that their theory is sometimes at odds with commonsense moral beliefs, although perhaps not as often as critics suggest. They admit, for instance, that utilitarianism sometimes requires rights violations, lying, promise breaking, and so forth, to produce the best result. Further, these utilitarians acknowledge that utilitarianism may sometimes prove to be extremely demanding, prohibiting the accumulation of luxuries and the privileging of family interests over the general good.[23] However, they argue that these implications are not flaws in the theory. Rather, they insist that, on reflection, their theory is preferable to commonsense moral beliefs. After all, commonsense morality has been terribly mistaken in the past. For instance, the keeping of slaves and the live vivisection of non-human animals were, for centuries, widely viewed as acceptable. So, we should not be too anxious if utilitarianism finds fault in some of our current moral beliefs. Rather than trust our prevailing mores, these utilitarians suggest that it is more reasonable to believe that what is morally right is to act in ways that maximize the good or minimize the bad for all concerned.[24]

RULE UTILITARIANISM

One further utilitarian reply to these criticisms should be mentioned. Utilitarians may concede that their theory is at odds with commonsense moral beliefs—such as respect for moral rights—and that it should be modified to make it more acceptable. One such modification is known as **rule utilitarianism.**[25] Rule utilitarianism says:

- The right thing to do is to follow the best rule.
- The best rule is defined as the one which, if consistently followed, will produce the greatest amount of good.

Thus, if given a choice between following a rule that says "respect people's rights" or "violate people's rights," for instance, it is clear that the former rule if consistently followed will have better consequences than consistently following the rule to violate people's rights. Thus, the former rule is best, and according to rule utilitarianism, the right thing to do would be to follow that rule and always respect people's rights. Thus, unlike the act utilitarian, who,

---

[23] See, for example, Peter Singer, "Famine, Affluence, and Morality," *Philosophy and Public Affairs* 1, no. 1 (1972): 229–43.

[24] An excellent defence of utilitarianism against the "rights" objection and the "too-demanding" objection can be found in J. J. C. Smart's "An Outline of a System of Utilitarian Ethics" in J. J. C. Smart and Bernard Williams, *Utilitarianism for and Against* (New York: Cambridge University Press, 1973). A more recent defence of consequentialism is Shelly Kagan's *The Limits of Morality* (Oxford: Oxford University Press, 1989).

[25] See, for instance, R. B. Brandt, *A Theory of the Good and the Right* (New York: Oxford University Press, 1979).

for example, would seem to support lying to the organ donor to save a life, the rule utilitarian would presumably view such a deception as morally wrong, since the rule, if always followed, would have very bad consequences.

In response to the objection that utilitarianism is too demanding, rule utilitarians may concede that insisting on a rule that is said to always produce the best consequences would likely be counterproductive, resulting in burnout or leading people to routinely ignore moral rules. Instead, they might reasonably suggest that the set of rules that would actually produce the most good, given the way human beings are, is one that is considerably less demanding—insisting on respecting people's rights, encouraging people to help others, and allowing people (to a degree) to show special concern for family and friends. Still, it is quite likely that rule utilitarianism would require considerable sacrifices on the part of individuals, for it seems likely that a rule that allowed people to acquire luxury goods and to take luxury vacations, instead of helping others who suffered from lack of food, shelter, and basic medical care, would not be the best rule from the point of view of maximizing the good. Instead, a far better rule might be one that required people to forgo their luxuries when doing so could greatly help the needy. Given this, it is fair to say that rule utilitarianism will still be rather demanding. It is certainly arguable, however, whether this should count as a reason against the theory, for it is unclear why a normative ethical theory should not be demanding.

Despite these arguments in its favour, rule utilitarianism faces a serious problem. Rule utilitarianism may still not be able to give a coherent response to the objection that focuses on people's rights. Here the problem becomes apparent when we ask the rule utilitarian how to determine what constitutes the best rule. Above, we considered only two possibilities: adopt a rule of violating people's rights or adopt a rule of respecting people's rights. Given these two options, it was only reasonable to think that the rule of respecting people's rights would lead to the best results and so is the best rule. But there is clearly a third rule we could adopt: respect people's rights, unless violating them is necessary to do a greater good. Now it seems that this third rule, if consistently followed, would have the best consequences. It would respect people's rights when that led to the greatest good, and it would violate people's rights (only) when *that* led to the greatest good—it is the rule, in short, that will always lead to the greatest good, if it is consistently followed. Thus, the critic argues, this rule is the one that ought to be adopted according to rule utilitarianism.

But, of course, this rule is really just another way of stating traditional act utilitarianism! On reflection, then, the critic argues that rule utilitarianism, if treated seriously, merely collapses into act utilitarianism. The rule that will lead to the best consequences if consistently followed is simply the rule that says to do whatever is necessary to produce the greatest good for all concerned—but that, of course, is just another way of stating act utilitarianism.[26]

---

[26] David Lyons, in *Forms and Limits of Utilitarianism* (Oxford: Oxford University Press, 1965), was perhaps the first to raise this objection to rule utilitarianism.

In response to this objection, rule utilitarians may argue that the rules that one is to choose between must be more general than a "rule" that merely says "follow the rule unless it is better not to do so." For, they may argue, a "rule" that is so easily disregarded would be no rule at all. Instead, rules must be more absolute, more exceptionless, than the objection supposes. However, if rule utilitarians insist that one ought to follow some rule like "never lie" even when a lie would produce better net results, then it seems that the position suffers from "irrational rule worship." Why should one agree to act in accordance with some optimal rule if one could occasionally break that rule and produce even more good? To say that such rule breaking would be wrong even if it did more good seems irrational.[27]

NON-CONSEQUENTIALISM AND DEONTOLOGY

Unlike utilitarians, many philosophers think that the rightness of an act is not solely determined by the goodness of its consequences. Such philosophers are called **non-consequentialists.** Some non-consequentialists are **deontologists.** Deontologists see morality as a matter of doing one's (moral) duty.[28] Many non-consequentialists (and deontologists) think that the consequences of an act are one determinant of the rightness of an action, but not the only determinant. Others think that the consequences of an act are simply irrelevant to the rightness or wrongness of an act. The latter view is famously held by the deontologist Immanuel Kant.[29]

KANT'S ETHICS

Kant argues that we are to evaluate the morality of an action by focusing on the agent's intentions rather than the results of the actions. More precisely, it

---

[27] Whether rule utilitarians can, in the final analysis, respond satisfactorily to these and other concerns remains a matter of significant debate. Perhaps rule utilitarians could argue that, given human nature, utility is best served by universal rules, since if exceptions are allowed, humans will make poor choices that do not maximize utility. Of course, this only invites the objection that rule utilitarianism would still collapse into act utilitarianism, and thus allow for rights violations, if only people were better rule followers and better judges of when exceptions were permitted. Students interested in this topic might want to turn first to Brad Hooker's entry on "rule consequentialism" in the *Stanford Encyclopedia of Philosophy,* http://plato.stanford.edu/entries/consequentialism-rule. Also, see R. B. Brandt's *Morality, Utilitarianism, and Rights* (New York: Cambridge University Press, 1992).

[28] *Deontology* comes from the Greek word *deon,* which means "duty." As we will see later, not all non-consequentialists are deontologists. Some non-consequentialists, for example, view morality as a matter of living virtuously or of caring for others.

[29] The following discussion of Kant's ethics is based on Chapters 1 and 2 of his *Groundwork of the Metaphysics of Morals,* trans. Arnulf Zweig (New York: Oxford University Press, 2002). An extremely helpful commentary on Kant's ethics is H. J. Paton's classic work, *The Categorical Imperative: A Study in Kant's Moral Philosophy* (Philadelphia: University of Pennsylvania Press, 1948).

is helpful to think of Kant's ethical theory as falling into two parts. First, Kant develops a view of when actions have "moral worth." Second, he defends a set of principles that determine whether one's acts are morally permissible (or morally wrong).

The Idea of Moral Worth

Kant observed that people act on the basis of two different sorts of reasons, which he called **hypothetical imperatives** and **categorical imperatives.** Both types of imperatives can be expressed in terms of "oughts." Hypothetical imperatives state what one ought to do given the presence of a particular desire or goal. Categorical imperatives state what one ought to do regardless of one's desires. Hypothetical imperatives are commonplace—for instance, "If I am thirsty, I ought to drink" or "If you want to do well in this course, you ought to read the book carefully, attend class meetings, and study hard." There is nothing special or mysterious about hypothetical imperatives. As rational beings, we rely on them all the time. That is, we set goals for ourselves and then determine the most effective ways to accomplish those goals.

As rational beings, however, we are also capable of following categorical imperatives. Categorical imperatives take the following form: "Do x" or "Don't do x," where the idea is that you must do or not do some act, regardless of your desires, goals, or other inclinations. Examples of such imperatives would be "Tell the truth," "Keep one's promises," "Don't steal," "Don't cheat," "Don't harm others," and so forth. Kant calls these categorical imperatives the *imperatives (commands) of morality.* These imperatives are said to apply to all of us, and we ought to follow them regardless of whether they further our desires. Thus, as a rational being, one is capable of acting according to hypothetical and categorical imperatives; that is, one can act in a way that furthers the goals one happens to have, and one can act according to commands (moral duties) that are not related to any particular goals that one may have.

Now, there is nothing necessarily wrong with acting on the basis of a hypothetical imperative, but Kant maintains that acts based on a hypothetical imperative have no moral worth. However, if one does an act out of respect for morality—out of respect for a categorical imperative—then one is said to have a good will, and so one's act has *moral worth*. Thus, the person who gives to charity because she wants to get a tax deduction, may be behaving rationally and certainly is doing the right thing, but nevertheless her act has no moral worth. Alternatively, if a person donates to a charity *because it is the right thing to do,* then not only is she doing the right act, but her act also has moral worth. For Kant, then, in order to have a good will, and for one's act to have moral worth, one must do the right act for the right reasons: namely, out of respect for morality. By contrast, if a person does an act not out of respect for morality, but because it furthers one of her own desires, then she may be doing nothing wrong, but her act has no moral worth.

The idea of moral worth is an extremely tricky one and gives rise to many questions. For instance, if a person donates to charity simply because she feels sorry for the needy and sympathizes with their plight, does her act have moral worth? Kant's answer is, surprisingly, "No." Such an act is still based on a hypothetical imperative—*If I feel sorry for someone, I ought to give that person charity*—and while such an act is certainly not morally wrong, it has no moral worth.

What about someone who gives to charity for several reasons—she wants a tax deduction, she feels sympathy for the poor, and she believes it is the right thing to do? The answer here is unclear. Some believe that Kant would say that such an act still has moral worth as long as respect for moral duty was a sufficient condition to motivate the person to do the charitable act. Others read Kant differently. They believe that such an act would not have moral worth because it was "polluted" by the presence of hypothetical imperatives. While it must be admitted that Kant is far from clear on this point, the former interpretation is the one we will adopt, since it seems to be both a reasonable interpretation of Kant's writings and it is the more *charitable* interpretation.[30]

The Categorical Imperative

By this point, the astute reader will wonder where these categorical imperatives come from. In other words, how does one determine what is and what is not a categorical imperative (a rule of morality)? This brings us to the second part of Kant's theory. Kant is famous for giving what he calls *the* **categorical imperative,** a test for determining whether a particular action is morally permissible or morally wrong. Indeed, Kant gives several different versions of the categorical imperative test. Two of his most influential versions will be examined here.

The Universal Law Formulation of the Categorical Imperative

One test that Kant gives to determine whether or not an action violates a moral rule is known as the **universal law version of the categorical imperative.** It says, "*Act only on those maxims that you can, at the same time, will as a universal law.*" In order to understand this principle, it is necessary to define its key terms. Specifically, we will need to clarify the terms **maxim, universal law,** and **will.** By the term *maxim,* Kant means the principle behind one's action.

---

[30] On this point, see Paton, *The Categorical Imperative,* 56. When given a choice between more than one interpretation of an argument or view, philosophers should follow the **principle of charity.** That is, they should go with the interpretation that is most reasonable. Philosophers do this in part because to do otherwise would be to commit the **straw man fallacy,** and in part because philosophers should be searching for the truth, and so it is only reasonable to go with the strongest interpretation of an argument or view. This is one way in which philosophy differs from debate—there, the goal is to persuade by any rhetorical means possible, including the deliberate oversimplification of the opponent's position.

Thus, in the case of the forged organ donation, the nurse's *action* is to give the patient a pen and paper, but her maxim is to act on the principle "When needed, I will deceive my patient into donating her organs."

A *universal law* is a principle that states that everyone follows this maxim all the time, as if it were a law of nature. Thus, in the organ donor example, the universal law would be "When needed, everyone always deceives patients into donating their organs."

Finally, before we can understand the test, we need to clarify the concept of being able to *will*. By this, Kant means two different things.[31] First, one is sometimes not able to will a maxim as a universal law because the practice would be self-defeating or self-contradictory if it were practised by everyone all the time. Kant calls this **a contradiction in conception,** and he maintains that if the maxim of one's actions yields a contradiction in conception when it is universalized, then the action violates a **perfect duty** and is therefore strictly forbidden. A perfect duty is one that must always be followed. At other times, Kant admits that one can conceive of a maxim as a universal law, but still not be able to will it because a contradiction will arise between the universal law and what a person will (later) want—Kant called this **a contradiction in will.** Kant claims that to act on principles which can be conceived but not consistently willed as universal law is to violate an **imperfect duty**—a duty that one must sometimes follow, but which need not be followed all the time.

So, if we look at the organ transplant case, we will need to know if we can will the universal law "*When needed, everyone will deceive patients into donating their organs.*" Now it seems that the answer is that such a universal law would yield a contradiction in conception, since if everyone, when necessary, deceived their patients into donating their organs, then such deception would be self-defeating—patients would simply not be deceived by such tricks. (In other words, it makes no sense to say everyone will tell a lie in situation *x,* since a lie would no longer work if everyone lied in that situation!) Thus, because the nurse's maxim cannot be conceived as a universal law, the Universal Law test tells us that it is morally wrong for the nurse to lie to the patient. She violates a perfect duty.

Let's now tweak the example slightly and consider what the Universal Law test says about the patient who chose not to give up her organs. Let's suppose her maxim to be as follows: "*I will keep my organs even when I have no use for them and others need them.*" We then universalize this maxim: "*No one will ever give up their organs to others even when others need them for survival and they are no longer needed by the donor.*" Obviously, there could be a world where no one donated organs to anyone—such a world has existed for most of human history—but could one always *will* this as a universal law?

---

[31] Kant's work is notoriously difficult to understand. Not surprisingly, then, there is a great deal of debate over how to interpret Kant's work. One such area of dispute is the nature of the contradiction, if any, in being unable to will a maxim as a universal law.

Apparently not, since one day you may be in need of an organ donor (or some other kind of benefactor), and then a contradiction will arise between the universal law of never donating organs (or more generally never helping those in need) and what you now want—an organ (or some other necessary good). Because there is a contradiction in will, it follows, on Kant's view, that there is an imperfect duty to donate one's organs (or at least to help others). What this entails is not exactly clear. Perhaps it means that all of us ought to donate some of our organs, although we are not obligated to donate all of our organs. Or perhaps it just means that we ought to help the needy at least sometimes, and not ignore their vital needs entirely.

By now it should be apparent that Kant's Universal Law test is extremely sophisticated and rather difficult to understand. It is sophisticated because this apparently simple statement—*to act only on maxims that can be willed as universal law*—purports to tell one not only whether one's act is morally permissible or a violation of moral duty, but also what kind of duty one is transgressing by one's act. This is truly an impressive accomplishment, especially if the test works! But, before we turn to possible difficulties with the test, it may be helpful to explain the basic insight that is informing Kant's reasoning when he proposes this test. It seems to be the commonsense idea that *when one acts immorally, one does something that one does not (or cannot) want everyone to do.* The mugger, who mugs, does not want everyone to mug. The shoplifter, who shoplifts, does not want everyone to shoplift. The promise breaker does not want everyone to break promises. Instead, the wrongdoer seeks to make an exception for himself—he wants to act in one way, while he wants others to act differently. But Kant's profound insight is that morality needs to be applied universally, or consistently: one should act only on principles that one can consistently will others to follow.

In turn, this point leads to another one of Kant's central claims: to act immorally is to somehow act in a manner that is contradictory. Kant's claim here is *not* that an act is immoral because it leads to bad consequences—he is no utilitarian. Rather, his claim is that to act immorally is to behave irrationally. The reason for this is that, in acting immorally, one acts on maxims that cannot rationally stand as universal laws.

Lastly, to simplify the Universal Law test, it may be helpful to think of it as a three-step procedure.

Step 1: Identify the maxim (principle) behind the action.

Step 2: Universalize the maxim, i.e., transform the maxim into a universal law (everyone acts on that principle, all the time).

Step 3: Consider whether the universalized maxim can be consistently willed.

　　a. If it can be consistently willed, then the act is morally permissible.

　　b. If it cannot be consistently willed, then determine why it cannot be consistently willed. If the maxim cannot even be *consistently thought of* as existing as a universal law, then the act violates a perfect duty and is morally forbidden. But if the universalized maxim can be consistently thought of as existing as a universal law but it cannot be *consistently willed,* then the act violates an imperfect duty—one that should not be ignored entirely but does not always have to be practised.

Before we move onto another key Kantian principle, it may be helpful to illustrate one more time how the Universal Law test can be applied. This time let's take one of Kant's own examples—a case of knowingly making someone a false promise.[32] Kant imagines that someone who is in need of money considers asking someone for a loan, even though he knows he will not be able to repay it. Here the maxim of the act is (Step 1) "When I need money, I will ask to borrow some money, promising to repay the loan, even though I know I won't be able to do so." Next, we need to universalize this maxim as (Step 2) "Whenever anyone needs money, that person will ask to borrow some money, promising to repay the loan, even though the borrower knows that he or she won't be able to do so." Kant then points out (Step 3) that such a universal law cannot be consistently conceived, and necessarily contradicts itself, for no one would lend money in such a world, and then the chance to make such promises could never arise. Thus, the Universal Law test tells us that knowingly telling a false promise violates a perfect duty, and it is always morally wrong to do.

The Humanity Version of the Categorical Imperative

Kant also developed another equally influential and important principle to test whether one is acting on maxims that are morally permissible. This principle, known as the **humanity version of the categorical imperative,** states that *one must treat humanity, whether in one's own person or that of another, always as an end and never merely as a means.* Once again, in order to understand Kant's test, certain key terms need to be clarified. Specifically, the terms **humanity, end,** and **means** need to be explicated. In order to do this, it is helpful to recall the earlier notion of categorical and hypothetical imperatives. Kant thought that **rational beings** are special insofar as they can follow hypothetical and categorical imperatives. That is, rational beings can freely set goals for themselves and then determine the various means to accomplish those goals (hypothetical imperatives). Rational beings can also recognize and choose to follow (or not to follow) moral rules (categorical imperatives). In this sense, rational beings differ from what Kant calls **things.** A *thing* can be defined as "not a rational being": things are not capable of following hypothetical and categorical

---

[32] Kant, *Groundwork,* p. 233. The example of making a lying promise, or of lying in general, could easily be related to issues in health care ethics. Examples are giving a patient a false promise of confidentiality, or telling a patient that his or her condition is treatable when in fact it is not.

imperatives. Thus, on Kant's definition, you are a rational being, but a chair, a cactus, and a cat are things (remember, rational beings are capable of following moral rules—cats are not, Kant assumes).

When it comes to rational beings, it should be noted that Kant says that people differ greatly in their chosen goals. You may choose to exercise regularly, read for fun, and pursue a career in journalism; someone else may prefer playing and performing music. But what all rational beings value is their **rational nature**—that is, their ability to make their own decisions and set their own goals. (Even the person who wants others to make his decisions for him wants to make the decision to let others decide for him, and it is the same with the person who is suicidal— she values the ability to decide to commit suicide!) Thus, Kant thought that while we may differ greatly in the ends in life that we choose, we, as rational beings, all necessarily value the ability to make our own decisions.

With this explained, we can return to the key terms in Kant's Humanity test. By *humanity*, Kant means "rational being." By *end*, Kant means "rational being," and by *mere means* he means "thing." Thus we can rewrite the Humanity test as follows:

> *Act so you treat* ~~humanity~~ *every rational being, whether in your own person or that of another, always as* ~~an end~~ *a rational being, and never* ~~merely~~ *as a* ~~means~~ *thing.*

This means you must always treat beings who are capable of making their own decisions as beings who are capable of making their own decisions, and not as if they were things that are incapable of making their own decisions.

Some examples will help to illustrate Kant's Humanity test. In the case of the deceived organ donor, the nurse certainly does not respect the patient's ability to decide for herself what should be done with her organs; instead, she disrespects this ability by manipulating her into signing the consent form. Or consider the case of rape. A rapist clearly treats his victim as a mere thing— that is, as someone who is incapable of making her own decisions. Instead, he forces his will upon another rational being, disregarding her ability to make her own decisions, and thereby dehumanizing her. Alternatively, the importance that contemporary ethicists place on obtaining informed consent prior to a medical intervention nicely illustrates the Kantian idea that people are rational beings who deserve to be respected by being given the information (or at least access to the information) that lets them make their own decisions.

At the heart of the Humanity test is the conviction that to behave immorally is to dehumanize. To behave immorally is to treat someone who is deserving of respect merely as though he or she were a thing to be used.

Moreover, like the Universal Law test, the Humanity test is able to distinguish between acts that violate perfect duties and acts that violate imperfect duties. Treating someone as a means only (as a thing) is strictly forbidden, a violation of a perfect duty. For instance, to lie or steal is to treat someone as a means only, and so these acts are violations of perfect duties. Failing *fully* to respect a person as a rational being is a violation of an imperfect duty. For instance, suppose my car battery is dead and I ask you for a boost, and you refuse to help me out even though you are able to do so. In such a case your refusal to help does not treat me as a means only—I am still free to ask someone else for a boost, or to call a tow truck—but your refusal to help me does not fully respect me as a rational being, either. For, if you fully respected me as a rational being, you would have assisted me in my (morally permissible) goal of getting my car started. In general, according to Kant, there is an imperfect duty to help others, a duty that he thinks follows from the imperative to respect rational beings.

Now, interestingly, despite the very different appearance of the Universal Law test and the Humanity test, Kant claims that they are equivalent—that is, they will always give the same answer about the moral permissibility or impermissibility of a given action. It is also fair to say that both tests have proven to be enormously influential—guiding people's thinking both within and beyond professional philosophical circles. Thus, it is quite common to hear the basic insight behind the Humanity test. People sometimes say, "He used me *as a means!*" Or someone may condemn an act on the grounds that "the ends don't justify the means." Likewise, echoes of the Universal Law test are found in such common expressions as "Don't keep things that don't belong to you, since you would not want others to do that if they found something of yours." Similarly, someone might complain to a litterer, "How would you like it if everyone did that?" These expressions give testimony to the currency of what are, at least in part, Kantian notions about the nature of morality.[33]

Objections to the Universal Law and Humanity Tests

Despite the power of Kant's ideas, both his Universal Law test and his Humanity test face serious challenges. One problem with the Universal Law test concerns the difficulty of identifying the principle behind one's actions (one's maxim). Kant's test instructs us first to identify the principle (or maxim) behind a person's action and then see if it can be willed as a universal law. But the problem is that the same act can be described by more than one principle (or maxim). Consider the act of giving the patient an organ donor consent form when the patient believes it is a form authorizing the refusal to donate her organs. This act can be described as falling under the maxim, "I will deceive the patient,"

---

[33] Some might hear echoes of the Golden Rule—"Do unto others as you would have them do unto you"—when they hear Kant's Universal Law test. Notice, though, that the tests differ. For one thing, the Golden Rule mentions only how to treat others, while Kant's principle deals with duties both to others and to oneself. There also certain difficulties with the application of the Golden Rule that do not apply to the Universal Law test. For example, according to the Golden Rule, it would be permissible for a person to break a promise if she did not mind other people breaking promises to her. But, on a Kantian view, such a person would still be obligated to keep her promises, since the maxim of promise-breaking cannot be universalized without contradiction.

but it also could be described as falling under the maxim, "I will procure an organ for a dying patient from someone who will no longer need her organs." Now, it seems that the former description of the action cannot be universalized, but the latter description of the action can be universalized. If so, this would mean that the same act can be both morally wrong and morally permissible depending on how its maxim is described. But this is highly problematic, for it now seems that a person who is careful to describe his acts according to the "right" maxims can do more or less whatever he wants.

Here is another problem with the Universal Law test. It seems too strict. There may well be morally permissible actions that the test views as wrong. For example, imagine a couple who decide to remain childless so that they can spend more time on important personal projects. (We needn't suppose they are selfish; we can suppose that one of their important projects is helping poor children around the world.) Now, there does not appear to be anything morally wrong with the couple's decision to remain childless, but the Universal Law test appears to claim otherwise. For here, the couple's maxim is "We will not have children, so that we may spend more time on important personal projects." Next, as a universal law, the maxim says, "No one will have children, so that everyone may spend time on important personal projects." But, clearly, this universal law is self-contradictory. For if no one ever had children, then no one would ever exist, and if no one ever existed then the decision not to have children could not be made. Thus the Universal Law test appears to tell us that it would be wrong for people to remain childless so as to be able to pursue important life projects. But contrary to this test, such a decision seems not to be wrong at all. The Universal Law test, therefore, sometimes gives the wrong answers; specifically, it views some morally permissible acts as morally impermissible.[34]

The Humanity test also faces a number of problems. First, it does not seem to be a principle that covers all of our moral obligations. Specifically, it tells us how we are to treat rational beings, but it is silent on the question of our moral obligations to non-rational beings. Indeed, the test suggests that non-rational beings are merely things that can be used for any purpose that a rational being chooses, provided our actions do not dehumanize a fellow rational being. But that seems highly problematic. Most people think that it is morally wrong, for instance, to torture a non-human animal, and that this wrong consists primarily in the fact that one is needlessly harming the animal. But the Kantian cannot do justice to this moral intuition. He could say that it is wrong to torture non-human animals if that animal belongs to (or is the pet of) another rational being, because that would disrespect the property rights of that other rational being.

For instance, if someone lights your puppy on fire for fun, the Kantian could say that this is wrong because *your* rights are violated, but the Kantian cannot

---

[34] The previous two objections may be related, in the sense that if the Kantian could solve the first objection by explaining how to unambiguously identify the maxims of our actions, then perhaps the problem raised in the second objection could be avoided.

recognize that anything wrong is done to the dog. Likewise, the Kantian will be hard pressed to satisfactorily explain why it is wrong for you to torture your own dog. Certainly, the main reason it is wrong to torture your dog is that it hurts your dog, but the Kantian cannot recognize this as a morally relevant reason, since he views dogs merely as things. Indeed, the Kantian would have to say that it is not wrong for you to torture your dog, or that if it is wrong it is only because it is likely to corrupt your character and make you more likely to injure a rational being in the future. But this seems to miss the principal wrong involved in harming the animal—namely, that it is wrong to make an animal suffer and it is wrong to act against its basic interests for no good reason.

It also worth observing that it is not only non-human animals that come out poorly on Kant's Humanity test: the test also has problems explaining why we have direct moral obligations to non-rational humans, such as those who are significantly mentally challenged. The Humanity test is (only) concerned with protecting the dignity of rational beings; it is the fact that we can freely choose goals for ourselves, and freely choose to follow moral rules, which marks rational beings out as possessors of dignity, and deserving of respect. What, then, does it say of our obligations to non-rational human beings? Surely, we think they warrant respect and special concern, and we do not accept the idea that they are mere things to be used for our purposes. It is extremely difficult, however, to see how the Humanity test can do justice to these important moral beliefs.

Lastly, one other problem with the Humanity test is worth considering. The claim that one may *never* treat a rational being merely as a means seems problematic. For sometimes, the only way to prevent serious harm to rational beings is by treating a rational being merely as a means. To see this, consider Kant's own infamous case of the inquiring murderer.[35] Suppose a person comes knocking on your door, looking for your friend, because he wants to kill her. The inquiring murderer asks you where your friend is hiding. Your friend is hiding in your house, and you have to decide what you should tell the inquiring murderer. If you lie, you will be treating a rational being—the inquiring murderer—merely as a means. If you tell him the truth, he will be free to make his own decisions, and you will have treated him as an end. Now, the Humanity test says that you must *always* treat rational beings as an end and *never* merely as a means. Thus, it seems clear that on Kant's view you must not lie to the inquiring murderer, even if that is the only way to save your friend. (Indeed, Kant explicitly states that lying to the inquiring murder would be wrong in this case.) But surely that is mistaken.

There seems to be something irrational in Kant's insistence that we never treat rational beings merely as means. For if rational beings possess dignity and ought to be respected, then (the critic argues) it seems to follow that one should be prepared to treat rational beings as mere means if that is necessary

---

[35] See his "On a Supposed Right to Lie from Philanthropy," in *Practical Philosophy*, trans. Mary Gregor (Cambridge: Cambridge University Press, 1996), 605–16.

to prevent even worse violations of rational nature. Thus, in the case of the inquiring murderer, it seems permissible, even required, to lie to the inquiring murderer, since that protects a rational being (the friend) from being destroyed, while, comparatively speaking, it only slightly devalues the rational nature of the inquiring murderer (he has been deceived, but his rational nature has not been destroyed). And surely, if rational nature is so important, we should prefer lesser violations to greater violations of rational nature.

Thus, like other moral theories, Kant's ethics faces numerous significant challenges. And yet, Kant's basic ideas—that we should act only on principles that could be applied to everyone alike, and that we ought to treat rational beings with respect—have undeniable appeal. Beyond that, in the field of health care ethics, Kant's ethical insights, particularly the emphasis on respect for individual autonomy and the dignity of persons, continue to make their mark. It is therefore not surprising that many philosophers continue to defend at least part of Kant's ethical theory.[36]

PLURALISTIC DEONTOLOGY

Thus far, we have seen that two very different ethical theories, utilitarianism and Kant's deontological view, possess impressive insights into the nature of morality. Most people recognize the importance of promoting good outcomes and avoiding bad outcomes; that the principles upon which persons act should apply to everyone in similar circumstances; and that we should not go around treating others as mere things. Nevertheless, it has also been argued that these two theories are in a sense too simple. Against the utilitarian, it seems that there is more to an act's being right than whether or not it promotes the best consequences—factors like promise-keeping, justice, and obligations based on special relationships seem important, too. Against the Kantian, it seems that moral rules need to allow for some flexibility. The objections discussed above suggest that our duties to keep promises, to not lie to others, and never to harm the innocent are not absolute. In some cases, at least where much more good could come from lying, for example, it seems morally permissible or even morally required to lie. Thus, we would not want to say that people who told lies in order to hide Jews in their homes during the German occupation of Holland did something morally forbidden.

Many therefore argue that we need a moral theory that recognizes a variety of moral duties, and also recognizes that these duties can sometimes be

---

[36] Important recent defences of Kant's ethics include works by Thomas E. Hill, *Commentary on the Groundwork* (New York: Oxford University Press, 2002); Christine Korsgaard, *Creating the Kingdom of Ends* (Cambridge: Cambridge University Press, 1996); Marcia Baron, *Kantian Ethics Almost without Apology* (Ithaca: Cornell University Press, 1995); and Barbara Herman, *The Practice of Moral Judgment* (Cambridge: Harvard University Press, 1993).

overridden by other duties. W. D. Ross attempts to develop just such a theory.[37] Ross is a *pluralist;* he does not think there is a single basic moral rule that explains all of our moral obligations. Instead, Ross argues that there are many general moral rules that generate the many different duties we have. Thus, for example, we have a duty to tell the truth, to keep our promises, to help others, and so on. He calls these *prima facie* duties. The usual translation of the Latin phrase *prima facie* is "on the face of it," but in this context, *prima facie* duties should be understood as *conditional* duties. A conditional or *prima facie* duty can then be contrasted with duties that remain for us *when all things are considered.*

To illustrate, we have a *prima facie* duty to tell the truth. We also have a *prima facie* duty to prevent harm to others. Now, suppose you find yourself in a situation where these duties conflict, such as in the case of the inquiring murderer. In this situation, you can prevent the murder of your friend only by telling a lie to his would-be murderer. It seems clear, as we suggested above, that the moral reasons in favour of saving your friend are much weightier than the moral reasons that support telling the truth. If this is correct, then Ross would claim that the *prima facie* duty to tell the truth is overridden in this case by another *prima facie* duty—namely, the duty to prevent harm. So in this situation, your **duty, all things considered** (that is, the duty you should act on), is to prevent serious harm to your friend.

An important feature of *prima facie* duties is that they are not absolute; they can be outweighed or overridden in various circumstances by other duties. When a *prima facie* duty is outweighed by another duty, the *prima facie* duty does not disappear. You still have a moral reason to tell the truth to the person who wants to murder your friend, for example, but there are weightier reasons in favour of protecting your friend. And since *prima facie* duties do not disappear in situations when they are outweighed, Ross suggests that we should feel a certain level of regret (or at least discomfort) for having violated a *prima facie* duty.

At this point, the thoughtful reader may be asking herself two questions: First, how does one know that something is a *prima facie* duty? Second, how does one know which duty is more pressing or weightier in a particular situation? That is, how do we know what our duties are, all things considered? Ross gives two very different answers to these questions. His response to the first question is this. *Prima facie* duties are known through what Ross calls **rational intuition.** Just as one "sees" that $2 + 3 = 5$, or that triangles have three sides, one just "sees" the truth of such general principles as "repay debts," "keep promises," "tell the truth," "help others," "don't harm others," and so on. The suggestion here is that our *prima facie* duties, like basic principles of mathematics and geometry, are *self-evident.* That is to say, they require no

---

[37] W. D. Ross, *The Right and the Good* (Oxford: Oxford University Press, 2002); first published 1930.

proof, and are not the result of rational argument or inference, but instead can be seen to be correct just by reflection.

When it comes to how we determine our duties, all things considered, Ross's answer is very different. They are not self-evident, so there is none of the certainty that one finds when apprehending the general (i.e., *prima facie*) principles of duty. Instead, all one can do is to study the situation as carefully as one can, paying special attention to which *prima facie* obligations are at play, and then make a judgment about which duty is most pressing in that situation. Here, one can follow general rules, like the rule that normally the duty not to harm is stronger than the duty to help, or that the duty to keep promises is usually stronger than the duty to give to a charity. But these rules are only general guidelines and may not apply to every case. In the end, Ross says, in judging what duty ought to be followed, one takes a moral risk.

Thus, for instance, consider a case where you need to decide whether to keep your appointments at work or to stay home to care for your sick child. Here it is clear that you have a duty to keep your appointments, and also a duty to care for your children. Let's suppose that these are the only relevant duties at play. You might try to resolve the conflict by finding someone else to care for your child or by rescheduling your appointments. But if that is not possible, then you must try to determine which duty is the more important in this situation, and then follow that duty. The duty that is more pressing—say it is staying home with your child—then becomes the duty, all things considered, in that situation. Of course, Ross notes, your judgment about which duty is the more pressing could turn out to be wrong—this is what he sees as the moral risk. You may have misunderstood the factors at play, or you may have misjudged the relative strengths of these factors. For example, if you decided to keep your appointments rather than to stay home with your sick child, and if it turned out that the meetings were not that important and your child was sicker than you thought, then you may well have judged incorrectly about which duty was more important in that situation.

We can now understand why Ross's theory is often referred to as both **intuitionism** and **pluralistic deontology**. It is called "intuitionism" because Ross claims that the general principles of duty are self-evidently true, and understood as such through a kind of intuition. And his view is known as "pluralistic deontology" because he recognizes that morality is a matter of balancing many competing duties.

Difficulties with Ross's Theory

It is fair to say that many philosophers find Ross's pluralistic moral theory quite attractive, since it avoids the single-mindedness of utilitarianism (rightness is solely a function of producing the best consequences) and the absolutism of Kant's ethics (there are *no exceptions at all* to the duty never to treat others merely as means). Nevertheless, critics of Ross's theory rightly raise several important objections.

First, many doubt that there can be self-evident moral principles that are analogous to the basic principles of mathematics and geometry. This is in part because it seems inconceivable that someone who has the concept of triangles can deny that triangles have three sides, but it does not seem inconceivable that someone can have the concept of the duty of beneficence, and yet deny that one has a *prima facie* duty to be beneficent.[38]

In response, Ross may claim that our *prima facie* duties are analogous to basic principles of mathematics and geometry only in the sense that we do not (or need not) infer these truths from other, more basic, principles. Rather, he may contend that both *prima facie* duties and basic truths of mathematics and geometry can be seen to be correct by anyone of sufficient mental maturity. Someone who cannot see that there is a reason to repay a debt is morally defective, just as someone who cannot see that the longest side of a triangle is opposite its largest angle is geometrically impaired. It is unclear, however, whether this response will satisfy Ross's critics, since at least some of his critics regard a faculty of moral intuition as something completely mysterious.[39]

Another objection to Ross's theory is that it gives too little guidance when it comes to determining our duties, all things considered. An important point of a normative ethical theory, one might argue, is to be action-guiding, that is, to give people a clear mechanism for determining how one ought to act. But Ross's theory is lacking at this point. He says, in effect, that one should identify the various *prima facie* duties in a particular situation and then *do the best one can* to decide which is most important. But many will find this to be too little guidance. Not only that, but such a procedure could simply lead people to embrace their pre-existing prejudices about right conduct. One could well imagine, for instance, two people following Ross's advice and coming to opposite conclusions. There is a *prima facie* duty to tell the truth and a *prima facie* duty not to harm others. When faced with a choice of telling someone the truth or harming that person, one person might conclude that telling the truth is more important here, while another might conclude that not harming that person is more pressing. On Ross's theory, we would have no way of telling whose view is correct. If his ethical theory cannot help us see which course of conduct is morally right in a particular situation, then it is not a very useful theory.

In response to this objection, Ross argues that any attempt to provide a formula to solve moral problems will be overly simplistic and will ultimately result in giving wrong answers to some moral problems. Instead, we have to accept that morality is messy, and that all we can do is be sensitive to the situations we find ourselves in, be aware of the *prima facie* duties involved, and

---

[38] The duty of beneficence is the duty to contribute to the well-being of others. Acccording to Ross, the duty rests "on the mere fact that there are beings in the world whose condition we can make better in respect of virtue, or of intelligence, or of pleasure." See Ross, *The Right and the Good*, 21.

[39] For a powerful, classic attack on the idea that moral truths can be known through moral intuition, see J. L. Mackie, *Inventing Right and Wrong* (London: Penguin, 1989).

then make the best judgment we can about which duty is most pressing in that circumstance.[40]

SOCIAL CONTRACT THEORY

Social contract theory suggests yet another way of understanding the nature of morality and of determining which acts and policies are morally right and wrong, and why. Social contractarians differ in the details of their theory, but they share the fundamental belief that justified moral rules are the ones that rational individuals would agree to for their own benefit. For example, contractarians would argue that a rule against murder is justified because we would each agree to this rule, since each of us benefits from it. In what follows, two versions of social contract theory are presented: the classic statement of the theory, defended by Thomas Hobbes, and a contemporary version of the theory, defended by John Rawls.

HOBBES'S SOCIAL CONTRACT THEORY

A classic defence of social contract theory is given by the seventeenth-century British philosopher, Thomas Hobbes. Hobbes, as a contractarian, thinks that moral rules are those that rational individuals agree to for their mutual benefit. To make his case, and to explain the nature of morality, Hobbes begins by asking what life would be like in a **state of nature,** that is, a time and place where there is no organized society and there are no recognized social rules, where everyone is free to do as he or she pleases.

What would life be like in a state of nature? You might think it would be a time of great peace, with no wars or conflicts over property, where people lived as free, independent individuals in harmony with nature. But this is not Hobbes's view. Instead, he suggests that life in a state of nature would be dreadful, a state of war of everyone against everyone else, where people would live in constant fear of being assaulted and killed, and where life would be, as Hobbes put it, "solitary, poor, nasty, brutish, and short."

You may suspect that Hobbes thinks that people are naturally evil, and that is why he believes the state of nature would be a state of war. But this is not the case. Instead, he makes the more modest assumption that people are primarily self-interested—typically caring more for their own well-being than the well-being of others—and they want to live and to have a better life. Next, he assumes that people need the same basic things: food, shelter, water, and so forth. Unfortunately, in a state of nature there is scarcity of the things needed. Food and shelter, for instance, are relatively scarce, given that they are needed

---

[40] For a contemporary defence of many of Ross's ideas, see Robert Audi, *The Good and the Right: A Theory of Intuition and Intrinsic Value* (Princeton: Princeton University Press, 2004).

by everyone, and yet there is no society to produce them. Finally, he assumes that people in the state of nature are roughly equal in power. That is, while some may be stronger or more rational than others, none is so strong or so rational that he or she can dominate for long over everyone else. Since people desire to live and lack the things needed for survival, they are going to be driven to fight for what they need. The result will be a war of everyone against everyone, where people live in continual fear of violent death.

Because life in the state of nature is so dreadful, and because people desire to live and to have a better life, they will eventually be driven to propose various "articles of peace." These articles of peace are moral rules—limitations on one's freedom—that each person accepts for his or her own benefit. For instance, it would be rational for everyone to agree to seek peace so far as others are willing to seek peace, to keep agreements with each other provided others are willing to do so, to not harm others provided others are willing not to harm them, and perhaps to even come to each other's aid, provided that too is agreed upon by others.[41] Thus, we can see that the rules of morality emerge as a tool that allows people to escape the misery of the state of nature and to obtain the benefits of social living. In short, moral rules are justified because they are in each person's self-interest: they are the rules that would be agreed upon by everyone so that all can live together and have a better life.

Now, it is important to realize that these rules of morality are supposed to be justified even if the state of nature did not actually exist, and even if they were not the product of an actual agreement. The social contractarian's point is that we all benefit from social living and by avoiding a state of nature, and the moral rules are justified because they are the rules needed for us to live together and to avoid this state of nature.

With this in mind, we can see why certain rules—those not needed for social living—would not be supported by social contract theory. For instance, rules prohibiting prostitution, same-sex relationships, or voluntary euthanasia would likely not be supported according to Hobbes's theory, since we could allow for such behaviour without threatening to fall back into a state of nature. On the other hand, rules that protect life and property do seem justified because they are needed for social living and to keep us out of the state of nature.

Hobbes's social contract theory has a number of attractive features. It does a good job of explaining and justifying some moral rules: justified moral rules are limited to those that everyone will agree to so as to enable people to live together in society. It also can explain why some of our most important moral rules are justified: rules against murder and violence, rules that require keeping one's promises and telling the truth are all justified. They all appear to be rules

---

[41] Hobbes also argues that in order to escape the state of nature and to gain the benefits of social living, people need to agree to the existence of a government that has the power of enforcing agreements and punishing wrongdoers. While Hobbes's insistence on the necessity of a government is crucial for understanding his political philosophy, it is not something that needs to be emphasized here.

needed for social living. Further, it can explain convincingly why practices like racial and sexual discrimination are morally wrong: people in the state of nature would certainly not agree to rules that said that they will get fewer rights and privileges than others.

Objections to Hobbes's Social Contract Theory

Nevertheless, Hobbes's social contract theory faces a number of objections. First, it seems unable to satisfactorily explain all of morality. For instance, we recognize obligations not to be cruel to non-human animals, to respect and to try to promote the interests of those humans who are born seriously mentally and physically disabled, and to provide for distant generations. Yet, social contract theory has a difficult time explaining the existence of such obligations. For, surely, self-interested humans could come together to form a society that benefits themselves without recognizing any of these moral obligations.

This objection seems to reveal a deeper problem with social contract theory. It views moral obligations as being justified because it is in each individual's interest to agree to them. But morality seems to be the kind of thing that it is not always in a person's interest to agree to: one might not benefit from living in a society that recognizes a duty not to torture animals or a duty not to be callous to those born with mental disabilities. Nevertheless, it seems clear that one has a duty to not do these things.

Further, it seems that social contract theory gets things wrong when it views morality as the product of agreement. For this implies that if we were in a state of nature, where there were no moral agreements, then nothing would be moral or immoral, just or unjust. Indeed, Hobbes admits this point when he writes of the state of nature that "the notions of right and wrong, justice and injustice, have there no place."[42] But that seems difficult to believe. Most would think that rape and torture would be wrong even in a state of nature (perhaps because it treats people merely as means or causes needless suffering); and kindness to children or sharing one's food with the hungry would be virtuous even if there were no social agreements (perhaps because they manifest respect for others or promote well-being). Yet social contract theory cannot explain these judgments.

Faced with these objections, social contract theorists have a number of responses. One line of response could go like this. First, social contract theorists may remind us that their theory is able to account for many of our moral obligations in a clear and convincing manner. As a result, they may argue that we should be confident in the truth of their ethical theory. With this confidence in mind, they may then simply bite the bullet and deny the commonsense moral claims that animals are directly protected by morality, and that there can be morality (or immorality) prior to agreements. As far as non-rational humans are concerned, social contract theorists might suggest that they would, in fact, be protected directly by a contract between rational individuals. The reason

---

[42] Hobbes, *Leviathan,* 108. (By convention, the page reference is to Hobbes's first edition.)

for this is that rational individuals may realize that it is in their best interest to accept a rule protecting vulnerable, non-rational humans, since one day they may become vulnerable and non-rational.

RAWLS'S SOCIAL CONTRACT THEORY: JUSTICE AS FAIRNESS

At any rate, even if some philosophers find Hobbes's social contract theory to be problematic, many accept some version of contract theory. For many, the guiding idea that moral principles are justified if and only if they would be agreed upon by everyone is a compelling one. Indeed, in recent years, numerous philosophers have tried to refine and defend certain aspects of social contract theory. The most influential modern social contract theorist is John Rawls.[43] Rawls's theory, called **justice as fairness,** is not intended as a comprehensive ethical theory, but rather as a theory of justice, aimed only at the question of how the major social institutions ought to be regulated.[44] Rather than beginning with the conception of a state of nature, Rawls begins with what he calls the **original position.** The original position is a hypothetical situation from which people are to choose the principles of justice to regulate the major social institutions. Like Hobbes, Rawls assumes that the people who are choosing the principles of justice are rational and primarily self-interested, and want to have a good life for themselves. However, unlike Hobbes, Rawls imagines that the people in the original position are behind a **veil of ignorance.** That is, he imagines them as not knowing any particular facts about themselves: for instance, they do not know their race, gender, class, natural abilities, religious convictions, specific values, goals in life, and so forth.

The purpose of the veil of ignorance is two-fold. First, ignorance of one's personal situation will facilitate agreement between people in the original position. If one is self-interested and knows one is from a wealthy family, one will choose principles that favour the wealthy, while those from impoverished backgrounds will favour principles that benefit the poor. Atheists will insist on principles that are beneficial to atheists, while strongly religious persons will seek principles advantageous to their particular religion, and so on. In short, if self-interested people know their personal situations and values, it will be very difficult, if not impossible, to reach unanimous agreement on principles of justice.

---

[43] John Rawls, *A Theory of Justice* (Cambridge: Harvard University Press, 1971).

[44] A comprehensive ethical theory is one that attempts to explain all of our moral obligations. An ethical theory that is not comprehensive aims at explaining a certain subset of our moral obligations. Rawls's theory is not comprehensive, since he attempts to use it only to arrive at an answer to the question "What is the just society?" He does not seek to solve moral questions that exist beyond this topic. Notice how this strategy avoids many of the objections raised against Hobbes's version of social contract theory.

Second, and more importantly, though, the point of the veil of ignorance is to ensure fairness in the choice of principles of justice. Since people in the original position lack all knowledge of their personal circumstances and attributes, they cannot tailor the principles of justice to benefit their own particular circumstances and views of the good life. Instead, people will be forced to choose fairly, or in an unbiased manner. Hence, we get the name of Rawls's theory—*justice as fairness*.

As parties in the original position do not know their particular conception of the good life nor have any particular information about themselves, Rawls believes that they will be extremely cautious in the choice of principles of justice. They will not, for instance, choose principles of justice that favour one race over another, since they may be in the racial group that is forced to form part of the underclass. Likewise, they will not choose a society that is radically inegalitarian when it comes to social opportunities and the distribution of wealth, since they do not know which economic group they will occupy. Thus, parties in the original position will adopt a choice strategy that Rawls calls **maximin:** *Choose in such a way so that you will be doing maximally well if you should turn out to be in the minimum (or worst off) position.* With this in mind, Rawls believes that rational, self-interested people behind a veil of ignorance will choose the following principles of justice:

1. The principle of maximal equal basic liberties: Each person is to have maximal equal basic liberties.
2a. The principle of fair equality of opportunity: Each person should have a meaningful opportunity to attain employment, education, and positions of power.
2b. The difference principle: There should be social and economic equality, unless inequality benefits everyone, especially those in the worst-off group.

According to Rawls, these principles are to be ranked in order of importance, with one being unable to relinquish, for instance, some basic liberties for the sake of greater wealth or greater opportunities.

Thus, Rawls believes that his two principles of justice are the result of a rational choice from an original position that is set up so as to be fair. Because the original position is fair, and because people would choose Rawls's two principles from the original position, it follows, Rawls argues, that the two principles of justice are themselves fair.

Rawls's theory of justice has been enormously influential in the areas of social and political philosophy. Feminists, for instance, have used Rawls's ideas to argue for justice within the family.[45] (Would people from behind a veil of ignorance agree that one sex would do most of the housework and child-rearing? Would they agree that those who stay home with the children so their

---

[45] Susan Moller Okin, *Justice, Gender and the Family* (New York: Basic Books, 1991).

partners can go out and work would receive no direct financial compensation for their decision?) Likewise, Rawls's ideas have been used to argue for justice in the distribution of health care. Not knowing in the original position if they were going to be healthy or unhealthy, or if they would be able to afford or not afford needed medical care, would lead people to make sure that everyone had access to health care, regardless of ability to pay. A system that allowed only the rich to get access to health care would certainly not be chosen by people in the original position, because of the risks people would run if it turned out that they were not healthy and not rich.[46]

Difficulties with Rawls's Social Contract Theory

Rawls's theory is widely recognized for its contribution to political and social philosophy. Nevertheless, it has its detractors. For one thing, as Rawls himself acknowledges, his theory of justice will not apply to all moral issues—rather, it is meant only to regulate major social institutions. What one owes to friends, what it is to lead a virtuous life, and how one ought to treat non-human animals are among the moral questions beyond the scope of his theory. (Of course, this is not really an *objection* to Rawls's theory, since he never intended his view to be comprehensive. The point, rather, is to note a limitation of the scope of his theory.)

Moreover, many have argued that Rawls's characterization of the original position is problematic. One concern is that while the original position is meant to be characterized as a fair situation from which one is to choose principles of justice, it is not a fair choice situation. For example, some claim that Rawls's characterization of the original position is biased against certain religious groups. Rawls assumes that people in the original position do not know whether they're religious. He also assumes that people in the original position want more **primary social goods** (liberty and rights, opportunities, income and wealth) rather than less. Rawls's motivation for these constraints on the principles of justice, as we have mentioned, is primarily to ensure fairness and a lack of bias. But the religious critic of Rawls's theory will say that these assumptions are actually biased against ultra-religious individuals and communities—the Amish or ultra-Orthodox Jews, for example. These individuals do not view their religion and its teachings as biasing conditions; rather, they view their religion and its teachings as the source of truth. Further, these religious groups likely do not value the so-called primary social goods of liberties, opportunities, income and wealth. Instead, what they may value is obedience to their religion and to their traditions, and the right to be left alone. And they may well view liberties, opportunities, and income and wealth as either not primary social goods or as positively harmful societal options.

---

[46] See, for instance, Norman Daniels, "Equal Opportunities and Health Care," reprinted in *Ethical Issues in Modern Medicine: Contemporary Readings in Bioethics,* 7th ed., ed. Bonnie Steinbock, John D. Arras, and Alex John London (Boston: McGraw-Hill, 2009).

Another objection to Rawls's theory concerns his claim that parties in the original position will choose the *difference principle* (which promotes social and economic equality) to regulate social and economic issues. Rawls argues that parties in the original position will choose the difference principle because they will want to guard against the possibility of being in an intolerable situation should they find themselves to be in the worst-off economic group. However, one could agree with Rawls that those in the original position will want to avoid intolerable outcomes, and yet deny that they would choose the difference principle to distribute income and wealth in society. Instead, in addition to a principle of maximal equal basic liberty and a principle of fair equality of opportunity, one might choose a principle that guaranteed that those in the worst-off group did tolerably well. In other words, people in the original position might accept a principle which allowed for significant economic inequality provided that those in the worst-off group have their basic needs met and have the meaningful opportunity to advance to a higher social and economic class.[47] Such a principle would allow people to prosper greatly economically and socially, should they be lucky to be born with the requisite natural skills and fortunate social circumstances; it would reward those who were hard working (and fortunate), enabling them to have a way to move from one class to another; and it would allow for protections should one find oneself in the worst-off group. Thus, it is at least unclear why the difference principle should be preferred to this less egalitarian principle of justice.

People on the political Left may also argue that Rawls's difference principle would not be chosen from behind a veil of ignorance. However, their argument would be that the difference principle is not sufficiently egalitarian. For the difference principle allows for *some* economic inequality—some people are allowed to have more income and wealth than others, provided that it maximally benefits those in the worst-off group. Thus, the difference principle is compatible with the formation of economic classes (though, to be sure, the degree of economic inequality will be much less than in most— probably all—industrial countries today). But the critic on the Left argues that people in the original position would not choose a principle that, by allowing the formation of economic classes, would underrepresent the interests of the poor in forming the political leadership and setting the political agenda. Instead, in order to safeguard their political voice and other basic liberties, it might be most rational for parties in the original position to prefer a system that required social and economic equality. Such a society may not be as wealthy as a society regulated by the difference principle, but it would be a more just society, since it would allow for more effective realization of people's basic liberties.

---

[47] We might call the idea that people in the original position will want to ensure a tolerable outcome should they turn out to be in the worst-off group *tolemin*, in contrast to Rawls's idea of *maximin*.

Further, many think that the difference principle is to be rejected because it is unfair. The concern is that it requires that the state assist people in the worst-off economic group regardless of why they are in that group. According to the difference principle, a person who is in the worst-off economic group because of illness or some other unfortunate circumstance has no greater claim to economic assistance than someone who is in the worst-off group because of laziness or choice. And this seems patently unfair. It is unfair to tax the hard work of some to assist those who are in the worst-off economic group because of choice, yet this is precisely what the difference principle requires.

Something like this unfairness criticism of Rawls's theory can also be raised against attempts to apply his theory to questions in health care. Is it right for the veil of ignorance to exclude knowledge of whether or not a person takes care of herself, or whether she is reckless with her health? If so, does that not penalize those who take great efforts to eat healthfully, exercise regularly, drink moderately, and refrain from tobacco use? And does it not reward people who make poor health choices? If that is the case, then one might rightly wonder if such an approach truly is a fair approach to questions of just health care.

Lastly, a concern with Rawls's theory is that it does not clearly settle problems of social justice, since it is sometimes unclear what the parties in the original position would choose. For instance, would parties in the original position opt for a single-payer health care system which covered everyone equally, or would they favour a two-tier system—one that gave basic coverage to everyone, but also allowed the rich to purchase private health care to buy more exotic medical treatments? Would parties in the original position support research into the development of cures for extremely rare diseases, or would they favour an emphasis on preventing illness and developing treatments for more common diseases?

Thus, it seems that Rawls's theory faces numerous problems. This is not to suggest that it cannot deal with these problems, or that a modified contractarian position could not do better. These matters are complex, and debates continue. It is fair to say that Rawls's theory is justly famous, for it gives us a fascinating way to think about just social institutions. The idea of evaluating social institutions from behind a veil of ignorance has widespread (if not universal) appeal; and it is an approach that has been adopted by many philosophers, even if they do not fully accept Rawls's principles of justice. Furthermore, Rawls and others have argued that even if the original position/ contract argument is rejected, other reasons can be marshalled in support of his principles—reasons that can appeal to religious minorities and non-religious groups alike.[48] Even if Rawls's theory does not get things exactly right, it may get many things right, and like all good philosophical theories, it points others in promising directions.

---

[48] John Rawls, *Political Liberalism* (New York: Columbia University Press, 1993).

ARISTOTLE'S VIRTUE THEORY

The ethical theories we have explored thus far have focused on identifying criteria for morally right and wrong actions, or on identifying just and unjust principles. **Virtue ethics** is commonly taken to represent a fundamentally different approach to ethics. Rather than focusing on right and wrong action, or justified or unjustified principles, virtue ethics is said to focus on *moral character*. While this distinction is somewhat misleading—the consequentialist and deontological theories explored above are concerned with moral character, and virtue ethicists are interested in right and wrong action—it does seem to capture an important difference between virtue ethics and these other normative theories. Consider a case of telling the truth. The utilitarian would say this is right (if it is right) because of its good consequences. The Kantian would say it is right because it is accordance with the injunction to treat others always as ends, and so on. The virtue ethicist will say it is right because it is a manifestation of the virtue *honesty*; it is the kind of thing an honest person would do.

The most influential virtue theorist is Aristotle.[49] According to Aristotle, the best life for a human being is a virtuous life—a life in which one exercises the virtues. A **virtue** is a character trait that disposes one to act and feel in a way that is appropriate. Thus, for instance, a person who possesses the virtue of compassion acts compassionately when circumstances call for it, takes pleasure in acting this way, and feels badly for others' misfortunes. (One does not have the virtue of compassion if one does the right act but feels nothing or feels pained while doing it.)

Aristotle adds that virtues are *positive* character traits, because they are necessary for the supreme good—**eudaimonia**. The term *eudaimonia* can be roughly translated as "flourishing" or "happiness." The suggestion, then, is that possession of the virtues is necessary for leading a flourishing or happy life as a human being. Aristotle recognizes that human beings are rational, social animals. In order to live successfully as rational, social animals, certain character traits are needed. For instance, in order to get along with others, one needs to be honest and trustworthy. These traits will benefit you in your life, since they facilitate cooperation with others. Likewise, a human being faces challenges in life and so will need courage to overcome these challenges. This will be true not only of people like soldiers, firefighters, and police officers, but of all people, since all people face challenges that require courage to overcome. Industriousness, understanding, self-control, beneficence, generosity, perseverance, and loyalty are virtues since these too seem to be important character traits to possess if one is to live well over a lifetime.

For the virtue theorist, then, the focus is not on formulating principles of right action (or rules) and then acting according to those principles. Instead, the focus is on developing a virtuous character. One becomes virtuous by

---

[49] See, especially, Aristotle's *Nicomachean Ethics*.

doing virtuous acts, and by learning over time to take pleasure in those acts. We begin to acquire the virtues, Aristotle suggests, in much the same way that we acquire special skills like playing a musical instrument or a sport. Consider two contemporary examples: learning to play guitar or tennis well takes much practice and proper training. Similarly, learning to be virtuous (courageous, honest, and so forth) requires that one practise doing virtuous acts and be properly educated in the virtues. Further (and unlike some special skill, like playing guitar), education and habituation (that is, practice) are crucial for developing the moral virtues so that one can also learn how to *feel* appropriately when doing virtuous actions.

According to Aristotle, part of understanding the virtues, and learning how to become virtuous, consists in recognizing that the virtues exist as a mean between two extremes—one of excess and the other of deficiency. This idea is known as the **doctrine of the mean.** For an explanation, consider the virtue of courage. This virtue is the mean between the extremes of cowardice (the deficiency) and rashness (the excess). A coward fails to stand up and fight the battles that ought to be fought. The person who is rash rushes to fight (physically, verbally, or emotionally) when fighting is not wise (as when one cannot win, or when one could win more easily by being diplomatic). The courageous person, by contrast, fights at the right time and in the right way. Another example is honesty. This virtue is the mean between the deficiency of being dishonest and the excess of being brutally honest. The dishonest person will conceal the truth when it ought to be told; the blunt person will state the truth when it should not be told or in a way that is inappropriate for the situation; the honest person, however, will be honest in the right way and at the right time, conveying what needs to be said but in a manner that is appropriately tactful. (Think about issues like telling a patient she has cancer. It is usually thought that one needs to be honest here, where this means communicating the truth, but in a sensitive and caring manner.)

That the virtues are characterized as means between two extremes is significant for several reasons. First, it helps people identify what the virtues are. Second, it can help one in becoming virtuous. For Aristotle points out that each of us has certain tendencies to go to one extreme or another, and that we are therefore more likely to hit the mark of acting virtuously if we aim at the opposite extreme. The excessively shy person, for instance, should know that she tends toward being shy, and so should aim at being excessively friendly and outgoing. In this way, she is more likely to overcome her shyness and develop the virtue of sociality.[50] Finally, the doctrine of the mean is an interesting idea because it explains why it is difficult to be virtuous: a given virtue is always

---

[50] Thus Aristotle speaks of the doctrine of the mean as being a mean relative to the individual. Just as it is true that all people should eat the proper amount of calories but this will mean different things for an Olympic athlete than for a couch potato, so all people should be honest, but one would expect a different degree of honesty from a close friend than from a mere acquaintance.

"surrounded" by specific vices, so it can be quite easy to slip into one of the vices, as opposed to hitting the mark of being virtuous.

Objections to Virtue Theory

There is much to recommend virtue theory. It is unclear, however, whether virtue theory is a comprehensive doctrine. Ethics concerns itself with more than matters of character; there are also questions, for instance, about how to design just institutions. What would be a fair tax code? How much tax money should go to public schools and how much to health care? Should Quebec be allowed to separate from Canada if 50 percent + 1 of Quebecers vote for secession? These are all important ethical questions insofar as they greatly influence people's well-being, autonomy, and opportunities. However, it is unclear whether virtue theory can contribute to these debates. Perhaps the virtue theorist could say, when it comes to an issue like Quebec separatism, or structuring our tax code, that we should do what a virtuous person would do—but the worry is that this admonition is too vague to be helpful.

On a related point, it is often unclear how useful virtue theory can actually be when it comes to issues involving tough ethical choices for which we need answers.[51] For instance, there are many cases where it seems that different virtues recommend different courses of action. For instance, would a virtuous person who has young children get a divorce if she is unhappy in her marriage? Loyalty, compassion, and concern for her children may speak against divorce; but courage, authenticity, and honesty might speak in favour of divorce. The virtue theorist tells us to do what a virtuous person would do, or to follow the virtues, but this seems unhelpful in a case where different virtues seem to push in different directions. Indeed, the *same* virtue seemingly can point in opposite directions. In the case of the unhappy woman, courage may speak in favour of staying and trying to make the marriage better, but courage may say to leave and try to make a fresh start on her own. Thus the instruction to be "courageous" appears unhelpful.

In response to these objections, the virtue theorist can plausibly say that hard cases are hard cases, and we should not expect an ethical theory to make hard choices easy. (Recall that Ross had a similar thing to say to similar objections to his theory.) Indeed, Aristotle famously, and some may say wisely, says that we should not expect more precision from a subject than the subject allows.[52] Perhaps, then, we can expect precise answers to problems in mathematics, but we cannot always expect neat answers to moral questions. Nevertheless, it does seem fair to worry that an ethical theory loses some of its appeal if the theory is too murky and too frequently lacking in guidance. And this is the worry that many have with virtue theory.

---

[51] Virtue theory is not alone in having to deal with the objection that it does not always give clear guidance. As we have seen, this is also a problem, for instance, for pluralistic deontology.
[52] Aristotle, *Nicomachean Ethics* 1094, 24–25.

Alternatively, the virtue theorist could try to overcome the murkiness objection by appealing to a decision procedure to decide what to do in cases of conflict. For instance, suppose a person asks you a question, and the truthful answer to that question would hurt his feelings. A virtue theorist could say that we have a conflict between honesty and compassion, and if more good will comes out of being compassionate than being honest, then a virtuous person would tactfully opt for compassion. But then, notice that the virtue theorist appears to be resolving ethical problems by ultimately appealing to their consequences. And thus, the worry is that virtue theory just collapses into a kind of consequentialism. Alternatively, if the virtue theorist says it is more important to be honest than compassionate, since a virtuous person would not be disrespectful of others, and to deceive the person would be disrespectful, then it appears that the virtue theorist has collapsed the view into something very much like Kantianism.

Thus, it seems that a real challenge faces the virtue theorist. Either the virtue theorist's view is frequently murky and unhelpful, or else it can give clear guidance, but only by resorting to a theory of right action. If it is frequently murky and unhelpful, then ultimately virtue theory is not a useful procedure for resolving ethical issues. Alternatively, if it gives clear guidance about how to prioritize or interpret the virtues, then it risks disappearing as a distinctive ethical position—that is, it threatens to collapse into consequentialism, Kantianism, or some other principle of right action.

Of course, virtue theorists today are trying to work out answers to these and others challenges to their view. We have already suggested one response—that it is a mistake to look for precise answers to complex moral problems. Also, virtue theorists could perhaps deal with the objection that their theory has little to say about moral problems that do not clearly involve issues of moral character by giving up the attempt to present their theory as the solution to all moral issues. Just as Rawls limited the scope of his theory to questions of social justice, virtue theorists may want to limit their theory's scope to questions of moral character and individual action. At any rate, many believe that virtue theory is particularly well suited to deal with a wide variety of ethical issues in health care, since so often these issues involve questions of character. Important ethical issues such as the virtues of the physician or nurse, the appropriate professional-patient relationship, and compassionate care for the dying are just a few of many possible examples.[53]

FEMINISM AND THE ETHICS OF CARE

Feminism may be defined as the view that women (and girls) have been, and in various ways continue to be, oppressed; it seeks to understand the nature of the

---

[53] Recent important works in virtue theory include Thomas Hurka, *Virtues, Vices and Morals* (New York: Oxford University Press, 2001); Rosalind Hursthouse, *On Virtue Ethics* (New York: Oxford University Press, 1999); and Philippa Foot, *Virtues and Vices and Other Essays in Moral Philosophy* (Berkeley: University of California Press, 1978).

oppression and to determine how best to overcome it. Some feminist philosophers embrace one of the standard ethical theories discussed above and use it to explain the wrongs women and girls experience. Thus, there are utilitarian feminists, Kantian feminists, contractarian feminists, and so forth. It seems that much headway can be made in promoting the cause of women's equality by applying these traditional theories to women's lives. Utilitarians could point to the great amount of needless suffering caused by patriarchy; Kantians can expose the various ways in which the historical treatment of women could not be willed as a universal law, as well as the many conventions and practices disrespectful to women's rational nature; social contract theorists could use the idea of the veil of ignorance to uncover how society would need to be reorganized to the benefit of many women; and virtue theorists could point to many instances of how mistreating women and girls is incompatible with being a virtuous person.[54]

Still other feminists have been skeptical of the traditional ethical approaches, suggesting that the ethical approaches are themselves inherently flawed or incomplete. There is much truth to the claim that traditional ethical theories, developed by men, have often failed to turn their attention to the plight of women. For instance, Kantians tend to emphasize the importance of acting on principle and out of respect for the moral law. This emphasis on respecting principle, as opposed to emphasizing context and the importance of caring relationships, may be indicative more of male bias than moral wisdom. Similarly, social contract theorists seem to emphasize self-interest and abstract principles of fairness, and they appear to ignore motivations of caring and the fact that people are embedded in a series of relationships. Instead of "an ethic of principle," it might be argued that we need a new ethical approach altogether. One such perspective that has received considerable attention in recent years is known as **the ethics of care.**

THE ETHICS OF CARE

The ethics of care begins with the observation that there are different kinds of moral knowledge.[55] There is moral knowledge that comes from the articulation and then application of abstract principles, as evidenced by such theories as utilitarianism, Kantianism, and contractarianism. But there is also a kind of moral knowledge that comes from attending to the relationships one finds oneself in. Sensing and interpreting the needs and interests of self and others, and learning how to appropriately respond to those needs and interests, one might argue, is every bit as important as being able to universalize maxims.

---

[54] An excellent introduction to the variety of feminist theories is Rosemary Tong's *Feminine and Feminist Ethics* (Belmont, CA: Wadsworth, 1993). For a fascinating feminist application of Rawls's theory, see Susan Moller Okin, *Justice, Gender, and the Family* (New York: Basic Books, 1989).

[55] Carol Gilligan, *In A Different Voice: Psychological Theory and Women's Development* (Cambridge: Harvard University Press, 1982).

Yet, this second way of moral knowing and acting has largely been ignored in the male-dominated history of moral philosophy.[56] The ethics of care aims at rectifying this omission.

Rather than using principles to arrive at the solutions to moral problems, one needs to adopt a perspective of caring. Here the focus is on maintaining and improving one's relationships. For instance, if a relative is sick and in the hospital, a Kantian may reason that one ought to visit the sick relative because one could not will it as a universal law that one should not care for the needy. Alternatively, the utilitarian may recommend visiting the hospital because he sees it as an effective way to promote overall welfare. But these seem like the wrong kind of reasons for visiting one's ill relative in the hospital. Instead, the reason one ought to visit one's relative in the hospital is because one *cares* about one's relative and one's ongoing relationship with him, and so one wants to be sensitive to and to attend to his needs.[57]

The ethics of care has been applied to health care ethics in interesting and important ways. For instance, feminists seek to deepen our understanding of such core notions as autonomy and competence, insisting that we become more sensitive to the background circumstances that affect people's understandings and choices. When thinking about the issue of abortion, for example, traditional philosophical approaches have focused on the alleged conflict of rights between the pregnant woman and the fetus. But the ethics of care might address this issue by focusing on different questions, such as "What circumstances led the woman to become pregnant?" and "What social supports are available to make it easier for women to not abort and to have the child?" Or, to take a different example, consider a case where patient autonomy and competency are at issue when it comes to accepting or rejecting some life-prolonging therapy. The ethics of care would insist on much more than just a meeting with the physician to explain the medical situation and a psychiatric evaluation to ensure that the patient understood her options and the likely consequences of her decisions. The ethics of care would encourage the patient and those close to her, including family and friends, nurses and physicians, to work together (in a non-hierarchical manner) to find a solution that would work best for all concerned. In short, the ethics of care rejects the idea of the individual as an isolated being, and sees her embedded in a series of relationships. Further, the ethics of care seeks to discover ways to understand, nurture, and support these relationships.

Difficulties with the Ethics of Care

While the ethics of care does well to remind us that ethics is more than just a matter of acting on principle, it is not at all clear that this approach can stand

---

[56] A noteworthy exception may be virtue theory, since, as we have seen, the virtues require not only right action, but also appropriate feelings.

[57] See, for instance, Nel Noddings, *Caring: A Feminine Approach to Ethics and Moral Education,* 2nd ed. (Berkeley: University of California Press, 2003).

on its own as a complete ethical theory. One concern about the ethics of care is that it is doubtful that all relationships requiring "attending to." Feminists are well aware that many relationships are exploitative or abusive. Often it seems best that these relationships be ended, and that the "needs" of the abusers *not* be attended to.

Another concern is that one often finds that one is involved in several important relationships, but that simultaneously attending to them all is not possible. At the same time, one's children may need looking after, relationships at work may require that one take a business trip, and an elderly parent may be ill and in need of one's presence. The claim that in such cases that one needs to be attentive and caring toward one's relationships now becomes unhelpful, since there is no way that all of these relationships can be jointly and simultaneously looked after.

The previous two points suggest a similar problem. It seems that the ethics of care needs to appeal to principles to help a person decide what to do. For instance, principles are needed to explain which relationships require nurturing and which require ending, which needs or interests within a loving and good relationship require attending to, and which are illegitimate and should be resisted. Similarly, when conflicting demands from distinct relationships arise, it seems one needs principles to help one decide which relationship should take priority, or which needs ought to be attended to first and which will have to wait, and which will have to be left unattended to. In short, it seems, there is no easy escape from the need for principles. The direction to "attend to relationships" seems inadequate and at times (in the case of abusive relationships) positively wrong-headed.[58]

A further limitation on the ethics of care is that it seems to limit the realm of ethics to the realm of one's relationships. But there may be ethical obligations that exist even in circumstances where relationships do not. For instance, most believe (1) we cannot have relationships with people that do not exist, and (2) we have ethical obligations to people living in future generations. But then it follows, (3) not all of our obligations are based on attending to relationships. (4) An ethics of care views all of morality as a matter of attending to relationships. Therefore, (5) an ethics of care cannot be correct.[59]

---

[58] A defender of the ethics of care may respond to these objections by trying to argue that we can best determine how to balance conflicting needs in different relationships, and how to best deal with destructive relationships, in a contextual manner, without appealing to principle. The idea may be that we bring the parties involved together (wherever possible) to try to work out for themselves acceptable solutions for that particular difficulty.

[59] Instead of the example of future generations, a similar point could be made with such examples as famine victims in a far-off land who need our aid, or people in our own society who are isolated and alone but in need of help. Surely we have moral obligations to assist these people in need, even though we are not in any sort of relationship with these people.

Now, it is unlikely that a defender of an ethics of care will resist premises (1) and (2). Line (3) of the argument logically follows from premises (1) and (2), so line (3) must be accepted if lines (1) and (2) are accepted. This leaves premise (4). It seems that the most promising strategy for a defender of the ethics of care may be to abandon premise (4) and to claim that not all of morality can be explained by an ethics of care. Instead, it could be maintained that a core part of morality can be explained in terms of meeting the needs of the relationships one finds oneself in. However, this is not all of morality: there are other ethical concerns that fall outside of one's relationships. And another normative theory needs to be invoked to deal with these ethical issues.

If the above is correct, then the ethics of care seems to provide an important insight into part of morality—part of the moral life involves the sensitive concern for the needs and interests of those one is in a relationship with. This will involve developing and prizing the sensibilities necessary for identifying others' needs, and understanding how to properly care for them. Nevertheless, it seems that it would be a serious mistake to think that this is all of morality. An appeal to principle appears necessary to tell people how to respond to the demands of conflicting relationships; how to determine which relationships (or needs within a relationship) are no longer worth attending to; and how to respond to the variety of ethical issues that do not involve relationships.[60]

CONCLUSION

As this chapter makes clear, normative ethical theory is a rich and complex area of philosophical inquiry. We have examined several different philosophies. Each of these theories contains compelling insights into the nature of right and wrong, and each of these theories faces objections. In the light of these objections, philosophers continue to develop and refine their theories. As in other areas of inquiry, disagreement persists over which theory is, on balance, best. In the following chapter, each author explains his favoured ethical theory. Specifically, you will see Doran defend a version of pluralistic deontology, Patrick defend a version of virtue theory, and Warren defend a version of social contract theory. These approaches will then guide each of us as we debate the ethical problems in health care that make up the remainder of the text. In addition to our favoured approaches, it is quite likely that readers will find it useful to appeal to the other ethical theories discussed in this chapter, as different ethical issues in health care are considered.

---

[60] Readers interested in pursuing these and related issues should see Susan Sherwin, *No Longer Patient: Feminist Ethics and Health Care* (Philadelphia: Temple University Press, 1992); Virginia Held, *Feminist Morality: Transforming Culture, Society, and Politics* (Chicago: University of Chicago Press, 1993); and Virginia Held, ed., *Justice and Care: Essential Readings in Feminist Ethics* (Boulder, CO: Westview, 1995).

Review Questions

1. Explain the difference between normative ethics, descriptive ethics, and metaethics.
2. What is the difference between ethical relativism and ethical objectivism?
3. Define classical act utilitarianism and explain why it is said to be too simple.
4. What is Kant's distinction between an action's having moral worth and an action's being morally right?
5. Use Kant's Universal Law version and the Humanity version of the categorical imperative test to explain why it is wrong for health care professionals to deceive their patients.
6. According to Ross, what is a *prima facie* duty, and how does it differ from a duty, all things considered?
7. According to social contract theory, what justifies a moral rule?
8. Explain why John Rawls's theory of justice is known as *justice as fairness*.
9. According to Aristotle, what is a moral virtue? In what way are the moral virtues similar and in what ways do they differ from other excellences, such as being an excellent musician?
10. What is the ethics of care? Explain two problems with an ethics of care.

WWW.MCGRAWHILL.CA/OLC/SMOLKIN

OUR PHILOSOPHICAL APPROACHES

INTRODUCTION

In the previous chapter, we critically examined some of the most important and influential normative ethical theories. While Doran, Patrick, and Warren subscribe to theories which were explained in that chapter, each has his own particular way of understanding and interpreting his favoured approach. The purpose of this chapter is for each author to explain and give his reasons for supporting his preferred normative ethical theory. This will help you to understand how each author approaches the ethical problems that will be debated in the coming chapters.

LEARNING OBJECTIVES

After completing this chapter, you should be able to:

- Explain and apply Doran's pluralist approach to ethics
- Describe Doran's objections to utilitarianism, Kantianism, social contract theory, and virtue ethics
- Distinguish metaethics from normative ethics
- Explain and apply Patrick's virtue-based approach to ethics
- Identify important similarities between colour properties and moral properties, on Patrick's view
- Explain and apply Warren's social contract theory
- Describe Warren's version of the original position, including the veil of ignorance and the sympathy metarule

DORAN'S PLURALISTIC APPROACH TO ETHICS

Philosophers have developed a wide variety of **normative ethical theories.** As was explained in the previous chapter, a normative ethical theory consists of a set of principles which purport to tell one how one ought to lead one's life. For some normative ethical theories the focus is on defending principles of right action; for other theories, the concern is more with determining which character traits ought to be developed. But all normative ethical theories share the common concern of determining how we are to lead ethically good lives. Although I cannot fully defend this here, I believe that each leading ethical theory provides important insights into the ethical life. However, I also find that each leading ethical theory fails to provide a complete explanation of right and wrong. As a result, I believe the best way to approach ethical problems is by adopting a kind of **moral pluralism.** That is, there are a *variety* of principles that help determine whether an act is morally right or wrong. As I explain below, the thoughtful philosopher draws on the insights of the leading philosophical theories, determines which particular moral principles are relevant to a given moral problem, and then uses those considerations to reason about what ought to be done. Such an approach to ethics is messy and unsystematic. However, I believe that rigidly following one ethical approach is less likely to provide reasonable answers to the variety of moral problems that we encounter. In what follows, I very briefly explain some of the main reasons why I find the leading ethical theories to be false, and what, in the light of this, is the best way to proceed.[1]

---

[1] Chapter 2 contains a more detailed discussion of the strengths and weaknesses of some of the leading normative ethical theories.

Leading Ethical Theories and Their Problems

Act utilitarians argue that the consequences of an action are the key factor in determining whether an action is morally right or wrong. Indeed, they believe that the right act in any situation is the one that produces the *best* consequences. I believe utilitarians are right to insist that the consequences of an action are important; however, like many, I believe that utilitarians err in thinking that the *only* determinant of a right act is its consequences. For example, when thinking about whether to honour a contract, one thing one should consider is the consequences of violating one's word. But, it seems, another reason to honour a contract, independent of consequences, is that it is in itself morally important to keep one's word. Further against utilitarianism, it seems that it gives the intuitively incorrect answer in many cases. For instance, a person can be quite confident that he should pay the teen who mowed his lawn the $20 he promised, rather than, say, give the money to UNICEF, even though he may not be at all certain that paying the teen will produce the most good.[2] Promoting good consequences is a morally significant factor, but it seems that it is not the only morally relevant consideration.

Kantians, by contrast, maintain that there are certain moral duties that are absolute, and must never be acted against. Keeping promises, not lying, not stealing, and not assaulting others are all examples of absolute moral duties, according to Kant. Underlying this belief is the idea that it is wrong to act on principles that one cannot consistently will that everyone follow. For instance, breaking a contract is wrong since one cannot always will that everyone break contracts. Also, Kantians defend the existence of these absolute moral duties because they think that it is wrong to act on principles that treat people (rational beings) merely as means (things). Thus, for example, it is wrong to lie to someone because it is disrespectful—it treats the person as a thing rather than an end in himself. But, unlike the Kantian, I do not think that these moral duties are absolute nor do I think that such considerations entirely determine the rightness or wrongness of an act. Failing to tell the truth, for example, may be disrespectful, but sometimes it is morally permissible or even morally required to lie, such as when it is the only way to save someone from being murdered. Similarly, on some occasions, an act may be morally permissible even when it is based on principles that cannot be followed by everyone. For instance, Kant claims it is always morally wrong not to keep one's contracts, but if repaying a bank loan (keeping one's contract) would mean that a parent would not have enough money to buy medicine for her very sick child, then it seems morally permissible not to repay the loan. Respecting people's rational nature and acting on principles that can be applied universally are important moral factors, but it appears that they are not all that is morally relevant.

---

[2] The example is based on a similar case initially introduced by R. Sartorius and used by Will Kymlicka in his *Contemporary Political Philosophy*, 24.

Social contract theory argues that moral rules are those that all rational people would agree to for their mutual benefit. Rules against stealing, murder, and mugging, for instance, are all justified because such rules would be chosen by everyone as a means of protecting their own self-interest. In contrast, limitations on free speech or on religious worship, for instance, are not necessarily mutually beneficial, and so would not be justified moral rules. Now, social contract theory does a nice job of explaining and justifying many core moral rules, but, nevertheless, I do not think that it explains all of morality. Social contract theory is notoriously weak, for example, in satisfactorily explaining our obligations to non-rational beings and entities, such as mentally incompetent humans, non-human animals, the natural environment, and future generations. Yet, it seems we do have direct moral obligations to at least some, if not all, of these things. However, it is very hard for contractarians to satisfactorily explain why there are such obligations.

Finally, I think **virtue** theory contains numerous profound insights into the nature of morality that are overlooked by other ethical theories. Rather than searching for criteria of right action, the focus of virtue theory is on such questions as "What is to be a good person?" and "What is it to live well?" Typically, virtue theorists argue that the character traits needed for being a good person and living well include the moral virtues: courage, honesty, industriousness, trustworthiness, compassion, loyalty, and other traits. While virtue theory provides an important approach to ethics, it too seems incomplete. Many critics think that it gives too little direction about how to act when the virtues conflict. For example, the virtues of honesty and compassion seem to frequently clash. The honest act may not be compassionate, while the compassionate act may not be honest. The virtue theorist's admonition "Be virtuous!" or "Do what a virtuous person would do!" is hardly helpful in such cases.

Moreover, the virtue theorist seems to miss the main reason an act is morally right or wrong. Consider, for example, animal abuse. Intuitively, the main reason it is wrong is not because it shows a lack of virtue on the part of the abuser, but because it causes needless suffering *to the animal*. It would be odd to say that animal abuse is wrong because it manifests a vicious character, since we think the animal abuser has a vicious character because he is doing something wrong. Indeed, I think that virtue theorists err when they conflate two distinct issues—what makes an act right or wrong and what makes a person morally good or bad. To see this, consider someone who performs an act that he reasonably thinks is beneficial, but which turns out to be harmful. Perhaps he donates to a charity because he wants to help famine victims; however, it turns out that the charity is a fraud, and the money actually supports the lavish and corrupt lifestyle of a con artist. In this case, it is clear that giving to the charity was *not* the right thing to do, although we may still want to view the person who donated as having a good character (as being charitable). But if this is correct, then right action cannot be understood simply in terms of virtuous character. What makes a person virtuous or vicious is one thing, and what makes an act right or wrong is another. If this is right, then again it seems that we have a moral theory that is of great interest—for assessment of a person's character *is* an important part of morality—but that still fails to capture all of morality.

Roughly analogous remarks apply to my analysis of an **ethics of care.** A complete moral theory ought to recognize the significance and importance of care and of attending to the needs of others. But an ethics of care seems to me to be incomplete in some important ways. That an act is caring may be a reason to perform the act, but other considerations also need to be taken into account, such as whether *other* obligations are more pressing. Also, it is not clear that one should, morally speaking, always care about caring. It seems morally permissible, for instance, not to care about the needs of an abusive partner or parent. But if these points are correct, then ethics is more than just a matter of caring.

Moral Pluralism

For the above reasons and others, I am in the rather uncomfortable position of appreciating both the insights and the difficulties of each of the leading ethical theories. Fortunately, I am not alone in this regard. Indeed, it seems that many philosophers working in ethics routinely appeal to the insights found in more than one ethical theory. Like these philosophers, when I approach a moral problem, I try to identify the moral reasons for or against the case: Will such an action have negative/positive consequences? Will such an action violate/respect someone's autonomy? Will such an action involve dishonesty/honesty, or the sacrifice/promotion of the agent's personal integrity? And so forth. I then try to weigh these varied considerations. In easy cases, these moral reasons all lean in the same direction. For example, murder is wrong since it tends to have harmful consequences, is disrespectful of rational nature, cannot be universalized, undermines social living, and for other reasons. Similarly, keeping one's promises is normally right, since it normally has good consequences, respects rational nature, can be universalized, facilitates social living, and involves personal integrity. These are the easy cases.

Our book is full of the hard cases—cases where respect for personal autonomy seems to conflict with the promotion of the best consequences, or with caring, or with respect for one's personal or professional integrity, and so on. Indeed, cases like these are interesting precisely because they are so difficult. My approach in these hard cases is to identify the moral reasons for and against, and to try to reach a determination about which moral reasons are most pressing in each case. In this regard, my work in ethics is most closely aligned with what is sometimes referred to as **pluralistic deontology.**

Following W. D. Ross, I'd say that morality consists in many conditional duties: to be honest, to promote good consequences, to repay debts, to not harm, to promote virtue, and so forth. In many cases, these conditional duties conflict. In cases of conflict, one must study the situation carefully and try to reach a considered judgment about which duties are most pressing in that situation. Whatever the strongest duties recommend in any situation constitutes the right thing to do in that situation.[3]

Here are some examples to make the point clearer. Recall the case of the homeowner who hires a teen to mow his lawn for $20. Upon completion of the task, the teen comes to collect his fee. The homeowner suddenly realizes that he could give this $20 to a charity like UNICEF or he could pay the teen what he promised. In this case, it seems quite clear that the duty to keep his promise is more important than the duty to help others. Thus, the right thing to do in this situation would be to pay the teen, and the reason is "he promised." In other situations, though, the duty to keep a promise may be outweighed by considerations of welfare. For instance, if forced to choose between keeping a promise to meet a student in my office at a certain time or to come to the aid of someone in mortal danger (say, another student who had just been hit by a truck and who needs my first aid skills in order to survive), then clearly my duty to help the needy would take priority in this situation over the duty to keep my promise, and it would be morally right (indeed, required) to help the needy student in this case.

Beyond the identification and weighing of competing duties in favour of and against a particular act, part of my approach to moral philosophy involves attempting to identify guiding principles to deal with cases that are similar in kind. For instance, I might try to defend the principle that says promises must be kept unless breaking them is necessary for preventing much greater harm or promoting much greater good. I would then test whether such a principle would give the right answer in a variety of situations. The more generalizable the principle, the greater the confidence I'd have that the principle is correct. If, however, it turns out that the principle is vulnerable to **counterexamples,** then I'd either have to modify the principle or scrap it entirely and search for another underlying rationale for our moral judgments in cases like these.

Finally, in addition to identifying general principles of right action that are able to yield reasonable answers in a variety of cases, I think it is important to be able to *explain* why the proposed principles are morally significant. Ideally, for instance, one should be able to say why it is normally right to keep promises even if doing so will not always do the most good, but why it is not always morally required to keep promises.

Thus, to summarize, when approaching a moral problem I consider the various morally relevant factors—such as consequences, virtue, care, universalizability, autonomy, and mutual benefit—weigh which factors are most pressing in this particular case, develop a principle that can handle other similar situations, and explain why this principle is reasonable independently of this

---

[3] Ross, *The Right and the Good.* While my approach to ethics is closest to Ross's theory, I do not necessarily accept Ross's claim that general moral principles are both self-evidently true and known through a faculty of moral intuition.

particular case. If I can do this, I then become reasonably confident that I have reached the right answer about the particular moral problem in question.[4]

The approach is messy. In hard cases, the conclusions are often tentative. But I think that is a virtue of my approach, for hard cases are hard, real-life scenarios are messy and complicated, and we are fallible in our moral judgments. Any moral theory that glosses over the complexities of the moral life is likely to be unsatisfying. All we can do is to try to sort things out, get some clarity on the issue, and reach a conclusion that is sensitive to as many considerations as possible.

PATRICK'S VIRTUE-BASED APPROACH TO ETHICS

My approach to ethics is the product of an investigation of issues in both **metaethics** and normative ethics. Let me begin, then, by saying a few words about this distinction. It is not easy to provide a precise account of the difference between these two levels of moral inquiry, but the rough idea is this: Metaethical issues are "second-order" issues; that is to say, they are issues *about* morality. Normative ethical issues, in contrast, are "first-order" issues— that is, issues *within* morality. For instance, normative ethics is concerned with questions about which moral principles are correct, and which actions are right and wrong. Metaethics focuses on more abstract questions *about* normative ethics. The normative ethicist asks: Are physicians always morally required to tell their patients the truth? The metaethicist asks: What does it *mean* to say that an action is morally required? Other examples of metaethical issues include the following: Are moral claims (such as the claim that eating meat is morally wrong) **descriptive** or merely **prescriptive?** If they are descriptive, are any moral claims true? That is, are there any moral truths or facts? If there are moral truths or facts, are they **objective** or **subjective?** Do our true moral claims describe a moral reality that is objective in some important sense, or do they merely describe the moral attitudes of particular individuals or cultures? Metaethical theories provide answers to these and other important questions about the nature of morality. These theories are typically characterized as either **realist** or **antirealist.** Realist theories hold that moral claims are (at least partly) descriptive, and that some of these descriptions are true. So realists hold that there are moral truths or facts. Antirealists either deny that moral claims are descriptive at all, or accept this but deny that any of the descriptions are true. So antirealists deny that there are any moral truths or facts. For reasons that I touch on below, I favour a realist theory of ethics.

---

[4] This is sometimes referred to as **reflective equilibrium,** a concept explained in somewhat greater detail in Chapter 1. An excellent discussion of reflective equilibrium can be found in the *Stanford Encyclopedia of Philosophy,* http://plato.stanford.edu/entries/reflective-equilibrium/#3.2.

Let's turn now to normative ethics. As mentioned above, normative ethics involves "first-order" issues—that is, issues *within* morality. These include questions about what sorts of things contribute to the rightness of actions and the goodness of persons. For instance, do consequences matter? If so, are consequences *all* that matter? Are people's motives also important? Among the most influential normative ethical theories are utilitarianism, deontological ethics, and virtue ethics. These theories generally aim to provide us with an account of the properties that make actions right (or wrong), and persons good (or bad).

The metaethical views one adopts put constraints on the normative views one can hold. For this reason, as I mentioned, my approach to ethics begins with an investigation of metaethical issues. As I explain below, this investigation lends support to a **secondary quality view** or, more specifically, **dispositional view of moral properties.** With this view in hand, I turn to normative ethics. I believe that virtue ethics provides a natural, and I think very plausible, way to fill in the details of the dispositional view. The end result is a realist version of virtue ethics: there are facts about what is right and wrong, and these facts are constituted, in part, by the judgments of virtuous persons.

Metaethics

Let's pretend, for the moment, that you and I have stepped outside of our normal moral practices and are observing what's going on "in" there. What will we see? Perhaps the first thing we'll notice is that people, in their day-to-day lives, make moral claims. People say things like the following: "Keeping one's promises is right," "Killing someone for no good reason is wrong," "Abortion is sometimes permissible," and so on. The **surface grammar** suggests that these and other ordinary moral claims may be (partly) descriptive, like familiar sorts of non-moral claims. And like ordinary non-moral claims, our moral claims seem capable of being true or false. We also think of ourselves and others as having moral beliefs and, in some cases, moral knowledge. We claim to know, for instance, that it is morally wrong to sexually abuse children. And we often engage in moral arguments with others about questions we take to have correct answers. These considerations strongly support a view called **cognitivism.** This is the view that our moral claims describe the moral features of actions, persons, and other things we evaluate morally. Consequently, moral claims are the kind of thing that are true or false, and that we believe, know, assert, doubt, and deny.[5]

A host of other considerations support the view that morality is *objective* in an important sense. Morality is objective in at least the (minimal) sense that the rightness and wrongness of actions is independent of the personal attitudes and feelings we happen to have toward the actions. For instance, many people in the past believed that it was morally permissible to keep slaves. But

---

[5] For the sake of simplicity, I ignore here potentially important distinctions among sentences, claims, and propositions.

the fact that these people happened to believe that slavery is permissible does not, according to ordinary moral thought, make it permissible. The thought is, rather, that these people had a mistaken view of the moral status of slavery. So we think that an action's being right or wrong is independent of whether you and I, in our ordinary circumstances, happen to think that it is right or wrong, or whether we happen to have a favourable attitude toward the action. In this sense, at least, morality is objective.[6]

The above two consideration suggest that moral claims are very much like familiar sorts of non-moral claims. Both are descriptive of a reality that is, in an important sense, independent of our feelings and attitudes. There is, however, a crucial difference between moral and many non-moral claims. Moral claims are prescriptive (or "normative"), whereas many non-moral claims are not. That is, moral claims give us reasons or motives for acting in certain ways;[7] familiar sorts of non-moral claims do not have this prescriptive force. For example, if you sincerely judge that it is wrong to eat meat, it seems you thereby have a reason or motive not to eat meat. The judgment, say, that your car's tires are black, however, does not automatically give you a reason or motive to act a certain way or adopt a certain attitude toward the car. These considerations help to support a view called **internalism**—the view that reasons or motives are in some sense internal to, or built into, the fact or judgment that an action is morally right (or wrong).

To sum up the discussion thus far, our ordinary moral claims are descriptive and, moreover, they describe a moral reality that is objective in an important sense. But, as we just saw, our moral claims are not merely descriptive; they are prescriptive or normative too. According to many philosophers, this prescriptive component is plausibly understood in terms of an internal connection between moral facts or judgments and our reasons or motives for action.

A common complaint of many metaethical theories is that they fail to capture one or more of the features described above. By construing moral properties as secondary qualities or, more specifically, dispositional properties, however, I believe we can accommodate the descriptive, objective, and prescriptive elements of morality.[8] The dispositional view I have in mind is analogous to a dispositional account of colours. A dispositional account of colours holds that an object's being red consists in the fact that it would appear red to "normal" observers under "normal" conditions. The dispositional account of moral properties I favour holds that an action's being right consists (roughly)

---

[6] The concept of *objectivity* is ambiguous. Readers should therefore be aware that different philosophers often mean different things when they speak of the objectivity of morality.

[7] Because this is an introductory text, I am ignoring potentially important differences between *reasons* and *motives*. Put very roughly, the difference is that reasons are considerations that *justify* one's actions, whereas motives are considerations that *explain* one's actions.

[8] My thinking about this issue was inspired by John McDowell's paper "Values and Secondary Qualities," which appears in Ted Honderich's book *Morality and Objectivity* (Boston: Routledge and Kegan Paul, 1985).

in the fact that it would appear right to appropriate observers when they are under appropriate sorts of conditions. The phrase "appear right" is shorthand for a more complicated psychological state—one that involves the apprehension of a reason or motive for action.

Now, notice that according to this dispositional view, moral claims are descriptive. They describe the dispositional properties of actions (or persons). And these properties are objective in the sense that an action might be right, even though you and I do not think or feel that it is right; similarly, an action might be wrong, even though you and I think or feel that it is right. Mistakes of this sort happen when either the evaluators or the conditions of evaluation are not appropriate. The dispositional view also (arguably) captures the prescriptive or normative element of morality, since it implies that reasons or motives are "built into" moral properties or judgments.[9]

Normative Ethics

I suggested above that central metaethical considerations support the view that an action's being right consists in the fact that it would appear right to appropriate observers when they are under appropriate sorts of conditions. But who are the appropriate observers? And what are the appropriate conditions? As I explain below, the appropriate observers are those who are virtuous, and the appropriate conditions are ones in which virtuous persons have, and fully appreciate, all relevant information. The upshot of this is the view that an action's being right consists in the fact that it would appear right to virtuous persons if they had, and fully appreciated, all relevant information.

Let's begin with the question, What are the appropriate conditions? What we are looking for here is a specification of the ideal conditions for evaluating the moral status of actions, persons, and other things we evaluate morally. We often make mistakes in moral evaluations when we lack an important piece of information or have incorrect information. For instance, suppose I hear that someone named Smith killed someone named Jones. Then, at first blush, I might judge that Smith did something wrong. But suppose I later learn that Smith killed Jones in self-defence. In that case, I might see my earlier judgment as mistaken, owing to a lack of relevant information. So the ideal conditions of evaluation are ones where we have all relevant information.

I'm not sure this is enough, however. It seems we can and do arrive at mistaken moral judgments, not because we lack information, but because we fail to appreciate the significance of some information, or fail to see how the information we have fits together to generate an obligation. To illustrate, suppose we are morally obligated to stop eating meat and become vegetarian, but I fail to see this, even though I know that meat production causes significant animal suffering. My failure here might be due to a failure to take sufficient note of

---

[9] The claims I assert here obviously require much more defence, but providing a more adequate defence is well beyond the scope of this section.

animal suffering, or perhaps to see how this suffering connects with other things I know to generate an obligation not to eat meat. Examples of this sort suggest that the appropriate conditions should require not just possession of all relevant information, but *full attention to,* or *appreciation of,* that information.

Let's now turn to the "appropriate persons" clause in the dispositional account I am proposing. Who are the appropriate persons? For reasons that I cannot fully defend here, I believe that the most plausible answer is that the appropriate persons are those who are morally good or virtuous.[10] Being virtuous in this sense consists in possessing particular virtues—for example, honesty, kindness, generosity, benevolence. Following Aristotle, I take these individual virtues to be deep and stable character traits that dispose those who possess them to act and feel in appropriate ways. Honest people, for instance, are disposed to act honestly, and to feel disapproval toward persons who are dishonest.

I believe that possession of virtue amounts, moreover, to possession of a certain kind of sensitivity or "perceptual capacity"—that is, a capacity to perceive the moral requirements situations impose on us. The rough idea here is this. We acquire virtue by acquiring certain sorts of concerns and feelings. These feelings and concerns enable us to clearly see the moral features of actions, persons, and so forth. Some simple examples will help to illustrate the idea I have in mind here. A sociopath might fail to see how his violent and abusive behaviour is wrong, because he is insensitive to the feelings and well-being of others. Similarly, a racist may fail to see how her discriminatory ways are insulting and disrespectful, because she lacks concern for the feelings of minorities. A good or virtuous person, however, has a concern for the feelings and well-being of others and therefore sees certain ways of treating others as morally better or worse, right or wrong. This is the rough idea, anyway.

Return now to the analogy between colour properties and moral properties. An object's being red consists in the fact that the object appears red to people with the right sort of perceptual equipment when they view the object in the right sort of light, under suitable conditions. Similarly, I am proposing, an action's being right consists in the fact that it appears right to people with the appropriate sorts of feelings and concerns—that is, virtuous people—when they have and appreciate all relevant information. And just as defects in our perceptual equipment can lead to colour blindness, defects in our moral character can lead to a kind of moral blindness.[11]

---

[10] The basic line of argument is that just as the redness of an object consists in the fact that it appears red *to those with a properly developed colour sensibility,* so the rightness of an action consists in the fact that it would appear right *to those with a properly developed moral sensibility.*

[11] There are, of course, important differences between a dispositional account of colours and the dispositional account of moral properties that I propose here. One important difference, for instance, is that the appropriate observers in a dispositional account of colours can be specified *statistically.* However, a statistical specification of the appropriate observers is not plausible in a dispositional account of moral properties. I do not believe that this difference undermines the value of the analogy, although some may disagree.

Some Objections and Responses

I would like to conclude by offering a brief defence of the view sketched above. I believe that perhaps the most attractive feature of this view is that it does a better job than other familiar metaethical views of accommodating and explaining the descriptive, objective, and prescriptive features of our moral discourse and practice. To repeat and expand on points made earlier, this view preserves the idea that moral claims are descriptive claims, just as their surface grammar suggests. It preserves the idea, moreover, that morality is objective, at least in the sense that what is right or wrong is not simply a matter of what you and I *happen* to think or feel. Finally, this view preserves the idea that there is an internal connection between moral properties or judgments and our reasons or motives. If one is virtuous, and one has and fully appreciates all relevant information, then one will have a reason or motive to do those acts that one perceives as right.[12]

Another supporting consideration is that this view is not vulnerable to the kinds of objections that pose a problem for utilitarian and Kantian theories.[13] On my virtue ethics perspective, consequences are not all that matter, as the utilitarian mistakenly argues. Nor, on my view, are moral rules absolute, as the Kantian claims. It is important to promote one's own good and the good of others. And it is also important to treat others with respect, to be kind, honest, generous, and loyal, and to practise other virtues. But all of these rules admit of exceptions.

I turn now to potential problems with the view. One common objection to dispositional accounts of colours is that they are **circular,** and some have argued that dispositional accounts of value properties suffer from the same problem. My simple response is this: Yes, the account is circular in a sense, for it holds that an action's being right consists (partly) in the fact that virtuous persons think it is right. But why is this circularity a problem? Is it supposed to be an **epistemic** problem? A **metaphysical** problem? Some other kind of problem? The alleged problem with circularity is, unfortunately, seldom explained. In any case, I believe that any circularity in my view is harmless, but showing this in detail would require a lengthy detour into the nature of properties and philosophical analyses. Since I can't take that detour here, I won't try.[14] However, let me say this: the circularity in my view is only at a surface

---

[12] This internal connection is admittedly rather loose. However, for reasons that I cannot defend here, I believe that any tighter internal connection is not plausible. But it is less plausible that there is no internal connection at all. David Lewis makes a similar point about his own view in "Dispositional Theories of Value," *Proceedings of the Aristotelian Society* suppl. vol. 63 (1989): 113–37.

[13] These objections are discussed at length in Chapter 2, where we critically examine the leading normative ethical theories.

[14] For an interesting discussion of dispositional views and the problem of circularity, see Jeffrey C. King's "On the Possibility of Correct Apparently Circular Dispositional Analyses," *Philosophical Studies* 98 (2000): 257–78.

level—an action's being right consists roughly in the fact that it would appear right to virtuous persons. But as I noted earlier, "appear right" is shorthand for a more complicated state involving the apprehension of a reason (or reasons) for action. At this point, the circle vanishes.

In the section explaining his favoured normative ethical theory, Doran raises several other common objections to virtue ethics which I would like to address. One of the alleged problems is that virtue ethics may provide little in the way of practical guidance, since it leads to conflicting rules or virtues. For instance, the virtuous person is one who is honest and kind. But suppose I ask my friend, who happens to be virtuous, what he thinks of my new jacket. Let's suppose that he hates it. Then, if he tells me the truth, I will be deeply hurt, and if he tells me a lie, he will be dishonest. So the virtues of honesty and kindness seem to conflict in this situation. The apparent problem, then, is that owing to these conflicts, virtue ethics provides little in the way of practical moral guidance.

One response to this objection is to find partners in crime. Conflicting virtues or rules is a potential problem not only for virtue ethics, but for any pluralistic view—that is, any view which asserts more than one moral rule. This is a frequently cited problem for contractarian and pluralistic deontological views, for instance. So, to the extent that this is a problem for virtue ethics, it is also a problem for many other moral theories, including the pluralistic approach Doran takes.

One way for pluralistic views to avoid conflicts is to provide a ranking of rules. Virtue ethics *can* similarly provide a ranking of the virtues. One might say, for instance, that honesty always trumps kindness. This ranking would then provide a way to resolve any conflicts among the virtues. I do not think, however, that this is a promising response to the objection. The problem is that there is no plausible ranking of the virtues that will hold true in all circumstances. In some situations, it is best to be honest, while in others it is best to be kind. Put otherwise, morality is not **codifiable,** as the point is sometimes put.[15] No matter how carefully we try to specify and rank moral virtues (or rules), we are bound to meet with exceptions. Notice that our experiences trying to reach correct moral decisions in hard cases helps to prove this point. In these cases, no simple rule, or ranking of rules, seems to lead to the correct answer. Rather, finding the correct answer requires the capacity to see which facts are most salient in the situation. There is no shortcut to the acquisition of this capacity; it comes from experience and wisdom. In hard cases, virtues or rules conflict, and we should expect moral theories to reflect this feature of our moral lives. The fact that virtue ethics does not provide simple answers to difficult moral questions is not, then, a problem with the view; rather, it is a point in its favour.

---

[15] This point has been made, in various ways, by several virtue ethicists, including Aristotle and John McDowell.

Another objection to virtue ethics that Doran raises is that virtue ethics gives the incorrect account of the reason why actions are right and wrong. He notes that the main reason why it is wrong to abuse animals, for instance, is not that it manifests a vicious character or because, on my view, virtuous persons would see it as wrong. The reason why animal abuse is wrong is that it causes needless suffering to the animal. But this is a point that virtue ethicists can fully agree with. The objection, I believe, is based on a failure to distinguish between two different questions: What *is* rightness/wrongness? and What *makes* an action right/wrong?[16] My answer to the first question is that rightness and wrongness are dispositional properties. More specifically, and simplifying somewhat: for an action to be right just *is* for it to be such that it would appear right to virtuous persons. And for an action to be wrong just *is* for it to be such that it would appear wrong to virtuous persons. When we consider the question What *makes* an action right or wrong? we are asking (on my view) what makes an action such that it appears right or wrong to virtuous persons. Now, to return to Doran's example, what makes animal abuse wrong is just what he says—that it involves the infliction of needless suffering. This is what makes the action wrong; that is, this is what makes the action such that it appears wrong to virtuous persons. Once we distinguish between these two questions—What *is* rightness/wrongness? and What *makes* an action right/ wrong?—I believe this objection evaporates.

A final objection that Doran raises is that virtue ethicists are themselves guilty of failing to draw an important distinction—in this case, the distinction between what makes an action right or wrong and what makes a person good or bad. The alleged failure to note this distinction is illustrated by considering well-meaning individuals who unwittingly act wrongly. In such cases, we may want to say that the individual did something wrong *and* that the individual is nonetheless morally good or virtuous. Doran provides a specific example to make the point: Consider someone who performs an act that he thinks is beneficial, but which turns out to be harmful. Perhaps he donates to a charity because he wants to help famine victims; however, it turns out that the charity is a fraud, and the money actually supports the lavish and corrupt lifestyle of a con artist. In this case, it is clear that giving to the charity was *not* the right thing to do, although we may still want to view the person who donated as having a good character (as being charitable).

Doran concludes that "if this is correct, then right action cannot be understood simply in terms of virtuous character." Perhaps this is a problem for some versions of virtue ethics; I'm not sure. But it is not a problem for my view. An action's being right or wrong, on my view, consists in the fact that it would appear right or wrong to *fully informed* virtuous persons. Since a fully

---

[16] This is a distinction that was intentionally ignored in the previous two chapters, given that it raises a number of complex issues. It is necessary to introduce the distinction here, however, in order for Patrick to respond to one of Doran's objections to virtue ethics.

informed virtuous person would know that the charity was a scam, then the act of giving to the charity would not appear as right to this person. So I have no difficulty saying that the action in question is not right. But can I also say that the person who gave to the charity has a good character, since he exemplifies the virtue of charity? Sure, there's nothing at all that prevents me from saying that the person is morally good (or virtuous, or praiseworthy) insofar as he was trying to be charitable. (I would add, however, that he might be also be deserving of some blame, if he *should have known* that the charity is a scam.)

So, how will I, from my virtue ethics perspective, attempt to answer difficult moral questions, such as the ones we will investigate in this book? The first thing I will try to do is get a firm grip on the relevant facts in the situation. Then I will ask what the virtuous person would do in the situation. More specifically, however, I will be asking what the kind, considerate, honest (and so forth) thing to do is in the cases discussed. Of course, it will not always be easy to determine this. And even when I can, the various virtues will often conflict. In these cases, I will rely on whatever moral experience and wisdom I've managed to acquire at this point in my life to determine which facts are most salient in the case, and so which virtue(s) should prevail in the situation.

WARREN'S APPROACH TO ETHICS: PRACTICAL SOCIAL CONTRACT THEORY
The Main Contractarian Ideas for Warren's Purposes

I defend the particular moral views I take by showing how they would be acceptable to a bunch of selfish, ignorant people. That is only partly a joke, as you will see. I will consider what rules self-interested people would choose if they were ignorant of their advantages, allegiances, biases, and the other particular things about them that determine what rules they accept. My view is inspired by a longstanding tradition in philosophy. Plato, Hobbes, Locke, Rousseau, and Kant, among the most famous of philosophers in history, have all been associated with some form of social contract theory. The contemporary philosopher John Rawls is a huge influence on my thinking, although Rawls would disagree with many of my uses of contract theory. Social contract theory is often used to justify claims about what political system is just. My use of the ideas of contractarians, however, is to generate a method for debating any moral rules that are proposed. I do not confine attention to questions about the justice of institutions. My question is, rather, how to fairly choose rules that guide us in what we ought to do in all areas, personal, political, and others.

Think for a moment about people who make rules. Members of the Canadian Parliament, for example, make laws. They also make many regulations that affect members of Parliament. For example, they, unlike most of us, determine what kind of pension plan their members will have. Not surprisingly, they gave themselves an astoundingly good pension plan, much better than the one nurses have, for instance. Even after being moderated in response to public outcry, it is still exceptionally generous. Now, many have thought this unfair. We might say that nobody who was not a parliamentarian or hoping to be one would have set up the rules in such a way as to give such a lush pension plan to that group.

Now, this is a crucial idea: nobody would accept the plan unless he or she was sure to be a member of Parliament. Ignorance of advantages and disadvantages is the kind of ignorance I want to build into my test of rules. I will take my cue from the contractarians who make use of a kind of ignorance of one's own contingencies. Here is a brief explanation of contractarian theory and my use of it.

Contractarians ask us to follow the rules of the **ideal social contract.** We discover what these rules are by asking what rules people in the **original position** would choose. The original position is a hypothetical situation in which people are:

1. equally powerful (so nobody can force others to accept a rule);
2. equally intelligent (so nobody can trick others into accepting a rule);
3. self-interested (so no other moral theory enters social contract theory in a Trojan Horse);[17] and
4. ignorant of their own advantages and disadvantages, loyalties, biases, or anything else about themselves that would influence their choices of rules that would govern their behaviour. (Behind this **veil of ignorance,** participants cannot skew the rules in their own favour or in favour of their group.)

People are never really in the original position. It is just a useful fiction that we can use to figure out what rules are fair. We can ask, What rules would people in the original position want to apply to themselves in the real world? Given that people in the original position are self-interested, they will want to choose rules that will benefit themselves in the real world. However, in the original position, people do not know any personal facts about themselves, including where they will end up in the real world. This means that they will not be able to tailor the rules to suit their own particular circumstances. It also means that in the original position, people will choose rules that give everyone in the real world a chance to successfully pursue their own interests.

Another major restriction on people in the original position comes into play when they choose the rules that will govern people's behaviour in the real world. This is the **human-sympathy metarule,** *a rule about how to make other rules.* It says: *Choose rules that people with ordinary human sympathies could follow.* I construe "sympathy" very broadly to include most of the positive

---

[17] The Trojan Horse was a hollow statue used to sneak soldiers into their enemy's city during a siege. Here it is being used to refer to a device for sneaking moral rules into the very procedure that is supposed to determine which moral rules are good ones.

emotions we have toward one another. Vague as "sympathy" is, people in the original position would still be restricted significantly in the rules they could choose. They could not, for example, choose a rule like this: *Maximize human happiness.* That rule requires, for example, a mother to starve her own children so that she can feed many more children in Peru if she knows the consequences for human happiness would certainly be better that way. That is clearly over the top. This human-sympathy restriction prevents the theory from asking too much of people. Rules that are too hard to follow will be ignored by people in the real world, so people in the original position would not choose them. The rules people would generate in the original position would be usable moral rules in the real world—rules that real people could follow. They would not require us to be saints or superhuman ethical calculators.

Of course, where some kinds of sympathy lie can depend on one's culture, or family or other ties. If we were in the original position, we could not rely on that kind of sympathy. We would not, after all, know what ties might bind us. Instead, we would have to attend to feelings that are common to human beings the world over, like the strong attachment of most mothers to their own children.

It may be objected that we need to know our personal degree of sympathy and other characteristics in order to choose rules in the original position. Otherwise we might end up making rules that favour people with an uncommonly high degree of sympathy. The solution to this problem is one that we would have to use widely if we were in the original position. Not knowing how sympathetic we might be to others, we would be wise to choose the *mean between extremes.* We should make rules appropriate for people who have neither the sympathy of saints nor a total lack of sympathy but who have sympathy to a moderate degree. In general, we would be guided by moderation if we were in the original position. It would keep us from going too far from where our interests lie.

The Committee Metaphor

Now consider a fanciful metaphor to explain what it would be like to choose rules in the original position. This metaphor makes limited sense, but is intended not as a genuine possibility but only to reveal what we believe about fairness in terms of two concepts: the *original position* and the subordinate concept of a *veil of ignorance.* You will, I hope, find the metaphor useful for revealing your own beliefs about what is fair.

Suppose that a new anesthetic has been developed which makes people temporarily **amnesiac.** They retain their general intellectual and emotional abilities, but they forget who they are and where they are. They are also temporarily blind. They cannot feel their bodies except to the extent that they can speak coherently. These people, though rational, are behind a veil of ignorance about their own personal advantages and disadvantages in society. They do not know if they are crippled, average, or athletic in their bodily capacities. They do not know their positions in society, what sort of personalities they have, nor any other personal information, not even their genders or ages. They retain general knowledge about the human condition, but no particular religious or moral beliefs. This peculiar **amnestic anesthetic** is put to an interesting political use.

Under the auspices of the Hospital Ethics Committee, a subcommittee of volunteers takes this anesthetic in order to approximate the original position from which to write a charter of rights of patients and health care providers. They communicate with each other only indirectly through intermediaries. As much as possible, the veil of ignorance is thickened. They do not know whether they are patients, administrators, physicians, nurses, or janitors. The anesthetized committee members are told that they may have children and grandchildren they care deeply about who are mentally impaired or much more brilliant than they are. The volunteers have been chosen to be equally intelligent, rational people.

These volunteers, acting in their own self-interest, have insufficient information to be unfair. They cannot even favour their own generation. The rules they choose must be acceptable to an arbitrarily chosen person, for the volunteers do not know who they will turn out to be. They also realize that they must choose rules that people with ordinary human sympathies can follow.

The point of this odd metaphor of the volunteers is to explain what the original position is like. Asking what rules the volunteers on this subcommittee would choose is like asking what we would choose if we were in the original position. The rules people would choose in the original position are the justified moral rules. They would form the fair rules of the ideal social contract. They might be a great deal like the rules that some other moral theorists choose to tell us what our moral rights and duties are, but their justification is different.

Whatever rules we come up with in any theory, if there is more than one rule and no rules are given priority over others, then we need to say what happens when rules conflict. Conflicts of rules are decided for my kind of contractarian by asking which rule would be given heavier weight in the original position if the choosers of rules were given the facts of the case but did not know their roles, if any, in the particular case.

Consider the case of a mentally fragile hospital patient, Zelda, who wants to know her diagnosis, and of her physician, Zeke, who thinks it will harm her to learn her diagnosis just now, although he knows that Zelda has a fatal illness. If you were in the original position you would not know if you were a patient like Zelda, a health care provider like Zeke, an administrator, a family member, or a person in some other role. You would have to select general rules to govern people's behaviour in such situations. These would be rules that you could live with no matter who you turned out to be in the real world. You would want honesty, in order to protect your own interests, but you would realize that brutal honesty might not be in your interest. While you would want the truth to be revealed, it might be allowed to emerge gradually with education and emotional support. You might try to write a rule of compassionate honesty into your social contract. Zeke would be required to educate his patients and break difficult news to them gradually and gently when possible.

If you were in the original position, you would want to protect your right to **autonomy,** your right to determine how your own life goes, by protecting your access to knowledge about yourself. You would know that few would look after your interests the way you would. At the same time, you would accept, in the original position, some limitations on autonomy that would be required to prevent you from getting too much choice when you could not handle it in the real world. If you are fragile, like Zelda, or if you are a child, you might want your autonomy in gentle doses.

One way to describe the balance to be achieved by those wishing to satisfy the requirements on the choosers of rules in the original position is to say it is a balance between protecting autonomy and **weak paternalism.** In other words, we are trying to balance protecting our ability to make choices for ourselves with allowing others to make choices for us that are intended to be in our own best interest. Those in the original position would accept certain slightly paternalistic rules the way we in the real world may accept seat belt legislation. This kind of legislation discourages us from temporary irrationality that would be contrary to our best interest. The freedom to drive without seat belts is not worth dying for. Some other more basic freedoms are worth dying for, and we want to make distinctions among the various types of freedom and the ways we should protect them. The choosers of rules in the original position would try to set the rules so as to protect their interests, primarily by ensuring respect for personal autonomy, but also by allowing for our protection against our own temporary irrationality. Any restriction on autonomy would have to be justified by an appeal to the protection of our interests.

The Video Game Metaphor

In another attempt to make the original position understandable, I am going to explain it in terms of an imaginary video game. Suppose you are playing a video game that you want badly to win—Sim Society. To win you must maximize the personal satisfaction of the character you control in an imaginary society and culture. You will do this through using opportunities for personal growth, wealth, health, and happiness. You do not, however, know in advance which of many characters you will control. The computer decides which one you get. Your character may turn out to be one with many advantages—wealth, beauty, family connections, a large inheritance, great intelligence, energy, strength, supportive social networks, and the like. Of course, your character might lack any or all of these advantages and and might even be extremely disadvantaged. Some characters suffer from poverty, membership in a despised group, physical and/or mental disabilities, living with drug-addicted parents, and other disadvantages.

Before you are given your character, you are asked to choose some rules that the characters will play by as they pursue fulfillment. Your only motivation is to win, but you don't know which character you will get. Your task is just to choose rules that will give your character the best chance no matter who he or she turns out to be. In choosing rules this way, you are like the choosers of rules in the original position in social contract theory, behind a veil of ignorance about the particulars of their lives. The sort of rules you would choose would be fair rules.

Warren's Use of Social Contract Theory

Let me assume that you have a rough idea of how a social contract theorist uses the fiction of the original position to argue for the acceptance of rules in the real world. The way I use it is not, as some have, to argue that any particular set of rules is an **absolute moral truth.** I am content to use it as a way to generate debate and to argue for rules. We cannot know for sure what rules people in the original position would accept. We do not have to know this. We only need be able to give reasons for or against accepting particular rules. Contractarian thinking gives us a way of justifying principles but does not guarantee that we will come up with a justification on which we can all agree. All I expect is a basis for public debate. I seek merely *intersubjective,* not absolute, principles.

Cultural Relativism

One might object that the contractarian method of justifying rules is a part of the culture of the West and not something that is genuinely universal. That may be so, but this method gives us a degree of objectivity that is as close as we can get to the probably unattainable absolute and universal rules for which we long. The choosers of rules in the original position would not know their country, culture, or religion. Hence they would, in their own self-interest, choose rules that encourage tolerance of various cultures, so long as those cultures were not harmful to each other or their own adherents. A cultural rule that requires human sacrifice would be contrary to the rules chosen by people in the original position, but cultures that live and let live would not run afoul of the rules chosen in the original position. Some would, nonetheless, call my view **cultural imperialism,** but the poor person on the sacrificial altar would probably (though not necessarily) welcome this sort of interference. Be that as it may, this is the most culturally neutral moral theory I have seen.[18]

Ethics Regarding Non-humans

Earlier in this chapter, Doran mentioned a serious criticism: "Social contract theory is notoriously weak, for example, in satisfactorily explaining our obligations to non-rational beings and entities, such as mentally incompetent humans,

---

[18] More detail on relativism can be found in Chapter 2's discussion of normative ethical theory.

non-human animals, the natural environment, and future generations." I have wrestled with this problem in my book *Persons: What Philosophers Say about You,* and I refer you there for more details.[19]

I do not recognize obligations to the natural environment, but this is no problem. It is in the interest of people in the original position to accept rules that preserve the natural environment, since their interests will be tied to that environment in the real world. The more difficult questions for me have to do with our obligations to incompetent humans and non-human animals.

Since I do not think that being human is essential for being a person, I have less trouble with this than some contractarians. Intelligent non-humans are not automatically banned from the moral community. One thing that is morally relevant on my view is ability. I think that human beings and any other creatures that are capable of the kind of mental and emotional feats that most humans can perform must be given special consideration in our moral judgments. We have capacities, for example, for anticipation of the future that some creatures do not have. These give us special capacities for pleasure and pain quite different from those of other animals. We are free to make choices. This makes praise and blame reasonable for people, though not for most other animals. Making rules in the original position, we could take such things into account and realize that they are matters of degree. In that position we would recognize, for instance, varying degrees of responsibility corresponding to varying degrees of capacity to understand what we are doing and anticipate consequences. It would make sense to distinguish between those who are competent to make decisions and those who are not, and to give those who are competent more power and responsibility. Because choosers of rules would not know whether their children might be mentally at a great disadvantage in the real world, they would want protections for human beings who are mentally disadvantaged, but they would not want these human beings to be given power or responsibility that they cannot reasonably exercise. That would be in nobody's interest.

This still leaves the problem of rights of non-human animals, since the choosers of rules know they are not in that group. Their children too will be human, however minimal their mental abilities turn out to be in the real world. Remember, however, that I have a special restriction on the choosers, the sympathy metarule. The choosers of rules must give us rules that people with ordinary human sympathies can follow. Our sympathies for a person remain even after that person's mental abilities have drained away. Our strong sympathies for animals and those among the mentally disabled who never did have the capacity to make free, informed choices are also important. I have argued in *Persons* that rights of animals and disadvantaged human beings would be preserved by the choosers of rules in the original position because it would be in their interest to nurture the kind of sympathy that they might very well need

---

[19] Warren Bourgeois, *Persons: What Philosophers Say About You,* 2nd ed. (Waterloo, ON: Wilfrid Laurier University Press, 2003).

for their children or, in the future, for themselves. We would give animals rights appropriate to beings that cannot bear responsibilities but that can feel pleasure and pain and have limited virtues. Unless our rules require their humane treatment, we encourage cruelty and risk that it will extend to us.

People manage to suppress sympathy for animals by keeping their suffering out of sight and out of mind. People who eat burgers would often go to great lengths to help a cow they found tangled in a barbed wire fence. In the original position, we would know that there is a danger that someone who could walk by the cow without a thought would also be able to suppress feelings for human beings. That is one reason why the rules would be set up to protect animals. Even if only a part (and I think the larger part) of the human population extends sympathy to animals and people in the same way, these rules protecting animals would be useful protection for interests of persons as seen from the original position. That is why fair rules would require us, for instance, to give up some of the cheap but inhumane food production methods on which agribusiness currently relies.

This does not mean that my theory supports fully the extreme animal rights movement. On a contractarian basis, animals can only gain rights via the interests of people. These interests, however, can be quite broad. Even if we knew that people would soon be extinct on Earth, it might be in our interest to set up arrangements to prevent animal suffering after our extinction. It might make us feel better in the present to work for a future with less animal suffering. Admittedly, saying that animal suffering only has importance with respect to interests of persons makes me uncomfortable. It does, however, give an intuitively right answer when we look at decisions like whether to save persons at the expense of animals. My view has the effect of putting persons first but avoiding the inhumane treatment of animals and human non-persons.

It is important, as well, that our moral rules in the ideal social contract be consistent with ordinary human sympathy. The rules affecting animals will have to take into account the strong sympathy people frequently have for non-human animals.

Social Contract Theory beyond Ethics

Another way in which I depart greatly from contractarian tradition is to extend the contractarian method to metaphysics (the theory of reality) and to epistemology (the theory of knowledge). I believe that our claims about what is real and what we can know are value-laden. These would be subject to the same test as our moral principles. Indeed, the advantage of this way of proceeding is that we get a unified theory of knowledge, morality, and reality just as Plato wanted, but without claims about such things as Platonic Forms or other absolutes that are just too hard to believe.

An example of this way of proceeding can be seen in my approach to **rationality,** a concept that draws deeply on our metaphysical and epistemological ideas. Rationality is a much-contested concept. Many think they have a lock on absolute truths about what is reasonable, but it turns out that others are equally convinced of contrary views on the subject. These views are often highly coincident with the advantage of those who adopt them. Behind a veil of ignorance, people might not be so confident. I think we should ask ourselves what we would accept as the mark of the rational if we did not already know where our advantages lay. I would say that the rules we follow to determine if a belief, a choice, a goal, or a person is rational would have to be rules we could agree to if we were in the original position. It would not be in our interest to allow others to declare us irrational to further their own interests. We need a standard of rationality we can live with in the real world, especially where this is used to determine the competence of patients to decide on their treatment.

Warning

In general, I will continually appeal to the original position to defend not only my ethical positions but also my other philosophical positions in the coming debate. This may become annoying after a while, but that is my job. I am a philosopher.

CONCLUSION

Each author has now explained his favoured approach to ethics. Doran will apply a version of pluralistic deontology, Patrick will use his distinctive virtue ethics approach, and Warren will turn to his social contract theory to address the moral problems in health care that are explored in subsequent chapters. Remember to return to this chapter from time to time, if you are having difficulty remembering the details of any of their approaches.

Review Questions

1. Explain why Doran's theory is called pluralistic deontology.
2. Why does Doran reject utilitarianism, Kantianism, social contract theory, and virtue ethics?
3. What steps does Doran think must be taken to resolve a particular moral problem?
4. What is the distinction between metaethics and normative ethics?
5. According to Patrick's version of virtue ethics, what does it mean to say that something is morally right or wrong?
6. In what ways does Patrick believe that colour properties and moral properties are analogous?
7. What is the original position? What is the veil of ignorance? What role do these concepts play in Warren's ethical theory?
8. Explain the sympathy metarule, and give an example to explain its use.
9. Consider a case of mercy killing—say it is the case of Tracy Latimer, where her father Robert deliberately ended Tracy's life so that she could avoid a life of horrible suffering. The details of this story can be found at http://www.robertlatimer.net/story/tracysillness.htm. How would Doran, Patrick, and Warren approach this difficult ethical issue?

WWW.MCGRAWHILL.CA/OLC/SMOLKIN

CHAPTER 4

EUTHANASIA

INTRODUCTION

The term **euthanasia** is most often used to refer to bringing about another individual's death for that individual's own good through some act or omission. Philosophers and health care professionals commonly distinguish *active* euthanasia from *passive* euthanasia. The distinction is based on an alleged difference between *killing* and *letting die*. Our main concern here is with *voluntary* **active euthanasia** (VAE), in which a patient who wants to die is killed, and *non-voluntary* **active euthanasia** (NAE), in which a patient who cannot express a wish to live or die is killed. In contemporary Canadian law, **competent** adults have a legal right to have medical treatment stopped, or to refuse treatment altogether. No one has a legal right, however, to be killed.[1] A physician who actively euthanizes an individual is therefore guilty of a criminal offence. Although the law is clear on this matter, there is considerable debate about the *morality* of voluntary and non-voluntary active euthanasia, and about whether the laws prohibiting VAE and NAE ought to be changed.

To explore these issues, we present a drama in which the characters discuss the movie *Million Dollar Baby*. This film tells the story of Maggie Fitzgerald, a poor 31-year-old woman who is determined to become a professional boxer. Maggie convinces Frankie Dunn, a jaded trainer who is estranged from his own daughter, to help her achieve her goal. Under the guidance of Frank and

---

[1] For a summary of Canadian law regarding euthanasia and assisted suicide, see http://www.parl.gc.ca/information/library/PRBpubs/919-e.htm.

his friend and assistant, Eddie Dupris, Maggie fights her way up the ranks of women's boxing to gain a shot at the reigning champ. In that match, however, Maggie is sucker-punched after the bell as she makes her way to her corner. She crashes into her stool and is paralyzed from the neck down. Feeling that her life is no longer worth living, and unable to kill herself, Maggie repeatedly asks Frank to end her life. He eventually agrees, removes her life support, and gives her an overdose of insulin to hasten her death.[2]

Maggie's ordeal presents us with a difficult case of VAE. She is killed at her request, and although she is a quadriplegic, she is not terminally ill. Our debate addresses the question whether VAE, in this case and in general, is morally permissible. We then turn our attention to consider the moral status of NAE. The difficult question of whether any form of active euthanasia ought to be legalized is not examined in this chapter, though we debate this issue at the Online Learning Centre, available at www.mcgrawhill.ca/olc/smolkin.

Doran, Patrick, and Warren agree that VAE is morally permissible in Maggie's case and in relevantly similar situations. They agree, moreover, that NAE is also morally permissible under certain conditions, although they concede that the arguments here are less decisive. That the authors reach the same conclusion, despite their different theoretical approaches, provides broad support for the moral permissibility of VAE and NAE.

LEARNING OBJECTIVES

After completing this chapter, you should be able to:

- Define *euthanasia*
- Distinguish the different types of euthanasia
- Explain why considerations of autonomy and best interests are not, without qualification, sufficient to show that voluntary active euthanasia (VAE) is permissible
- Outline Doran's, Patrick's, and Warren's ultimate positions on the moral permissibility of voluntary active euthanasia
- Describe the Sanctity of Life and the God's Ownership objections to voluntary active euthanasia and why they fail
- State the Best Interest argument given in support of the moral permissibility of non-voluntary active euthanasia (NAE)
- Explain Philippa Foot's argument against the moral permissibility of non-voluntary active euthanasia and why her argument is rejected
- Develop your own arguments for or against the permissibility of voluntary active euthanasia and non-voluntary active euthanasia

---

[2] Removing life support would normally be considered an act of passive euthanasia, but because she is given an overdose of insulin, this is a case of active euthanasia.

DRAMA

Please note: This case is based on various true stories, although names, places, and some uncontroversial elements of the case have been changed to preserve anonymity and confidentiality. Discussions of this and similar cases with health care professionals have also informed this fictional case. The drama merely raises issues. The philosophical arguments are to be found in the debate following the drama.

A group of students is discussing the film *Million Dollar Baby.*

CHARACTERS

Bob: *a law student*   **Ted:** *a religious studies major*
Carol: *a nursing student*   **Alice:** *a fine arts student*

Bob: That was intense.

Alice: What?

Bob: Carol and I just saw a film, *Million Dollar Baby,* about euthanasia.

Ted: Oh yeah, I heard it was great.

Carol: Well, my emotions were all over the place. I don't know what to think about it. I hate boxing. Still, I can see how Maggie would be thrilled to be a fighter. It was the only way to pull herself out of her poverty-ridden sink-hole, and I was really on her side even though it kind of makes me sick to see fights.

Ted: Whoa—what has this got to do with euthanasia?

Bob: Maggie is this gutsy woman who joins a gym run by a boxing trainer, Frankie. She wants him to train her, but he just says stuff like "Tough ain't enough, girlie," "I don't train girls," and "You're too old." She's thirty-something.

Alice: God, I hate Frankie already.

Bob: Eddie is this wise old boxing trainer who works for Frankie and gets him to take Maggie on as a fighter.

Carol: Don't tell them the whole thing. You'll ruin it.

Alice: Forget it. I'm not going to go watch Frankie mouth off.

Bob: Besides, the power of the film isn't from some surprise ending. It's the way it makes you think about dying on your own terms.

Carol: Yeah, and the acting is excellent. Clint Eastwood takes this Neolithic old bugger, Frankie, and makes you see through his attitudes to a really good heart.

I don't know how he does it. I guess it doesn't matter if you know that Frankie kills Maggie in the end.

Ted: Cheery. Anyway, go ahead and tell us about it.

Bob: Well, Eddie talks Frankie into training Maggie. She goes from being this dirt-poor unknown to having millions of adoring fans.

Carol: Yeah, she is going for the world championship when it happens.

Alice: It?

Carol: This really dirty fighter she is beating in the championship sucker-punches Maggie between rounds when her back is turned. Maggie falls and hits her head on the stool in her corner.

Bob: She's left quadriplegic. Bottom to top of the world and back again in short order.

Alice: So she wants to die because she's depressed about it or something?

Carol: It's deeper than that. Her whole life, her whole sense of self was wrapped up in being a fighter. You might be able to live as a quadriplegic and have a good life, but she was destroyed. You kind of have to see it. She's just lost everything she lives for.

Bob: It really makes sense in the film. I'd want to die if I was in Maggie's shoes.

Alice: Bob! What about your family?

Bob: That's one of the master strokes in this film. Her family is particularly vicious and selfish. When they come to visit her in the hospital to try to get Maggie's money, you see that Frankie is more like family to her than those fools.

Alice: Well, what about Frankie, then? If he loves her or something, shouldn't she stay alive for him?

Carol: They're both tough. Still, there's a way in which they have a kind of father-daughter love. That's why he kills her. After she bites her tongue at night to try to bleed herself to death, he knows that the most horrible thing for her is being pathetic. In Maggie's mind, and I think in Frankie's, her life is intolerable. She was a champion. Now she feels useless.

Bob: Yeah, they stop her from bleeding to death at the hospital. They are forcing her to live. One night, Frankie finally gives in to her constant demands and removes the respirator. Just to be sure she doesn't suffer, he gives her an overdose of insulin and she dies instantly.

Ted: You sound like you sympathize with Frankie, but he is no hero. God gave us our lives. Only he can take them.

Carol: Ted, that's just your religion talking. The rest of us aren't Catholic.

Ted: I don't know how you expect to settle moral questions without asking what God wants.

Alice: But Ted, why does God want us to live no matter what? Wouldn't you say He wants that because it's the right thing to do? He doesn't just arbitrarily want it, right?

Ted: I guess.

Alice: So then there must be a reason why it's right before God wants us to do it. So maybe we should ask about that reason. I mean, God gave us the brains to figure it out or he can't blame us if we don't get it, right?

Bob: Alice, you should join me in law school. That was brilliant!

Carol: Yeah, and I think what Frankie did was not just right, it was noble. It was courageous. It was loving.

Ted: I seem to be all on my own here.

Alice: I don't know what to think, actually. I'm on the fence.

Carol: Maybe mercy in a case like Maggie's is what makes it okay to do. Her life was just a torture to her. Think of her biting her tongue to try to bleed herself slowly to death. She really needed to die.

Alice: This stuff is really hard to think about. She must have been just desperate to die.

Bob: Morally, I think that if you respect somebody as a person, you should honour her wishes about what to do with her own body.

Alice: I guess so. We always say, "My body, my choice," when we're talking about abortion. It's the same thing here.

Ted: But remember, Bob, that it is one thing to let a person die. It's another thing altogether to kill somebody. If an old man says, "Don't thump on my chest if I have a heart attack, let me go," I can go with that. If he says, "Stab me," that's where I draw the line.

Carol: Well, maybe we can all agree that at least Maggie should be able to refuse treatment and be allowed to die.

Alice: Time's up. We've got to run. The movie is almost starting.

Bob: What are you two going to see?

Ted: This flick about a bunch of penguins. It's deep.

DEBATE
Clarifying the Case and Identifying Relevant Facts

Warren says: In order to have a case of euthanasia before us, let's recall what happened in the movie *Million Dollar Baby*. Maggie had been a champion boxer. Her whole self-concept and self-worth were wrapped up in her achievements in the ring. As a result of a treacherous attack from behind, she was rendered **quadriplegic.** Maggie was unable to move or feel from the neck down, could

BACKGROUND

There is a recent and very similar case involving assisted suicide. A 23-year-old semi-pro rugby player was paralyzed from the neck down in a rugby practice. He really wanted to die and tried to kill himself several times. After 18 months of this, his parents took him to the Dignitas clinic in Switzerland where he obtained an assisted suicide.

Source: http://news.bbc.co.uk/2/hi/uk_news/england/hereford/worcs/7676812.stm.

breathe only with the assistance of a respirator, and had no hope of physical improvement. In fact, her body was continuing to slowly deteriorate due to infection, requiring amputation of her leg. She consistently requested that she be allowed to die. Life in her condition was pointless to her. She attempted to kill herself by trying to bite her tongue off so that she would bleed to death before the injury was discovered. She was, however, kept alive by the hospital staff. Frankie, her manager, trainer and father-figure, finally accepted her request for death. He took two measures. First, he removed her respirator. This removal of treatment would have allowed her to die. Next, in order to hasten death, he injected her with a dose of insulin following which the line on her monitor went flat. It appears that the dose was fatal. The only other person who knew of this was their mutual friend, Eddie, the caretaker at the gym.

What Is Euthanasia?

Doran says: Maggie's tragic case clearly involves euthanasia. But beyond the example, we need a general definition of *euthanasia.*

Patrick says: Consider the etymology of the term *euthanasia*. It derives from the Greek prefix *eu,* which means "good," and the word *thanatos,* which means "death." This suggests that *euthanasia* means "good death."

Warren says: Right, but that definition is much too vague and ambiguous. Many things may be viewed as good

TECHNIQUE

It may seem odd to introductory students that we do not just look up the term *euthanasia* in the dictionary to answer the question of what euthanasia is. In this section we illustrate a philosophical technique of conceptual analysis. Inadequacies of some common definitions are noted. Progressively better definitions of euthanasia are produced in response to objections.

deaths that would not qualify as euthanasia—dying for a just cause, for instance, may be a good death, but would not be euthanasia. So, we need a much more precise definition of the term.

Patrick says: There was an interesting discussion of euthanasia recently on the CBC, in which euthanasia was defined as bringing about the death of a terminally ill person through the omission or commission of an act. This definition is moving in the right direction, but needs refinement.

Doran says: I agree that this definition moves us in the right direction, but it still is somewhat problematic. One problem is that euthanasia need not be performed on *persons;* we can and do euthanize non-persons—for instance, pets. Another problem is that euthanasia need not involve bringing about the death of *terminally ill* individuals. We can euthanize individuals who suffer from very serious disabilities or injuries, yet who are not terminally ill. Maggie's euthanasia is a case in point.

Warren says: A third problem with that definition is that it does not acknowledge that euthanasia involves bringing about an individual's death *for the sake of that individual.* Ending the life of a person who is terminally ill in order to get her insurance money is certainly not euthanasia.

Patrick says: Right, of course. In the light of these points, let's try this: *Euthanasia is an intentional act, or omission, that brings about the death of an individual for that individual's own good.*

Warren says: That looks better. The definition rightly recognizes that the individual being euthanized need not be terminally ill, and it also correctly states that euthanasia is something performed with specific intentions. That is, one intentionally allows or brings about an individual's death with the intention of benefiting that individual.

Patrick says: Given this definition, the intention behind the act will greatly affect whether or not some act is a case of euthanasia. For instance, if a physician gives a patient a large quantity of medication—say, morphine—with the intention to ease the patient's pain, while foreseeing that the drug will likely kill the patient, then this would not count as a case of euthanasia. However, if the patient was given the same dose of morphine with the intent to kill him for his own good, then that would be a case of euthanasia. Thus, the same behaviour could amount to an act of euthanasia or not, depending on the intention of the person who behaves in this way.

Warren says: It is true that doctors, and others, often want to draw this distinction, so I suppose it is good that our definition allows for this distinction to be made.

But a different concern is with the idea of "an individual's own good." Perhaps we need to limit the idea of an individual's good to health-related concerns, such as extreme pain or incapacity. For if we do not limit the idea, it may turn out that we would have to view certain killings as instances of euthanasia when they are not really cases of euthanasia. For instance, it could be for an individual's own good if he is killed rather than having to spend his life in a notoriously brutal maximum security prison, but it seems odd to count such an act as euthanasia, even if it was done at that person's request and intending his own good.

Patrick says: Well, I am not so sure that it would be odd to count that as an act of euthanasia, if we assume that there was no other option for this person, and that life in that prison would be absolutely dreadful. But, given that our present concern is with health care situations, perhaps we would be wise to avoid controversy and to stipulate that whenever we speak of the individual's best interest, we mean the individual's *health-related* interests.

Warren says: All right, just to stick with what we perceive to be common usage, let's stipulate that the benefits are health-related.

In order to stick to common usage, we might also want to distinguish euthanasia from suicide, and this definition does not do that.

UP FOR DISCUSSION

Do you think that ending a person's life for his or her own good for non-medical reasons should count as euthanasia?

Doran says: I think you are right, Warren. Our definition entails that some suicides can be cases of euthanasia, but I think that is fine. When a person intentionally kills himself for his own good, he performs an act of euthanasia on himself. For example, imagine a person who is diagnosed with an extremely painful cancer—say, mouth cancer. Suppose, after several surgeries, and much suffering, the cancer has returned and the end is near. Not wanting to face the horrific pain of untreatable mouth cancer, and not wanting to take so much medication that he would be rendered barely conscious for the rest of his natural life, suppose this person opts to take his own life by taking an overdose of barbiturates. I see no problem with viewing his act as a case of euthanasia. Indeed, to say he

UP FOR DISCUSSION

Do you think that some suicides should count as instances of euthanasia?

simply "committed suicide" would be to under-describe his act. Nevertheless, I admit that my use of the term is idiosyncratic, and since our focus here is on euthanasia when performed on others, let's stipulate that when we use the term *euthanasia*, we mean it to involve one or more individuals performing it on another.

Warren says: Agreed. Our definition is now this: *Euthanasia is an intentional act, or omission, that brings about the death of another individual for that individual's own health-related good.*

Different Kinds of Euthanasia

UP FOR DISCUSSION

The concept of euthanasia is closely related to another concept—physician-assisted suicide. Physician-assisted suicide (PAS) occurs when a physician provides a hopeless, usually terminally ill patient with the means (such as a prescription for a lethal dose of a drug) to commit suicide. A noteworthy example of PAS is the case of Sue Rodriguez, a victim of ALS. After Canada's highest court denied her the right to voluntary active euthanasia, a sympathetic physician assisted her to die. She was paralyzed and unable to take her own life, but she was clearly rational, competent, well informed, and willing to die.

Source: http://archives.cbc.ca/IDD-1-74-1135/life_society/sue_rodriguez/.

Why would our definition of euthanasia not include PAS? Do you think there is a morally significant difference between PAS and euthanasia?

Patrick says: Even though we now have a working definition of *euthanasia*, there is still more work to do in order to clarify the concept. This is because there are different types of euthanasia. Let's begin by noting the difference between active and passive euthanasia.

Active versus Passive Euthanasia

Doran says: Roughly, active euthanasia occurs when one *directly causes* another individual's death—for instance, by administering a lethal injection—for that individual's own health-related good. Passive euthanasia occurs when one *allows* another individual to die—by withholding life-prolonging treatment, for example—for the sake of that individual's health-related good. It must be said that the boundaries between active and passive euthanasia are not always clear, however.

Warren says: Yes, but in spite of the penumbral area, we can often agree on the distinction in health care contexts. For instance, it was a case of active euthanasia when Frankie gave Maggie a lethal injection. But it would have been a case of passive euthanasia if, instead, Maggie's breathing tube or respirator had stopped functioning, and Frankie chose not to notify the nurse so that Maggie could be allowed to die.

Perhaps we can just say that intentionally refraining from treatment so that it will lead to death for the patient's good counts as passive euthanasia, while intentionally providing treatment that will lead to death for the patient's good counts as active euthanasia.

Doran says: But what about cases where a feeding tube or respirator is removed from a terminally ill patient? In a sense this is active, since it requires action, and yet in a sense it is passive, since the act stops treatment and so allows the patient to die of a natural cause.

Patrick says: Interestingly, such cases are usually viewed as passive euthanasia. Perhaps that is because what marks the distinction between passive and active is the cause of death. Roughly, the idea is that if one intends to let the disease kill the patient for the patient's own good, then it is passive. But if one intends to cause "non-naturally" the death for the patient's own good, then it is active. Thus, not treating the cancer or the infection, or removing the respirator and "letting nature take its course" are cases of passive euthanasia, while giving a lethal dose of drugs, for instance, is active.

Warren says: I think that drawing the exact boundaries between passive and active euthanasia is very tricky, but the basic idea is quite clear, and in many cases we can confidently judge whether it is passive or active euthanasia.

Doran says: Even if we can draw a reasonably sharp distinction between active and passive euthanasia, there may be no morally relevant difference between these two kinds of euthanasia.

Patrick says: Right. James Rachels famously argues that there is no intrinsic, morally relevant difference between killing someone and letting someone die. Given this, he argues, there is no intrinsic, morally relevant difference between active and passive euthanasia.[3]

BACKGROUND

The case of Nancy B. is a famous Canadian case of voluntary passive euthanasia. Nancy B. was paralyzed by a rare neurological disease and refused to be kept on a respirator. The case came to court where a judge agreed that she had the right to refuse treatment. She was tranquillized and then removed from the respirator, and she subsequently died.

Source: http://archives.cbc.ca/IDCC-1-74-1135-6406/life_society/sue_rodriguez/.

UP FOR DISCUSSION

Explain why rationing health care—for instance, denying needed heart transplants to elderly people so that younger people can get them instead—is not passive euthanasia.

UP FOR DISCUSSION

Do you think there is a morally relevant difference between euthanasia that occurs as a result of removing a patient from a respirator and euthanasia that occurs as a result of administering a lethal injection?

---

[3] James Rachels, *The End of Life* (New York: Oxford University Press), 106–28. An online version of this book is available at the Online Learning Centre.

Voluntary, Non-voluntary, and Involuntary Euthanasia

Patrick says: We're not finished with drawing distinctions yet! We should note that active and passive euthanasia can be done either voluntarily, involuntarily, or non-voluntarily.

Doran says: Right. **Voluntary euthanasia** occurs when a competent individual consents to his death; **involuntary euthanasia** occurs when a competent individual does not consent to his death; and finally, non-voluntary euthanasia occurs when it involves mentally incompetent individuals who lack the decision-making capacity to express a preference to live or die.

Patrick says: Those definitions look good, but a few clarifications are in order. We should note, for instance, that voluntary euthanasia can occur with the patient consenting at the time of the euthanasia, or prior to that time, through an **advance directive**. So, it is important to realize that a person need not be competent at the time of his or her death for it to count as a form of voluntary euthanasia.

Doran says: Right. And notice also that we've defined non-voluntary euthanasia in such a way that it applies to individuals who lack the ability to make a decision. This would include young children, for example, and the severely cognitively impaired. A broader definition might include the very rare cases of individuals who are mentally competent to make the decision but unable to communicate their preferences.

BACKGROUND

A famous Canadian example of non-voluntary active euthanasia is the case of Tracy Latimer. Tracy was a twelve-year-old quadriplegic who functioned at the level of a three- or four-month-old infant. She suffered from excruciating pain, underwent repeated surgeries, and required further surgeries to remove her thigh bone. In 1993, her father, Robert, unwilling to see his daughter suffer any longer, placed her inside his pick-up truck, ran a hose from the exhaust pipe to the inside of the cab, and watched as his daughter died. He then turned himself in to the police, admitting that he killed his daughter. Latimer was convicted of second-degree murder. The jury recommended parole, and the trial judge agreed, even though the minimum sentence for second-degree murder is ten years in prison. This decision, however, was repeatedly appealed, going all the way to Canada's Supreme Court. In the end, it was ruled that the minimum sentencing laws needed to be followed, and Robert was sentence to life in prison, with no eligibility for parole for ten years. In 2007, Robert was denied parole for failing to express remorse. In 2008, however, Robert was finally granted day parole. See http://www.cbc.ca/news/background/latimer/ for a brief overview.

Warren says: Finally, there are cases of involuntary euthanasia. These would be rare cases, but they could happen. It is not unrealistic to think that a physician, or, more likely, a family member, might, on grounds of compassion, decide not to tell her competent patient or loved one that she is going to be allowed to die or to receive a lethal injection.

Patrick says: True, Warren, but it takes some imagination to come up with cases of involuntary euthanasia that seem permissible.

Warren says: Yes, of course.

Doran says: I agree. And once again there can be grey areas that divide these different categories, but the distinction between these types of euthanasia usually seems quite clear.

Warren says: Good. With these definitions in hand, we can now turn to the moral questions about euthanasia raised by the particular case under consideration.

DECIDING WHICH ISSUES TO DEBATE

Doran says: There are a variety of ethical issues surrounding euthanasia. These ethical questions concern the moral permissibility of the various kinds of euthanasia, as well as ethical questions over whether such actions should be legalized.

Warren says: Right, these are two different issues that are best kept separate. One can think that certain kinds of euthanasia are morally permissible without also thinking that they should be legally permissible, and vice versa.

Patrick says: Let's focus here on questions about the *moral* permissibility of euthanasia. Whether euthanasia should be legalized is an issue we dicuss at the Online Learning Centre.

In Maggie's case, we have a clear case of voluntary active euthanasia. Frankie intentionally causes Maggie's death at her request and for her sake. We can start by asking whether this case of VAE is morally permissible.

Warren says: We should also consider the moral status of non-voluntary active euthanasia, since VAE and NAE are the most controversial

UP FOR DISCUSSION

Suppose there was someone who was mentally competent, yet who was unable to communicate any of his preferences as a result of permanent and complete paralysis. If this person was intentionally allowed to die or intentionally killed for his own good, would it be a case of non-voluntary or involuntary euthanasia? Could it be neither of these? Explain your answer.

BACKGROUND

Here's a table that lists the six possible kinds of euthanasia:

Voluntary active (VAE)	Non-voluntary active (NAE)	Involuntary active (IAE)
Voluntary passive (VPE)	Non-voluntary passive (NPE)	Involuntary passive (IPE)

THEORY AND DISCUSSION

Moral principles and their legal counterparts are two different things. Laws may be moral, immoral, or amoral, and moral principles may not be legally enforceable. Discuss an example of an act that is morally wrong but should not be illegal. Give an example of an act that is not morally wrong but should be illegal.

BACKGROUND

The CMA (Canadian Medical Association) defines euthanasia as follows:

Euthanasia means knowingly and intentionally performing an act that is explicitly intended to end another person's life and that includes the following elements: the subject is a competent, informed person with an incurable illness who has voluntarily asked for his or her life to be ended; the agent knows about the person's condition and desire to die, and commits the act with the primary intention of ending the life of that person; and the act is undertaken with empathy and compassion and without personal gain....

Source: Canadian Medical Association, "Euthanasia and Assisted Suicide" (policy document approved by the CMA Board of Directors, 19 June 1998).

The CMA's definition seems too narrow, as it precludes many of the distinctions drawn in the previous section.

THEORY

Appeals to the moral importance of respecting autonomy are often Kantian in nature. Appeals to the moral importance of welfare are consequentialist in spirit. As explained in Chapter 3, Doran's pluralist theory recognizes the importance of both considerations.

kinds of euthanasia and the most discussed in public debate.

Doran says: Sounds good. Let's start with Maggie's case and consider the morality of VAE in general. Later we can debate the morality of NAE.

THE MORALITY OF VOLUNTARY ACTIVE EUTHANASIA

Warren says: I think VAE is justified in some cases, including Maggie's. In the **original position** it would be in our interest to accept a rule that would allow us to choose the manner and time of our own deaths. There may be all sorts of restrictions we would want to put on the practice of euthanasia, however. Things like psychological evaluations and the availability of good comfort care would be adopted to protect our interests as seen from the original position. But the basic right to voluntary active euthanasia would be acknowledged in the original position as being in one's interest.

Patrick says: I agree that VAE is permissible in many cases, including the case of Maggie. Compassion, kindness, charity, empathy, respect, and other virtues speak in favour of voluntary active euthanasia in this case and relevantly similar cases. And I also agree that various restrictions will likely be needed to protect people from such things as temporary depression, irrationality, etc.

Doran says: I also think VAE is morally acceptable in Maggie's case, as well as in many other cases. I have many reasons for my view. One of my arguments is, roughly, that respect for autonomy and considerations of welfare constitute reasons in favour of euthanasia that, in many cases, including Maggie's, overwhelm any arguments against it.

Warren says: Well, why don't we begin, Doran, by taking a closer look at your arguments in support of VAE?

Doran says: Sure. I'd like to begin by identifying some fairly familiar reasons which speak in favour of VAE, and then I will point out that these reasons are not by themselves sufficient to justify VAE. I will argue, however, that, suitably modified, these reasons form the basis of a sound argument for the morality of VAE.[4]

Patrick says: Sounds good.

The Autonomy and Best Interest Argument for VAE

Doran says: Two basic sorts of arguments are frequently voiced in support of VAE. One sort of argument raises the idea of autonomy—the basic refrain is that competent people should have the right to determine their own futures, euthanasia allows for death with dignity, etc. Another strain of argument in favour of active euthanasia emphasizes that sometimes it is in the best interest of a person to no longer continue living. Often this is because of the tremendous hopeless suffering, both physical and psychological, experienced by some patients, but it may also be because the patient is in a condition where life is no longer a benefit to her (say, because she is able to exist without horrible pain only if she is in a drug-hazed stupor). It is this appeal to the patient's best interest that constitutes another powerful reason in support of active euthanasia.

Patrick says: Both strands of argument seem to introduce powerful considerations in favour of VAE, although without qualification they may not be sufficient to make the case for VAE.

Doran says: I agree. Let's begin with an initial statement of what we might call the *Autonomy and Best Interest argument*. This version of the argument will be too simple, but understanding its weaknesses will enable us to revise the initial argument into something that I take to be sound.

(1) If a person freely chooses some action, and that action is in that person's best interest, then the act is morally permissible.

(2) In some cases, including Maggie's, a person freely chooses VAE and it is in that person's best interest.

(3) Therefore, in these cases, including Maggie's, VAE is morally permissible.

---

[4] Doran's argumentative strategy for VAE is modelled on a similar set of arguments offered by James Rachels, "Euthanasia," in *Matters of Life and Death: New Introductory Essays in Moral Philosophy,* 3rd ed., ed. Tom Regan (New York: McGraw Hill, 1993).

Patrick says: The argument is valid, but it is likely unsound. Some may try to reject this argument by attacking premise (2). The critic may deny, for instance, that a person could ever have a life that is not worth living and, hence, that death is ever in a person's best interest. But that objection is weak and is, I believe, refuted by Maggie's case, and by other cases that are particularly grim.

Warren says: Others will suggest, more plausibly, that VAE will be misapplied and performed on people who don't really freely choose it, or on people whose lives could still be a benefit to them. Of course, these are serious concerns, but they speak to the issue of whether VAE should be practised, and to the dangers of legalization, and not to the present issue of whether VAE is, in principle, morally wrong.

Patrick says: Agreed. The critic is better off attacking premise (1) of the argument. An act can be morally wrong even if it is freely chosen and in the best interest of those primarily concerned. One way it could be wrong is if such an act violated the rights of others. For example, it may be in the best interest of a person who just found out that he needed a liver transplant to have his friend put him at the head of the queue, but such an act—though freely chosen and in the best interest of the person primarily involved—would be wrong since it would violate the rights of those who had a prior claim to the transplant.

TECHNIQUE

Patrick and Warren are adopting the standard philosophical technique of using counterexamples to disprove a moral principle. In this case, it is the principle expressed by premise (1) that is under attack. In the light of their objections, Doran must either abandon or revise premise (1).

Warren says: Notice further that freely chosen acts that are in a person's best interest can be wrong even if they do not violate anyone else's rights. Think of a case such as this. Suppose there is a person, call him Zeke, who is fabulously rich, and who is soon going to die. As a last act of pleasure for himself, he decides he will collect his millions and light it all on fire. The decision to burn the money may be an autonomous decision, and perhaps it is in Zeke's best interest to do so, since his choice will give him pleasure. But it also certainly seems wrong for Zeke to engage in such a wasteful, selfish action, given that Zeke could instead have used his wealth to benefit many people in great need. And if this is right, then we have another reason to reject premise (1).

The Revised Autonomy and Best Interest Argument

Doran says: Your counterexamples show that premise (1) of the above argument is false. It is too simple to say that euthanasia would be justified if it was freely chosen and in a person's best interest. But suitably modified, I think this argument can be saved. So consider what may be called the *Revised Autonomy and Best Interest argument* for VAE.

(1) If a person freely chooses some action, and that action is in that person's best interest, and it neither violates anyone's rights nor sets back anyone's very important interests, then it is morally permissible.

(2) In some circumstances, a person freely chooses VAE, and it is in that person's best interest, and it neither violates anyone's rights nor sets back anyone's very important interests.

(3) Therefore, in those circumstances, VAE is morally permissible.

I believe that Maggie's case of euthanasia is a case where VAE is justified because it satisfies the conditions set forth in premise (1). She freely chose euthanasia; euthanasia was (tragically) in her best interest; it did not violate anyone else's rights; and it did not set back very important interests of others. Therefore, it was permissible for her to receive VAE.

Of course, in other cases, euthanasia may not be permissible. For example, if euthanasia was not freely chosen, or if receiving it violated others' rights or seriously harmed others, then it may be wrong. But, other things being equal, the fact that VAE is sometimes an expression of one's deepest preferences and is necessary to serve one's best interests, and can be done without setting back even more important moral considerations, means that VAE is sometimes morally permissible.

Warren says: It is good that your modified premise (1) can avoid our previous counterexamples. The revised premise (1) does not support putting one's name at the top of the transplant list, since such an act violates the rights of others. And the revised premise avoids the thrust of the case of Zeke, since his action would set back the very important interests of others.

Patrick says: But there's still room for objections to premise (1), even with the revision.

Warren says: I suppose that opponents of VAE will try to reject your premise (1) by arguing that freely chosen acts that serve a person's best interest, and violate no one else's rights nor set back any very important

TECHNIQUE

Frequently in philosophical debate, the response to a counterexample is to revise the statement that it attacked, explicitly stating exceptions so as to avoid the counterexample. The process may then be repeated until all the necessary exceptions are explicit in the statement. A concern with this sort of process, however, is that the revisions to the principle become merely ad hoc. One wants the principles one defends not only to avoid counterexamples but also to have an underlying rationale that is itself morally significant.

UP FOR DISCUSSION

Note that some could still challenge premise (2). They might maintain that euthanasia violates God's right to say when we die. Is this a plausible position? What would that imply about other sorts of killing?

UP FOR
DISCUSSION

Do you think that the revised Autonomy and Best Interest argument is sound?

interests of others, can still be wrong if they transgress other important values. For instance, they might think that such acts would be wrong if they violate the sanctity of human life or if they are contrary to God's will. We should, therefore, consider those arguments against VAE.

The Sanctity of Life Objection to the Morality of VAE

Doran says: Right. Those who oppose VAE often argue that it is wrong because it would allow for the intentional killing of innocent human beings, and that killing innocent humans is always immoral. Given that this is a common argument against AE, and given that it could be used to counter my premise (1), we should consider it.

Warren says: Yes, that is a standard objection. It is derived from the **Sanctity of Life principle.**

Doran says: I think the objection is mistaken.

TECHNIQUE

Notice that Patrick is pointing to frequently overlooked features of the Sanctity of Life objection to active euthanasia: (1) it applies only to human life; (2) it typically is said to apply only to innocent human life; and (3) it assumes that if a life is sacred it is always wrong to end it.

Patrick says: I do too, but before we look at problems with this objection, I think we need to spell it out in more detail. This view is often characterized as the view that it is wrong to kill, because life is sacred. But proponents of this view are surely not claiming that *all* life is sacred. The suggestion seems to be, rather, that *human* life—specifically, *innocent* human life—is sacred. But why do proponents of this view believe that there is something special about the lives of humans, and only humans? And how is it supposed to follow from this that it's always wrong to kill an innocent human?

Doran says: Various reasons are given for why human life is "sacred." Often, arguments that appeal to God are invoked in support of this claim. God created humans in His image, and so they are special, and deserving of special respect.

Other times, non-religious reasons are given for the view that human life is sacred. Kant, for instance, could be seen as (to some degree) relevant here, since he famously claims that humanity is an end in itself, and as such, has a special dignity. By *humanity,* however, he means "rational agents," not "human beings." So it is the lives of rational beings that are "sacred" for Kant.

But, Patrick, you raise an interesting question. What does it mean to say a human life is sacred? I take it, the claim is not that human beings may never be killed, since, as you suggest, most who espouse this view accept the legitimacy of killing humans in some cases, such as self-defence, a just war, or maybe even capital punishment. So, most likely, to say that a human life is sacred is to say that an innocent human life may not be taken, or may not be taken intentionally. Thus, perhaps the principle should really be called *the sanctity of innocent human life.*

BACKGROUND

One statement of the Sanctity of Life view is as follows: "Lutherans for Life–Canada is an organization whose mission is to 'witness to the sanctity of human life through education based on the Word of God.' Lutherans for Life–Canada believes every human life—from conception to natural death regardless of physical or mental challenges or condition of dependence—is precious in God's sight."

Source: Glenn Schaeffer, Lutherans for Life—Canada, http://www.lutheransforlife-canada.ca/.

Patrick says: Yes, I think that better captures the principle behind the Sanctity of Life view, as I understand it.

Doran says: Still, you're right that one may wonder why the sanctity of innocent human life entails that innocent humans may never be killed. After all, proponents of the view are willing to make exceptions in cases like self-defence. Why should they not make an exception when life is no longer a benefit to the person, and when that person no longer wants to live?

Warren says: More to the point, there are compelling counterexamples to the principle that innocent humans may never be intentionally killed. Suppose that a totally incompetent patient has been infected with an incurable disease that is easily spread, and that the patient has escaped custody and is running toward a crowd. Now, suppose a police officer shoots and kills that patient to avert what could be a global disaster, a plague. In this case it would be permissible to kill an innocent human being so as to avoid a world-wide plague, and so the sanctity of innocent human life principle must be false.

UP FOR DISCUSSION

Do you think the case of the innocent plague victim is a successful counterexample to the claim that innocent human beings must never be intentionally killed? Why or why not?

Doran says: I take it that this patient is innocent in virtue of being "totally incompetent," and so the doctrine which says it is always wrong to kill an innocent human being would imply that it was wrong to kill the plague victim. But it would clearly not be wrong to kill this innocent human being, given that it was necessary to avert a global disaster. Therefore, the claim that innocent human beings may never be intentionally killed must be false.

Patrick says: Although I agree that it would not be wrong to kill the innocent person in this example, we should, in my view, feel badly about having taken an innocent life in this situation.

It's also worth noting that not everyone would agree with our conclusion concerning the permissibility of killing the plague victim in this case. A Kantian would argue, for instance, that it is always wrong to use persons as a mere means to an end. Assuming the innocent human is a person—which is questionable, I suppose, given his incompetence—then some may argue that it would be wrong to kill him, even if it is necessary to save the lives of others. So the example might be unpersuasive for some.

Warren says: It is only problematic if we think, like Kant, that we must be so non-consequentialist that we would risk all of humanity to save one person who will die from his illness in any case. I think it presents a counterexample to Kantian thought and, more generally, to the principle that it is always wrong to kill innocent human beings intentionally.

Patrick says: I agree, Warren. As you know, I'm no Kantian.

Doran says: I believe your case presents a counterexample to most versions of the principle of the sanctity of innocent human life, Warren. Kantians maintain that it is wrong to treat rational beings merely as a means; they could then point out that a totally incompetent person is no longer a rational being, and so the injunction not to treat him merely as a means no longer applies. But a different case could serve as a counterexample even to the Kantian version of the sanctity of human life (that is, the sanctity of *rational* life).

Patrick says: Let's hear your counterexample, Doran.

Hare's Lorry Driver—A Counterexample to the Sanctity of Life Principle

Doran says: The Christian philosopher R. M. Hare gives this case: a petrol lorry driver (gasoline tanker truck driver) gets into an accident and is trapped in his vehicle as flames begin to engulf him. He screams for someone to kill him, so that he does not have to roast to death. A bystander, understanding the situation, takes action and ends the petrol lorry driver's life. Does the bystander act permissibly? It seems so. And if that is the case, then we have a clear counterexample to the Sanctity of Life principle. For the petrol lorry driver is an innocent person who is permissibly killed by another person.[5]

Patrick says: Good. This example seems to be a clear case where it is not wrong to end the life of an innocent person, as it would be cruel not to comply with his request. Further, it is a useful example to show the implausibility of the claim that it is never in one's best interest to die.

Still, although we agree with Hare's counterexample, I suspect some would argue that killing the lorry driver is wrong, because it is sinful or cowardly for the driver to want to die.

Warren says: That response to Hare's example confuses, as Nowell-Smith says, a right to live with a duty to live.[6] If one has a right to live, then one may sometimes waive the right and release others from their duty not to kill one. That is what the driver does. The idea that it is sinful to want to die, however, probably rests on the mistaken view that one has not just a right to live but a duty to live. Those who think wanting death is cowardly are, moreover, being quite unrealistic about pain. What do you think, Patrick?

Patrick says: I agree, it is certainly not cowardly for the driver to want to be killed when the alternative is burning to death. If anything, it would perhaps be cowardly not to comply with the driver's request to be killed. I believe this case shows that it is sometimes morally permissible to kill innocent persons. If that's correct, then the main premise in the Sanctity of Life objection to VAE is false, and that objection is therefore unsound.

Doran says: Beyond giving a clear counterexample to the Sanctity of Life principle, I would like to explain why it is a mistake to claim that killing innocents is always wrong.

Warren says: Go ahead.

THEORY

Hare defends the permissibility of active euthanasia in the case of the petrol lorry driver by employing an idea that is similar both to the Golden Rule—"Do unto others as you would have them do unto you"—and to Kant's universal law version of the categorical imperative, "Act only according to that maxim which you can at the same time will that it should become a universal law." Kant's basic idea is that we should act only on principles that we can consistently will everyone to follow. Since we cannot consistently will to universalize a principle that prevents us from being killed were we in a situation like that of the lorry driver, we should reject a principle that prohibited killing in such situations.

There is considerable irony in using a Christian- and Kantian-inspired argument to support VAE, since many Christians think that their faith requires them to oppose active euthanasia, and since, as we have seen, Kant is usually interpreted as a defender of the principle of the sanctity of human life.

For a more detailed discussion of Kant's ethics, see Chapter 2.

---

[5] R. M. Hare, *Essays on Religion and Education* (Oxford: Oxford University Press, 1998).

[6] Patrick Nowell-Smith, "The Right to Die," in *Contemporary Moral Issues*, 3rd ed., ed. Wesley Cragg, (Toronto: McGraw-Hill Ryerson, 1992), 8.

An Argument That the Moral Reasons against Killing Do Not Apply to VAE

Doran says: Normally, there are many reasons that explain why killing an innocent person is wrong. The thing is, though, none of these reasons speak against VAE, and some seem to actually support the moral permissibility of VAE.[7]

For instance, consider a typical murder—say, a drive-by shooting. Why is that act wrong? Reasons why it is wrong include (1) it harms the victim—he is deprived the goods that his life had to offer and would have come to offer; (2) it goes against his preferences—he did not want to die, yet his preferences were disregarded; (3) it violates the victim's autonomy—he had various plans in his life, yet this killing took away his ability to control his life choices; (4) it spreads fear in the community—knowing that there is a murderer on the loose who kills people against their will is bound to terrify others. Perhaps there are other reasons that make the act of murder wrong, but these seem to be the principal ones.

But notice that none of these reasons apply to VAE. It does not deprive the "victim" of a good future (since it is only to be performed on individuals whose life is no longer a good for them); it does not act against the "victim's" preferences—it honours them; it does not violate the "victim's" autonomy; it respects it; and it need not spread fear in the community, since VAE is limited to people who both need it and want it. So the standard reasons which make killing people normally wrong do not apply to VAE, and so that is why it makes sense to say that VAE is an important exception to the moral rule against killing innocent humans. Perhaps there is some other reason why killing is wrong that I have overlooked, and which applies to VAE, but the onus is on opponents of VAE to identify that reason.

An Argument That Euthanasia Is Wrong Because It Destroys What Belongs to God

Patrick says: I agree with you, Doran, that the considerations that typically make it wrong to kill innocent human beings tend to speak in favour or VAE, rather than against it. Once this point is made explicit, it seems implausible to suppose that VAE is always morally wrong.

[7] On this point, see Peter Singer, *Practical Ethics*, 2nd ed. (Cambridge: Cambridge University Press, 1993), 175–217. Also available online, http://www.utilitarian.net/singer/by/1993----.htm.

I doubt, however, that your argument will persuade many proponents of the Sanctity of Life view. This is because the reasons you cite for why killing is generally wrong are not the principal reasons why many advocates of this view think killing is wrong. What principally makes killing humans wrong, on this view, usually turns on the fact that humans are God's creation. So whether you kill someone in a drive-by shooting or you kill a terminally ill person, you are killing one of God's creations either way. This is often why both are regarded as wrong, according to their view.

Doran says: You may be right, Patrick. But those who appeal to this theistic argument are in trouble, since, as we have seen, there are clear counterexamples to the Sanctity of Life view they wish to defend—the petrol lorry driver case, for instance. Further, this argument has other problems.

Patrick says: I agree—I think that this line of argument is indefensible. One additional and obvious problem is that it presupposes that God exists. This is something that I, and many others, would deny.

Doran says: Yes, plus setting that question aside, notice that *everything* (or at least every "natural" thing) on a theological view is God's creation, and so it would turn out that it would be wrong to destroy anything (or any natural thing)—bacteria, plants, weeds, animals, etc. Clearly, however, that is an absurd consequence. Instead, for this argument even to get off the ground, we should revise it so that it says that *human life* belongs to God, and so to destroy it (whether one's own or others') is wrong, because it destroys something that belongs to God.

Warren says: Yes, one often hears that only God can take human life because human life belongs to God, but those who say this may nonetheless accept capital punishment, or killing in self-defence, or killing in defence of one's country, or killing the *innocent* plague-stricken incompetent in our earlier example. Whatever is meant by "sanctity of life," if human beings' intentional killing of human beings is sometimes justified in God's eyes, according to this religious view, then it may well be justified in the case of euthanasia. Instead of pointing to their view that our lives belong to God, they should face the justificatory arguments already given, if they are to be consistent, or deny

TECHNIQUE

Warren is setting up an argument called a **dilemma**. A dilemma shows that one's opponent is faced with only two or more logical alternatives, none of which the opponent would accept. If these opponents insist that only God may destroy human life, then they have a problem, for they would not be able to explain why it is wrong to kill the innocent plague victim. But if they say humans may justifiably kill in some cases, then they have not yet provided an argument against active euthanasia.

UP FOR DISCUSSION

In the final analysis, do you think it was morally permissible for Frankie to perform VAE on Maggie?

BACKGROUND

One of the most common arguments against VAE is the "slippery slope" objection. Roughly, this is the concern that if VAE is accepted, it will lead to other kinds of killing that are morally unacceptable, for example, killing patients who do not really choose euthanasia, or killing patients who could have had lives that were worth living. These slippery slope arguments raise serious concerns regarding legalization of VAE, but they do not show that any particular instance of VAE, such as Maggie's, is morally wrong. An examination of the arguments for and against legalizing VAE can be found at the Online Learning Centre.

that any killing of human beings, who are God's creation, innocent or not, is ever justified, even in self-defence.

Patrick says: Right. To sum up, then, either it is always wrong to kill human beings or it is not always wrong. Proponents of the Sanctity of Life view would not—or at least cannot plausibly—hold the former view. They would, or should, accept that killing humans is sometimes permissible. But then they cannot object to VAE simply on the ground that human life is sacred or that human life belongs to God. Further argument is needed.

THE MORALITY OF NON-VOLUNTARY ACTIVE EUTHANASIA

Doran says: Okay, so it looks like we all agree that the Sanctity of Life objection fails, and that VAE is morally permissible in certain situations. There are, of course, other objections to VAE, but perhaps we should now consider the difficult issue of NAE, *non-voluntary* active euthanasia.

Patrick says: Yes, it's one thing to say that if a competent person regards his or her life as no longer worth living and expresses a clear preference for euthanasia, then it may be permissible to end that person's life. It's quite another thing, however, to say that it's permissible to euthanize an individual if he or she does not, because he or she *cannot,* consent to the act. This, of course, is different from Maggie's case. But we can easily imagine that her opponent's sucker punch not only paralyzed Maggie, but also caused significant brain damage which rendered her mentally incompetent to make her own medical decisions, and ask whether NAE would then be permissible.

Doran says: Things are especially difficult when it comes to NAE, since my favoured argument for VAE appealed, in part, to a person's right to control her own future in matters that primarily concerned her. But this appeal to control one's own future, and the right to make one's own decisions, is not something that applies to human infants or to humans with severe mental incapacities. In general, we do not say that a young child, for instance, has a right to make her own decisions about matters that could seriously affect her well-being. So this argument cannot be used to support NAE, where the individual cannot consent.

Warren says: So, Doran, if your main argument for VAE won't apply to NAE, then what is your view on the morality of NAE?

The Best Interest Argument for NAE

Doran says: I think NAE is sometimes morally permissible. I think the crucial issue is what we should do for individuals who cannot make their own decisions. Here it might be instructive to consider one's beloved pet, when it comes to end-of-life decisions. It is quite clear that when it comes to one's dog, for instance, one has a moral duty to euthanize him, if continued existence harms the dog because he is in unremitting pain, or cannot do the basic activities that dogs do—like eat, play, move, etc. In the case of one's dog, questions of what the dog wants, or getting consent from the dog, are obviously out of place. What is relevant is helping the dog avoid misery.

If we turn from one's pet to an incompetent human being, it seems that here, too, questions of respecting autonomy are out of place. When a child does not want to go to the dentist, or wants to eat a pound of junk food, the responsible adult should not be concerned with respecting the child's "autonomy," since the child is not competent to make her own decisions about such matters, but rather should do what is in the child's best interest. Likewise, those individuals who are not competent to make their own decisions need others to do what is in their best interest. Similarly, when it comes to active euthanasia of incompetent human beings, I believe that the primary concern needs to be with doing what is in the best interest of the patient.

Warren says: I have a caution to offer. I have noticed that examples of euthanasia of pets are red flags to some critics of a liberal position on euthanasia. They say that promoters of euthanasia value human beings no more than dogs. It bears emphasis, then, that the point is to look at the reasons for mercy killing, not to compare the value of the lives of humans and dogs.

Doran says: Point taken. Nonetheless, I always find that reply odd, since it is tempting to say, "You would do it for your dog—why wouldn't you do it for a person?" Why should someone who is supposedly worth more have to suffer in ways that we would not dream of making a dog suffer?

Patrick says: A related point is that we agreed that VAE is morally permissible in certain cases. Given this, it is arguably unfair to make certain individuals suffer needlessly, simply because they are unable to give consent.

Doran says: That's a good point, Patrick. Let's now get back to the best interest argument for NAE. My argument is as follows:

(1) If an action is in an incompetent patient's best interest,
is performed for that patient's sake, and neither violates
anyone's rights nor sets back anyone's very important
interests, then it is morally permissible.

(2) NAE is in an incompetent patient's best interest, is
performed for the sake of that patient, and, in some
circumstances, neither violates anyone's rights nor sets back
anyone's very important interests.

(3) Therefore, in some cases, NAE is morally permissible.

Patrick says: Let's consider what premises (1) and (2) imply with respect to the
modified case of Maggie mentioned earlier—that is, the case in
which the sucker punch left her mentally incompetent.

Warren says: Euthanasia is performed for her sake. It is consistent with both
her best interests and her rights. If she is suffering, it is in her best
interest and it is her right to avoid pointless suffering. She also has
an interest in and a right to dignity. But a dignified existence is
not possible in her current condition. Euthanasia would serve her
right to avoid indignity.

Doran says: Yes, and given the sort of family she has, Maggie's euthanasia
does not violate anyone else's rights or very important interests.

Patrick says: Well, it seems in this modified case that NAE would be justified
for Maggie, assuming she is suffering pointlessly. Though I am not
sure it is fundamentally a matter of respecting rights, as Warren
suggests. I believe a virtuous person would be moved by considerations of mercy and charity to do what Maggie is unable to do
for herself—put an end to her pointless suffering and allow her a
more dignified death.

Warren says: Before we move on, though, the critic might attack the second
premise of Doran's argument, specifically the part which asserts
the moral claim that NAE can be consistent with everyone's rights.
For NAE involves killing a patient without his or her consent, and
surely that would violate his or her right to life.

Doran says: In response to that objection, I would deny the claim that killing
violates the patient's rights in justifiable cases of NAE. We must
remember that rights exist to protect one's important interests,

and these include autonomy interests as well as interests in not being harmed. But in cases of the incompetent, autonomy interests do not apply since incompetent individuals lack the capacity for autonomy. And while they certainly have an interest in not being harmed, this is, in fact, respected by NAE. This may be borne out by a straightforward analogy with the vaccination of a young child. We do not (and should not) say it violates her rights because she never consented, and we do say that it is in her interest in not being harmed since the painful poke protects her from contracting a much more serious setback to her well-being. Similarly, we should not say that NAE violates the rights of the incompetent patient since the patient never consented. Instead, we should say that NAE is justifiable if it is in the best interest of the patient, done for the sake of that patient, and neither violates anyone's rights nor sets back anyone's very important interests.

Patrick says: So you agree, Doran, that incompetent individuals have a basic right to life. But you deny that the right is violated in cases where death is in the patient's best interest?

Doran says: That is a fair way to put my point. The right to life protects persons who have an interest in living. But in justifiable cases of NAE, the patients—tragically—do not have an interest in living.

Patrick says: I agree with you that NAE is sometimes permissible, though my argument might look a little different from yours. As I suggested above, I believe it is primarily virtues such as compassion, charity, etc., that justify NAE in certain situations. There are, however, other virtue ethicists who would disagree with me—and with your argument. Philippa Foot is one.

Doran says: Yes, let's consider Foot's view. Opponents to my argument must either reject my claim that NAE does not violate anyone's rights, or reject my claim that NAE is sometimes in the patient's best interest. Why don't we begin with an examination of Foot's objection? She claims that NAE violates the patient's right to life.

Philippa Foot's Objection to NAE

Warren says: Okay. Philippa Foot, a prominent virtue theorist, argues that NAE is unjust since it violates the right to life of the incompetent individual who is euthanized. Her argument is that we should assume that an act that infringes a right violates that right unless that right is positively waived, or unless we can assume that it would be waived. In the case of non-voluntary active euthanasia, the patient has not waived her right to life (obviously). So the question is whether or not we can assume that the right would be waived. She says we can make this assumption when it comes to NPE (non-voluntary passive euthanasia) but not when it comes to NAE: this is because there is a widespread feeling in society that one would not want to be kept alive indefinitely when there is no hope for recovery, but there is no widespread consensus that people would want to be killed if they were in a hopeless condition. Thus, in the end, she supports the permissibility of NPE but opposes NAE, on the grounds that the latter (but not the former) violates the individual's right to life.[8]

Patrick says: I think Foot is mistaken. We must show compassion and sympathy for the suffering of incompetent individuals. When it is clear that continued life is of no value, the compassionate thing to do is to end the suffering by ending the life. Moreover, as I suggested earlier, it may well be unjust, or unfair, *not* to perform NAE in certain cases. Both competent and incompetent individuals have an interest in avoiding pointless suffering and dying with dignity. Given this, it seems rather unfair to grant active euthanasia to the former but not the latter.

Doran says: I believe Foot is mistaken, too. In general, I think it is a mistake to decide what is right (or wrong) by appealing to prevailing consensus. It is odd to think that whether NAE is justified or not depends on prevailing social mores. Why should it be wrong in Canada, but right in Holland, for instance? Such relativism seems problematic.

Moreover, I think we can understand, as I tried to explain above, why a right to life is not relevant when speaking of non-voluntary euthanasia. Here, the function of rights is to protect the person's interests in general, to protect autonomy, and to ensure that a person has the ability to make his own decisions in matters that intimately concern his life. But in cases of euthanasia, it is not in the interest of the person to continue to exist, and when considering those who are not competent there is no autonomy to protect and no decision-making capability to honour. Instead, what needs to be done is to do what is most merciful for the person whose life is in a hopeless condition.

UP FOR DISCUSSION

Do you think that NAE violates the individual's right to life? Why or why not?

---

[8] Philippa Foot, "Euthanasia," in *Virtues and Vices* (Oxford: Oxford University Press, 2002).

Warren says: I also reject Foot's view. In the original position, we would not want to be at the mercy of the majority in the real world. At the same time, we would recognize that if we were permanently disabled to the point of being unable to make a decision, we would want others to make decisions for us in our best interest. These interests should be judged, with notable and rare exceptions, from the viewpoint of the patient.

Doran says: I am glad to hear, Warren, that your argument from the original position also supports the moral permissibility of some NAE. Likewise, I am pleased that Patrick's appeal to considerations of virtue also supports NAE. This is a very difficult issue, so it is good to know that there is more than one support for my conclusion.

The Never-Best-Interest Objection to NAE

Patrick says: Even if the critic accepts your first premise, Doran, there's room to argue that your second premise is false, by insisting that killing a person can never be in the best interest of that person. The underlying idea is that NAE is never in a person's best interest, because death removes all possibility of future benefit for the patient. In a sense, this is a concern for any kind of euthanasia, but it is a particular concern for non-voluntary cases. For, in such cases, the sole justification is an appeal to the best interest of the patient.

Warren says: Right. When discussing this in class, students often bring up cases of so-called miraculous recoveries, where seemingly hopeless people turn out to have good lives.

Doran says: Yes, but this line of objection is unsound. We certainly think that actively killing a dying pet can sometimes be in the pet's best interest. Further, it is reasonable to say, "It was for the best," when a loved one dies after enduring the end stages of terrible diseases like throat cancer. And finally, virtually everyone thinks it is sometimes in the best interest of a person to be allowed to die (VPE or NPE). So, it is difficult to see how one could plausibly deny that it could be in one's best interest to have that death brought about by active, quicker, less painful means.

Patrick says: It would also be rather cruel to expect people to hold out for a miraculous recovery when they are suffering horribly and the likelihood of such a recovery is virtually nil.

Warren says: I agree. To demonstrate that NAE could be in the best interest of the person, we could adapt Hare's example of the truck driver in the burning cab. Suppose the driver hit his head in the accident and is no longer competent to request death but is still conscious and dying in unbearable agony. It seems clear that it would be in his best interest to receive euthanasia in this case, and cruel to allow him to burn to death instead. It would also seem strange to suppose that VAE would be right in the original case and that NAE would be wrong in this case just because the driver cannot ask for death. While it is somewhat less obvious, I think the same sorts of things can be said about Maggie concerning the modified case where she is incompetent.

UP FOR DISCUSSION

Opponents of NAE often argue that it is wrong because it discriminates against incompetent humans. However, Patrick argues that not supporting NAE actually discriminates against those who are not competent. What do you think?

Patrick says: I agree. The modified example pretty clearly shows, I believe, that it would be both cruel and unfair not to kill the driver simply because he cannot express a desire to be killed, when it is quite clear that that is what he'd want. The examples considered defeat the objection that NAE can never really be in the best interest of the patient, and support the view that NAE is at least sometimes permissible.

Warren says: Nevertheless, there remain serious objections to *implementing* active euthanasia, both voluntary and non-voluntary. At present, active euthanasia is criminal in Canada. Perhaps there are good reasons for this? If that is the case, then even if we are right that some instances of voluntary and non-voluntary active euthanasia are morally permissible, it could still be the case that it ought to be legally impermissible to perform active euthanasia.

Patrick says: Right. It does not follow from the fact that VAE and NAE are morally permissible that they should also be *legally* permissible. But the question of whether active euthanasia should be legalized is exceedingly complicated, so perhaps we ought to leave that debate for another time. (Please see the Online Learning Centre for a further discussion of this topic.)

Doran says: Agreed.

Warren says: Well, this is a good beginning to a debate about the moral permissibility of various kinds of euthanasia that could go on a long way yet.

Doran says: No doubt there is much more that can be said both for and against VAE and NAE, and the other kinds of euthanasia we didn't address in this chapter.

Patrick says: Right. But let's call it a day.

SUMMARY

Here is a summary of the main questions, concepts, and arguments covered in this chapter:

- The main questions explored in this chapter are "When, if ever, is voluntary active euthanasia (VAE) morally permissible?" and "When if ever, is non-voluntary active euthanasia (NAE) morally permissible?" These questions are initially motivated by a drama which raises the tragic case of Maggie in the film *Million Dollar Baby.*
- Euthanasia is defined as an intentional act, or omission, that brings about the death of another individual for that individual's own health-related good.
- Active euthanasia is distinguished from passive euthanasia.
- Voluntary, non-voluntary, and involuntary euthanasia are distinguished.
- Doran, Patrick, and Warren agree that both voluntary and non-voluntary active euthanasia are morally permissible in some circumstances. They also agree that Frankie acted permissibly when he performed voluntary active euthanasia on Maggie.
- Doran initially presents the Autonomy and Best Interest argument *for* voluntary active euthanasia, but Warren and Patrick show this argument to be unsound. In its place, Doran defends the Revised Autonomy and Best Interest argument.
- Various versions of the Sanctity of Life and God's Ownership arguments *against* voluntary active euthanasia are considered and rejected.
- The Best Interest argument *for* non-voluntary active euthanasia is presented and defended against objections.

Review Questions

1. Why is the definition of *euthanasia* as "a good death" rejected? How, instead, do Doran, Patrick, and Warren finally define the term?
2. What are the six types of euthanasia? Give an example of each.
3. Explain the distinction between active and passive euthanasia.
4. Why is the initial statement of the Autonomy and Best Interest argument for VAE unsound?
5. Explain the Revised Autonomy and Best Interest argument.
6. Explain the Sanctity of Life objection, and explain why this objection is rejected. What example does Warren give to show that it is sometimes morally permissible, and perhaps morally required, to kill an innocent human being intentionally?
7. R. M. Hare's case of the petrol lorry driver is a counterexample to what principles?
8. Why do the normal explanations of the wrongness of killing fail to show that VAE is wrong?
9. What is the Best Interest argument for NAE?
10. Why does Philippa Foot think that NAE violates the right to life of the individual who is to be euthanized?
11. What responses do Doran, Warren, and Patrick each give to Foot's argument against NAE?

WWW.MCGRAWHILL.CA/OLC/SMOLKIN

AUTONOMY AND THE RIGHT TO REFUSE TREATMENT

INTRODUCTION

Commonsense moral thinking strongly supports a principle of respect for **autonomy.** The rough idea here is that we ought to respect individuals' right to choose how to lead their lives. Within a medical context, this principle suggests that we ought to respect the right of patients—at least insofar as they are **competent**—to choose their own course of care. Respecting patient autonomy seems to imply, among other things, that we recognize a right to refuse medical care. These basic points are relatively uncontroversial. Controversy quickly emerges, however, when we attempt to get beyond the basics and specify more precisely what we mean when we speak of autonomy, competence, and the right to refuse medical care.

To help us think through these issues, we consider the case of Jillian Edwards. Mrs. Edwards was recently diagnosed with **multiple sclerosis (MS).** Because of her MS, she also suffers from **dysphagia,** a potentially very dangerous condition where one is prone to choke. She recently had a choking incident, and has been admitted to the hospital for observation. Her doctor prescribed a soft diet. However, Mrs. Edwards is in denial about her condition (both her MS and the dysphagia), and she insists on eating solid foods. She is at times disoriented and confused, but at other times she seems to understand her doctor's warnings, and just thinks they're overblown. Mrs. Edwards is a very strong-willed individual and she is determined not to have her diet restricted, yet allowing her to eat solid foods would put her at a high risk of serious harm. After arguing with her physician over her diet, Mrs. Edwards insists on being discharged from the hospital. Her doctor and nurses are concerned that if she is allowed to leave the hospital she will return to her normal diet and will be risking grave harm to herself. A psychiatric assessment finds Mrs. Edwards competent, but her eccentric and at times seemingly irrational behaviour leads most of her physicians and nurses to believe otherwise.

By debating Mrs. Edwards's case, we are able to explore the difficult issues of autonomy, competence, **informed** or **valid consent,** and the right to refuse care. Was Mrs. Edwards competent to make her health care decisions? Was Mrs. Edwards's refusal of care valid? As you read through the drama and the debate, be mindful of such issues as when a competent person's liberty may be interfered with for that person's own good, and under what conditions a person should be permitted to make his or her own health care decisions. Focusing on these general questions may help you to develop a clear approach not only to the issue of whether Mrs. Edwards was competent to make her health care decisions, and whether the hospital staff erred in releasing her when they did, but also to a wide variety of cases involving patient autonomy and the right to refuse medical care.

LEARNING OBJECTIVES

After completing this chapter, you should be able to:

- Define *autonomy* as that term is used in this chapter
- Explain what it means for a person to be competent (or incompetent)
- Distinguish soft paternalism from hard paternalism, and weak paternalism from strong paternalism
- Discuss Patrick's and Doran's view that greater paternalistic interferences were warranted in Mrs. Edwards's case, even if she was competent to make her own health care decisions
- Discuss what is required for a person to be competent to make his or her own health care decisions
- Distinguish informed consent or informed refusal from what Warren views as valid consent or valid refusal
- Understand the relationship between autonomy, competence, and valid consent or refusal
- Describe Warren's reasons for thinking the hospital staff did not err in releasing Mrs. Edwards from the hospital when they did
- Explain Patrick's and Doran's reasons for thinking the hospital staff erred in releasing Mrs. Edwards from the hospital when they did

DRAMA

Please note: This case is based on various true stories, although names, places, and some uncontroversial elements of the case have been changed to preserve anonymity and confidentiality. Discussions of this and similar cases with health care professionals have also informed this fictional case. The drama merely raises issues. The philosophical arguments are to be found in the debate following the drama.

CHARACTERS

Jillian Edwards: *a patient with MS causing dysphagia*	**Dr. Paula Paladin:** *the attending physician*
John Edwards: *Jillian's husband*	**Eva Kowolski:** *the head nurse*
Chantal Nolet: *a nurse assigned to Mrs. Edwards's care and her friend of many years*	**Jane Kruala:** *a social worker*

Scene 1

A patient, Jillian Edwards, is talking animatedly to nobody while her friend and nurse, Chantal Nolet, observes her, unseen, from the door to the ward.

Jillian: Nonsense! The idea! Me, with multiple sclerosis? Why, I'm as healthy as a horse. I'm sure my problems come from something much less exotic than MS. (She spots Chantal, who walks in with her arms out to her old friend.) Oh! Dear me. (*Laughs*) You caught me rehearsing, my dear. How are you?

Chantal: Very well, Jilly, but how are *you*?

Jillian: Oh, never mind about me, dear. Oh, it's so good to see you. Your mother said you were working here and I knew I'd be getting a visit.

Chantal: More than that. I got myself assigned to your care, Jilly. Nothing but the best for you.

Jillian: Oh, you are a sweetheart. It is a bit of luck too, since that silly little girl they call my doctor is trying to starve me to death. John brought me in a nice chop. Even if it is cold, it's better than that hideous gruel they expect me to put up with. I won't have it. It is utterly *nauseating*.

Chantal: Let's see your chart. Ah, yes. Dr. Paladin ordered a soft diet. She thinks you're having trouble with your swallowing reflex. The **motility** test they gave you . . .

DEFINITION

Multiple sclerosis or **MS** is a disease in which the central nervous system is damaged by deterioration of a protective covering called the myelin sheath. It causes a variety of symptoms including weakness, lack of coordination, speech disturbances, vision problems and strange sensations. It can also cause dysphagia, i.e., difficulty in swallowing. MS can vary from mild to debilitating. The course of the disease is usually prolonged with remissions and relapses over years. The cause is unknown.

Source: Dorland's Illustrated Medical Dictionary.

DEFINITION

Motility is the ability to move spontaneously. If this ability is lost in the parts of the body used to swallow, dysphagia results.

Jillian: I swear, that young doctor hasn't a brain in her head. My chop was delicious, thank you, and I swallowed it all. Yes, I choked once upon a time, but who hasn't done that? No doctor is going to tell me what to do.

Chantal: Well, I see you're just as naughty as ever.

Jillian: Naughtier. By the way, dear, I'll need your help. I can get to the kitchen to get the little care packages my family leaves in the fridge, but I can't reach the food when it is pushed to the back. Be a dear and pull it up to the front for me, will you? My things all have a little green ribbon taped on them. Oh, and one more thing, that chair that John has to sit in when he visits is so hard on his bad back. What possessed them to buy such ridiculous chairs? See if you can get something else, will you, Chantal?

Chantal: I'll see what I can do, Jilly.

Jillian: That's a love. I think I'll just nap now. The door isn't open, is it? There's a draft. We wouldn't want Nettles to get out.

Chantal: Nettles?

Jillian: Yes, my cat. Oh of course, you went away before Brambles died, poor old thing. Nettles can't hold a candle to Brambles, you know. Do see that the door is closed and ask John to open a tin for little Nettles, won't you?

Chantal: I will.

Scene 2

Chantal and Eva Kowolski, the head nurse, are discussing Mrs. Edwards.

Eva: Well, there is a question of competence.

Chantal: Oh, Jilly's okay. I've known her for years. She's always been a little bit dotty—well, *eccentric,* you know—but she's got all her marbles, all right.

Eva: Maybe knowing her for years clouds your objectivity about this patient just a little.

Chantal: What do you mean?

Eva: She refused to get an MRI scan because she doesn't think she needs one and thinks it's a waste of tax dollars. She says she's perfectly healthy when she can barely get into her wheelchair. Chantal, she talks to herself. She shouts and gesticulates at the empty air. She's forever pushing the call button to have us feed her imaginary cat or put it out or let it in. Alice in Wonderland was straighter.

Chantal: She's always been like that. She built and ran a travel agency talking to herself all the while. She calls that talking to nobody "rehearsing." It's just a quirk.

Eva: Did she always have a Cheshire Cat?

Chantal: Okay, she is a bit confused about being here or being at home sometimes. Nettles is a real cat, just not here.

Eva: Look, Chantal, she's practically family to you. You said she helped finance your education as a nurse. Gratitude would make you want to give her the benefit of the doubt.

Chantal: Of course I'm grateful to Jilly. But that isn't the whole thing. You have to know her. She's always been so peculiar. People thought she was crazy before, and she was crazy like a fox. She's made millions being different, and she put a lot of that loot into this hospital. Maybe she is a little bit confused, but I owe it to her—we all owe it to her—not to write her off too soon. I swear, when I'm talking to her, dear Jilly can be as sharp as a tack.

Eva: You not only admire her, you're starting to talk like her too, *dear*. Watch out. But seriously, think about the possibility of her choking. I think we should make sure Dr. Paladin's order for a soft diet is strictly followed.

Chantal: I'll see what I can do, Eva.

Scene 3

A patient-care conference between Paula Paladin (physician), Eva Kowalski (head nurse), Jane Kruala (social worker), and Chantal Nolet (nurse), concerning Mrs. Edwards

Paula: Have there been any incidents of choking since the first one that led us to do the motility test?

Eva: No, we've been lucky.

Paula: I don't want to depend on luck. Let's keep her on soft foods.

Jane: Mrs. Edwards is in denial. Until she's convinced and her family is convinced that she really has MS and really has a problem with swallowing, we aren't going to get co-operation.

Paula: Well, Mrs. Edwards is not competent to consent.

Chantal: We can't say that. She does some quirky things, but she's right on top of it when we discuss her treatment.

Paula: So why doesn't she comply?

Chantal: Because she doesn't agree that it is necessary. I've discussed the risks with her and she says she is willing to take those risks. She's been a big risk-taker all of her life.

Eva: Yeah, well I don't want her aspirating on my watch.

Paula: A rational person wouldn't risk death for a lamb chop.

Chantal: We all eat fast food, and that box of doughnuts John left for us disappeared pretty quick. We're slowly digging our graves with our teeth, and we know it. She's just making tougher choices. The threat of death is a little closer. We might not share her values, but anyway, she's one of the most rational people I know.

Paula: So what do the rest of you think? Is Mrs. Edwards competent? Should we respect her autonomy?

Eva: I don't know. She seems too scattered to me.

Jane: Well, let's have the psychiatrist test her. If she really understands the consequences of her choices, then we should respect those choices.

Paula: Okay, but keep a close eye on her in the meantime. Be ready to suction her. Try to talk her into accepting the soft diet.

Eva: (*laughs*) Nobody talks Jillian Edwards into anything.

Chantal: She's got a strong mind.

Eva: A strong will, anyhow.

Paula: Well, Chantal, you're close to her. See if you can persuade her to be a little more co-operative.

Chantal: I'll see what I can do.

Scene 4

Dr. Paula Paladin and Jillian Edwards talk about Jillian's second choking incident.

DEFINITION

Hypoxia is a reduction of oxygen to tissue in spite of adequate blood circulation. In this case, the brain is deprived of oxygen, causing damage.

Paula: You don't seem to appreciate the situation. If Chantal had not been right there to help you out, you could have suffered some serious long-term consequences.

Jillian: Like what?

Paula: Brain damage from **hypoxia** or death, for instance.

Jillian: What was that, dear? High what?

Paula: Hypoxia is not getting enough oxygen. When you can't breathe, you're in deep trouble.

Jillian: Oxygen, my word. There's none in this stuffy little room, in any case. Of course if we leave the window open, Nettles will get out. Now, don't roll your eyes, young lady. Nettles may be just a cat, but she's a dear little thing. Now, about this choking business, what this tells me is that I need somebody to stand by with one of those dreary little suction machines when I eat. Giving me baby food, my dear, is not an acceptable solution.

Paula: Mrs. Edwards, we haven't the staff to watch over every patient who might choke and aspirate during every meal. For us to help you, you must listen to some of our advice.

Jillian: I'm not sure I like your tone, doctor. The very independence of mind that seems to be such a problem at this institution has served me so well in life that I can afford to hire some twit to stand around with a tube in hand while I have my meals.

Paula: Speaking of tone, do you think that the people who have been caring for you deserve a little respect? Chantal . . .

Jillian: Oh, the girls here have been lovely. Don't put words in my mouth.

Paula: Words like "twit"?

Jillian: What are you saying? I have never used such language.

Paula: Mrs. Edwards, you seem rather unhappy with your care here.

Jillian: What gives you that impression? Nettles and I are quite happy here, I assure you. I don't know where he has gotten to. Frisky little thing. Always off and about somewhere.

Paula: We were just speaking of your soft diet . . .

Jillian: Out of the question, my dear.

Paula: And this latest choking incident of yours. I was saying that we couldn't provide staff to watch over you at every meal.

Jillian: Then I will provide staff. There are lots of young girls about who can lollygag around with a tube in hand waiting to suction me if need be.

Paula: Your life depends on it. You need a trained nurse. This is not a task for an unskilled person.

Jillian: Stuff and nonsense! There's nothing to it. My cleaning woman could do it.

Paula: Trained nurses know how to deal with quite a variety of complications that can arise as a result of choking and aspirating. Speedy responses are vital when you're not getting air.

Jillian: As an employer, I am used to staff exaggerating their own importance. Suctioning me is a minor task. Don't you make much of it just to justify the high-priced help.

Paula: If you don't want our advice and care, then you can seek help elsewhere, but . . .

Jillian: I shall. Thank you for your efforts. And really, dear, don't take it ill. It's not that I'm an ingrate. I'm sure you're all quite sincere and doing your best with a difficult old woman, but I am accustomed to acting on my own opinions, isn't that right, John?

Paula: Your husband is not here at the moment, Mrs. Edwards, nor is your cat in this hospital room.

Jillian: Oh! Oh, yes, of course.

Paula: Why don't you rest? We'll talk tomorrow.

Jillian: Excellent idea.

Scene 5

A patient-care conference with Eva, Jane, Paula, and Chantal

Eva: So Jillian's back, but she's not going to be a difficult patient this time. She still protests, but she is barely coherent and certainly incompetent.

Jane: What happened?

DEFINITION

Dementia is a loss of intellectual function, in this case from severe brain damage. Jillian is reduced to an infantile state intellectually.

Paula: Predictably, she got into trouble at home under her husband's care, and by the time he got her to Emerg she was hypoxic. **Dementia** has set in thoroughly now.

Jane: Weird! I just talked to John in the cafeteria and he said that he thought Jillian was finally going to listen to him and be a good girl about treatment now.

Chantal: Jillian's gone. Unfortunately, her body is still alive. She would have hated that. Poor John, he's finally going to take charge.

Paula: It was all so maddeningly preventable. I don't think she was competent to book herself out and decide on her own care. I just could not get through to her.

Chantal: Nobody ever could. She was a wonderful person but never did really listen to anyone. If she could look at the whole thing right now, she would just say, "Well, I made my choice and I was wrong. Win some, lose some."

Jane: Well, the psychiatrist said she was competent. We had to respect her autonomy.

Paula: Autonomy comes in degrees. It's wrong to treat it as all or nothing. You wouldn't have let her drive if she were drunk. Why should we have let her book herself out when she was in the initial stages of dementia? People ought not to be allowed to risk their lives when they are not on top of things. We should have got a second psychiatric opinion. Jillian had some good years left.

Jane: Maybe so, but wouldn't it look different to you if you were in her shoes? Physicians themselves are always difficult patients just because they want to take charge of their own care, just as Jillian did.

Chantal: I visited her at home and described to her in detail the dangers she was facing. She thanked me and said that she used to ride a motorcycle without a helmet to feel the wind in her hair. I'm not saying she was totally sharp at the end or able to keep the risks in mind, but if she had her old self back, she would still make the same decision.

Paula: I don't see that. She would have at least hired a home-care nurse if she really was sharp and appreciated the dangers. She was not suicidal. Come on, let's face it. We did the wrong thing. We should have fought harder to keep her. It's a damn good thing we're not bartenders or we'd all be in big trouble for giving her back her keys.

DEBATE
Clarifying the Case and Identifying Relevant Facts

Patrick says: Let's, as usual, clarify some relevant facts before we begin our debate. How old was Mrs. Edwards?

Warren says: She was 62.

Patrick says: What were her long-term prospects? Suppose Mrs. Edwards had followed her doctor's orders: How long, and how well, would she have been expected to live?

Warren says: MS patients may live long lives, but with limitations. These can be quite minor, but in Mrs. Edwards's case, the dysphagia could be quite limiting and dangerous. Dysphagia is difficulty in swallowing, in this case due to a failure of the swallowing reflex. People can choke to death if this reflex does not work properly. Mrs. Edwards's prognosis would have depended on her co-operation with a treatment plan.

Patrick says: I'm familiar with the basic challenges MS patients face, and I understand that sometimes the problems can be quite minor, while other times the problems can be very significant. Where on this scale did Mrs. Edwards fall?

Warren says: Mrs. Edwards was in the middle of the scale of harms from MS. She could have had a decent life, but she would've been low on energy.

Patrick says: Okay. So she wasn't obviously doomed to a life of pain and suffering.

Warren says: No, she had a chance, at least, of a good life.

Patrick says: How about her mobility? I recall something about her having trouble getting in and out of a wheelchair.

Warren says: Yes, it was something like having a flu all the time. The disease has both remitting and chronic progressive forms, however. Which one Mrs. Edwards had was not yet determined.

Doran says: Was her confusion the result of the MS or was it something unrelated to the MS? Was there any reason to think her state of mind would have improved, or deteriorated, if she had followed the treatment plan?

Warren says: Her confusion could've been the result of her MS, but that only happens in a minority of cases. It was also possible that she was suffering from dementia from organic causes. It was possible that her confusion could have stabilized. We just don't know.

Doran says: What do you mean "her confusion could have stabilized"?

Warren says: She might not have become progressively more confused. If her condition turned out to have been chronic progressive, she would have become more confused to the point of complete dementia. If she had the remitting form, she might even have improved for a while, and then relapsed later.

Doran says: What were her husband's views? It seems they had a good relationship, though he had little influence over her decisions. Is that right?

Warren says: Yes, he tended to follow her lead rather than taking a position himself. As usual, her family agreed with her.

Patrick says: Her family agreed with her that she could eat solid food?

Warren says: Yes.

Doran says: Did her family understand that there was a good chance that eating solid food without a nurse's constant supervision could cause her to choke so badly that she'd become a vegetable?

Warren says: Her family accepted her position that this danger was exaggerated.

Doran says: But they were mistaken?

Warren says: Yes, they were mistaken.

Patrick says: Why would her family accept her position, rather than the position of the medical professionals?

Warren says: There was some history there of her brooking no opposition and having all the say in family matters. This is based on a real case.

Doran says: Ouch! I assume the family realized they made a mistake. Is that true?

Warren says: They realized the mistake too late. Paula, Mrs. Edwards's attending physician, was convinced that all the staff should have been working to make the truth known and that they slipped in their clear moral duty.

Patrick says: Did the family genuinely believe that the danger was exaggerated, or were they just afraid to speak up and tell Mrs. Edwards what they really thought?

Warren says: Mrs. Edwards was always right. After a point in the family history, nobody disagreed with her because she could out-think them and browbeat them all. If they had opinions different from hers, they did not reveal them.

Patrick says: So the family might have thought she was mistaken, but felt that there was no point in trying to convince her of that?

Warren says: Right.

Doran says: It is mentioned in the case that a psychiatrist found Mrs. Edwards competent. Can you say more about that, please?

Warren says: The psychiatrist saw Mrs. Edwards at a good time for her and questioned her in ways that did not involve Nettles the cat. Before the examination, nobody talked to the psychiatrist about Mrs. Edwards's odd behaviour, although it would have been noted in her chart. Perhaps the chart was not clear. For whatever reason, the psychiatrist did not take much notice of the apparent hallucinations.

Doran says: Did the psychiatrist know the doctor's opinion that Mrs. Edwards would likely choke again if she ate solid foods, like lamb chops, and that it could make her hypoxic, that Mrs. Edwards insisted on eating the chops nevertheless, and that she denied that there was a serious risk of harming herself?

Warren says: The psychiatrist did not talk to anyone before the examination. This particular psychiatrist thought that it was best to see a patient before getting prejudicial comment. In the hurly-burly of hospital life, there was no coordination or communication with the rest of the health care team, partly by accident and partly by the psychiatrist's design. However, he would have seen Mrs. Edwards's chart, so he would have had some idea of Dr. Paladin's view of the matter.

Doran says: Did the psychiatrist know about Mrs. Edwards's hallucinations?

Warren says: If he did, he did not seem to take account of them. Perhaps talking to him about the hallucinations and asking for a further evaluation could have delayed Mrs. Edwards's departure from the hospital. That is what the attending physician, Dr. Paladin, was berating herself for not doing.

Doran says: Did any of the doctors meet with Mr. and Mrs. Edwards before she was released, to explain the situation to them?

DEFINITION

AMA in this context stands for "against medical advice." Patients like Mrs. Edwards who leave when their doctors tell them to stay in the hospital are asked to sign a form certifying that they know their physician wants them to stay. It gives legal certitude that the patient was warned against leaving.

Warren says: Before Mrs. Edwards even tried to leave, Paula had patiently explained the dangers of hypoxia to her, but Mrs. Edwards was dismissive. Mr. Edwards had been told about the dangers too, but did what Mrs. Edwards told him to do, including smuggling in lamb chops.

Doran says: Did the psychiatrist have Mrs. Edwards sign an AMA?

Warren says: No, but there is no doubt that Mrs. Edwards was adequately warned and refused to listen. Chantal even went to her home and thoroughly briefed her after she had been discharged from the hospital. While Mrs. Edwards was at the hospital, everybody got too busy. The psychiatrist did not communicate with Paula, Chantal, and Eva, who could have given him more information about Mrs. Edwards's hallucinations. Mrs. Edwards could appear quite reasonable at times and very dotty at others, so the psychiatrist might have seen her on a good day.

Patrick says: Do you think that the psychiatrist would have reversed his decision that Mrs. Edwards was competent, had he gotten acquainted with her "dotty" side?

Warren says: Probably not. Psychiatrists are not usually willing to ask the courts to force involuntary treatment on patients. Paula just thought they should have used the second evaluation to delay Mrs. Edwards's departure. She wanted another chance for the staff to get through to Mrs. Edwards about the dangers.

Doran says: Okay. Patrick, do you have any more questions about the facts of the case?

Patrick says: Not now, although more questions will probably arise once we start the discussion.

MORAL ISSUES RAISED BY THE CASE

Doran says: This case raises a number of ethical issues we could explore. Warren, do you want to suggest a proposition to debate?

Warren says: How about the following proposition: *It was a moral error for the staff to allow Mrs. Edwards to discharge herself without further evaluation.*

Patrick says: Good—this seems to be the main ethical issue raised by this case. So, what do you guys think? Was it morally wrong for the staff to let Mrs. Edwards leave the hospital without further evaluation, when they had doubts about her mental health and knew she would likely do things that might seriously harm herself?

Stating Our Positions

Doran says: I agree with the proposition. It was a moral error for the staff to allow Mrs. Edwards to discharge herself without first making a greater effort to protect her from harm.

Warren says: You are saying that patient autonomy can be restricted even for a patient who has been certified as competent?

Doran says: Yes.

Patrick says: I also agree with the proposition. Although Mrs. Edwards had been certified as competent, it seems the testing of her competence was incomplete. So it was not an accurate measure of her competence, right?

Doran says: Right, that is what I was thinking, too.

Warren says: Although I find this to be a very hard case, ultimately I disagree with the proposition. Imagine yourself having been certified as competent and having the staff tell you that's not good enough. They want a second opinion on whether you are competent. You would rightly feel that they want to keep trying until they can restrict you unfairly.

Patrick says: Well, if I were in a situation relevantly similar to Mrs. Edwards's, I probably wouldn't like the staff telling me that further evaluations were necessary. But that's not the appropriate question to ask. The question to ask is, Would you and I—or some other person whose competence is not in question—object to further evaluations and restrictions on our liberty, if we were displaying symptoms similar to Mrs. Edwards's? I suspect we wouldn't now object to **paternalistic** interferences with our liberty if we were later to find ourselves in a situation like Mrs. Edwards's. In fact, I think I'd be prepared to sign an advance directive now specifying that I should be kept in the hospital if I were hallucinating and insisting on doing things that, according to medical experts, were likely to kill or seriously harm me.

DEFINITION

Paternalism is interference in the liberty of another for that person's good. There is an ongoing controversy about the extent to which paternalism may be morally justified. For a good brief overview, see the entry "Paternalism" in the *Stanford Encyclopedia of Philosophy:* http://plato.stanford.edu/entries/paternalism/.

Warren says: Mrs. Edwards's hallucinations were not clearly relevant to the determination of her competence to make medical decisions. Competence is context-relative. Mrs. Edwards may not have been competent to judge the presence of Nettles, her cat, but she was competent to understand the risks she was running according to Dr. Paladin. She was competent to decide to dismiss those warnings. It was morally permissible for the staff to release her when they did.

Doran says: I agree with Patrick that the hospital staff erred in releasing Mrs. Edwards without further evaluation, but I would not agree that she should be kept indefinitely. If I were to be in her situation, I would not agree to being kept in the hospital indefinitely, although I would agree to delaying my discharge for a short period of time to give caregivers a better opportunity to explain the situation to me, and to give me more of a chance to come to terms with my situation.

Patrick says: Well, Doran and I have serious doubts about whether the hospital acted permissibly. So we affirm the proposition that *it was a moral error for the staff to allow Mrs. Edwards to discharge herself without further evaluation.* Warren, why don't you present your argument to see if you can convince us otherwise?

AN ARGUMENT FOR THE RIGHT TO IGNORE EXPERTS

Warren says: The real issue here has to do with valid refusal of treatment by competent people. The right to have one's refusal of treatment respected is, in turn, dependent on the right to **autonomy.** In the **original position,** we would insist on a strong right to autonomy because without that, others would be able to limit us in ways they might think are in our interests. When others try to run our lives for us, they often make a bad job of it, despite good intentions. Our interests are best protected when we have the right to assert and protect those interests on our own. That is why one's competent, free refusal of treatment must be respected.

In this case, if Mrs. Edwards knowingly chose not to respect the expertise of her doctor and nurses, and not to take precautions, she may still have given valid refusal of treatment. The idea that she was incompetent if she did not respect medical expertise or believe what experts told her is inimical to a basic right to autonomy. As a competent adult, she could have chosen what information she wished to accept or to consider. She could have also chosen what risks she wished to take, including the risk of ignorance. To deny this is to slip into a kind of paternalism that would not be tolerated by those in the original position.

DEFINITION

Autonomy is derived from the Greek *autos* ("self") and *nomos* ("rule," "governance," or "law"). It has come to have many meanings, among them the capacity for, or the right to, self-government. We prefer to use *autonomy* to mean "self-determination." When the context is clear, though, we will also use *autonomy* to mean "the right to self-determination." For a good discussion of autonomy, see Tom L. Beauchamp and James F. Childress, *Principles of Biomedical Ethics,* 5th ed. (New York: Oxford University Press, 2001), chap. 3.

BACKGROUND

Warren is relying on a version of **social contract theory.** See Chapter 3 for an explanation of this approach.

Doran says: That's an interesting argument. For purposes of evaluation, I would like to restate part of your argument in **standard form**:

(1) Actions are morally justified if they are consistent with the rules that would be chosen by people in the original position to form the ideal social contract.

(2) People in the original position would choose rules to protect their own interests in the real world.

(3) In order to protect their own interests, people in the original position would choose rules that secure a strong right to autonomy as part of the social contract.

(4) This strong right to autonomy entails that competent patients have a right to information about their condition, a right to accept or reject that information, and a right to refuse treatment with or without use of the information that is available.

(5) Mrs. Edwards was a competent patient who was given access to information about her condition, but deliberately chose to ignore that information and to leave the hospital against the medical recommendations of her physician and nurses.

(6) As a competent individual who refused information, Mrs. Edwards was within her rights to leave the hospital against the medical recommendations of her physician and nurses.

(7) If Mrs. Edwards was within her rights to refuse treatment, then the hospital was morally required to respect this choice.

(8) Therefore, the hospital did not err in releasing Mrs. Edwards.

Is that what you intended to argue?

Warren says: That is a good start. There's more to it that I hinted at, but let's see what you think of this bit.

Clarifying Premise (3)

Patrick says: Let's start with the third premise. You claim that people in the original position will pick rules granting them a strong right to autonomy. What do you mean by a right to autonomy?

Warren says: Autonomy is a complex notion. But the basic idea is that an autonomous person is self-determining: an autonomous person makes her own choices, free of external controls or internal compulsions. To say that people in the original position will want to

---

TECHNIQUE

Part of Warren's argument is put in **standard form** (a numbered list). This helps with clarifying the argument and makes it easier to consider targeted objections to specific premises.

make sure that they have a strong *right* to autonomy or (a strong right to self-determination) is to say that they will pick rules that protect their right to make their own decisions and to lead their own lives—that is, they will want to ensure that others are not justified in controlling their choices; they may also want to make sure that they have the social conditions necessary to make their own decisions.

Doran says: And why do you think that people in the original position would choose a strong right to autonomy?

Warren says: I reiterate, when others try to run our lives, they may make a hack job of it. Only we can know what our real preferences are. To protect our interests fully we need to control our lives. That is one reason why we would choose a strong right to autonomy in the original position.

BACKGROUND

A classic defence of individual liberty can be found in John Stuart Mill's *On Liberty*, chap. 4. Mill, too, thinks that the strongest argument against interfering with a competent person's liberty for his own good is that such interference is likely to be done poorly.

Patrick says: I notice that just now you slip between speaking of interests and preferences. In the original position, would we insist on a strong right to autonomy to protect our interests or our preferences? Preferences and interests seem importantly different.

Warren says: They are different, but preferences can determine interests. For instance, someone who has a preference for risky activities like rock climbing will have an interest in rock climbing, while someone who has a preference for less extreme activities will have different interests.

Patrick says: I see. So your position is that we would insist on a strong right to autonomy in the original position in order to protect our interests. And protecting our interests will enable us to pursue the satisfaction of our preferences. Is that right?

Warren says: Well, the satisfaction of our preferences is one of our main interests. It may, at times, conflict with other interests. In the original position we would not want others to decide which interests we must pursue in cases where our interests conflict. The right to autonomy lets us be the judge of which interests we want to pursue. We might choose to satisfy preferences that conflict with our interest in safety, for instance.

THEORY

Warren slides between preferences and interests, although of course he realizes that what we prefer may not be in our interest. In this case, however, preference for risk is a major determinant of interests. In the original position we would not know our preferences for taking risks in the real world, so we would want those to be taken into account when the right to autonomy is applied. If we have a strong risk tolerance in the real world, for instance, we should be allowed to take risks under the system of rules chosen in the original position.

Patrick says: Okay, I think I see how you understand the relation between preferences and interests.

Doran says: And I see why you think people in the original position would choose rules giving them a strong right to autonomy. But just how strong is this right?

Patrick says: Good question. In the original position we would of course want to secure a right to autonomy, but presumably we wouldn't want the right to be so strong that we'd end up undermining others' autonomy, and presumably we would want to limit our autonomy so as to prevent serious harms to ourselves through foolish, uninformed, or irrational choices.

Warren says: It is clear that people in the original position would want to limit everyone's right to autonomy in order to protect their own autonomy. On this point, I agree with John Rawls that people in the original position would choose what he calls the **liberty principle.**

A more difficult question concerns identifying the conditions, if any, under which people in the original position would agree to limit their right to autonomy for the sake of self-protection. For, on the one hand, people in the original position would certainly not want to be treated like children whenever experts think their choices are foolish. Yet, on the other hand, it also seems that people in the original position would want to protect themselves from their reckless, ill-conceived choices.

Patrick says: Under what conditions, then, would people in the original position accept paternalistic interferences with their liberty?

Warren says: I think that when interferences in one's liberty are relatively minor and when the benefits of interference are great, then paternalism would be accepted by people in the original position. Seat belt legislation is a case in point. Here the benefits of seat belt wearing are clear and substantial, while the interference in a person's liberty is relatively minor, so requiring seat belt use could be justified for paternalistic reasons.

Contrast this with interferences that are significant—say, total bans on tobacco use, or on gambling, or on backcountry skiing. Likewise, preventing people from acting AMA—against medical advice—would be too great an interference in a person's liberty. Unlike the case of seat belt legislation, where there is at most minor frustration of people's preferences and minor interference in people's liberty, not allowing people to discharge themselves from the hospital when it is against medical advice would constitute a major interference in people's liberty, and would likely greatly frustrate the satisfaction of people's preferences.

DEFINITION

John Rawls's **liberty principle** states: "Each person is to have an equal right to the most extensive basic liberty compatible with a similar liberty for others" (*A Theory of Justice,* 60).

THEORY

Here Warren assumes that seat belt legislation could be justified on paternalistic grounds. Of course, other reasons could be given in defence of seat belt laws. For example, one could argue that such a law is justified on the basis of trying to reduce economic costs to society. Whether a piece of legislation is paternalistic or non-paternalistic depends on why it was passed. Legislation is often considered paternalistic only if it is justified at least partly on the ground that it prevents people from harming themselves.

Patrick says: I still wonder, though, why simply warning people about the risks of not wearing seat belts is not enough on your view. Why wouldn't people in the original position just accept a rule that they be warned of harms to self, and then let competent people make their own decisions?

Warren says: We would recognize, in the original position, our vulnerability to rash decision making. Seat belt legislation is an instance of insurance against such decisions. Not wearing a seat belt can be a moment of foolishness for no significant personal gain which leads to huge personal pain. Booking out AMA is different, and much more complex.

Patrick says: All right, but given that acting AMA can also be foolish and lead to great personal pain, wouldn't it be justified to also take steps to protect patients from their own rash choices?

Warren says: I agree that some limited steps would be agreed to by people in the original position to protect themselves from reckless decisions when it came to acting AMA. They would agree to testing for competence, and perhaps to brief delays to allow a person to change her mind. But they would accept only limited interference with their autonomy. The decision to act AMA is too important to a person to have it indefinitely interfered with by others. Ultimately, it must be up to the competent patient to determine what information to accept, believe, and act on.

Doran says: I am beginning to get a clearer idea of your view of the right to self-determination as it relates to those who are competent, but what about incompetent individuals? I imagine that paternalism is more easily justified for those who are unable to competently decide for themselves.

Warren says: I agree that with respect to those who are not competent to make their own decisions, such as young children, paternalism is easier to justify. The state, for instance, may be justified in requiring those who are not competent not only to wear seat belts, but also to refrain from tobacco and alcohol use, to receive an education, to undergo certain medical procedures, etc. But,

> **UP FOR DISCUSSION**
> How would you distinguish a minor interference in a person's liberty from a significant interference in a person's liberty?

> **BACKGROUND**
> Philosophers sometimes distinguish between different sorts of paternalism. For example, **hard paternalism** is the interference in a competent person's liberty for his or her own good. **Soft paternalism** is the interference in an incompetent person's liberty for his or her own good. It is generally recognized that the latter sort of paternalism is much easier to justify than the former. It should also be noted that different philosophers differ slightly on how they define these terms.

here too, there has to be clear evidence that the incursion on liberty is necessary to protect the important interests of those whose liberty is restricted.

Doran says: Okay, you have suggested two ways in which paternalism may be justified. With respect to competent individuals, liberty may be interfered with for paternalistic reasons only when there is very clear evidence that the interference will be greatly in the person's interest, and the interference is slight. Both conditions are necessary for the competent. With respect to incompetent individuals, such as young children, interference with a person's choices for that person's own good can be more extensive and will be easier to justify. Is that right?

Warren says: Right.

UP FOR DISCUSSION

When, if ever, do you think hard paternalism is justified?

Patrick says: Although a lot more could be said about when paternalism is justified, perhaps we should now turn back to Mrs. Edwards's case, and consider what your view implies about her case.

Assuming Mrs. Edwards Was Competent, Did the Hospital Staff Err in Releasing Her from the Hospital When They Did?

TECHNIQUE

It is common for philosophers to grant a claim *for the sake of argument*—that is, to accept a claim not because they think it is true, but because they want to focus on another aspect of the argument. In this case, Patrick is not agreeing that Mrs. Edwards is competent, he is only assuming it for the sake of argument. For he wants to consider whether it was wrong for the hospital to discharge Mrs. Edwards from the hospital if she was competent. Later he and Doran will challenge Warren's premise that Mrs. Edwards was competent to make her health care decisions.

Patrick says: Given that you think that the hospital staff did not err in releasing Mrs. Edwards from the hospital when they did, I assume you think that she was competent to make the decision to act AMA and that her decision to refuse care was valid. I have serious doubts about Mrs. Edwards's competence and whether her refusal of care was valid. But let's set that aside for the time being. It seems to me that the hospital staff should have done more to protect Mrs. Edwards from her reckless decision not to follow a soft diet, even if we assume she was competent to make that decision. I think it was pretty clearly a foregone conclusion that Mrs. Edwards would not do well. Everyone knew that she would continue to eat meat, and everyone but her (and perhaps her husband) knew that this would kill or seriously harm her. Letting her discharge herself from the hospital when they did seems rather irresponsible to me.

Warren says: Some staff thought Mrs. Edwards would be killed or seriously harmed, but nobody knew. Patients surprise the experts often enough. The staff took the key steps to protect Mrs. Edwards from her reckless decisions. They obtained a competence evaluation; they repeatedly warned her about what they took to be the dangers of her eating solid foods. In other words, they discharged their duty of protecting persons from harming themselves. Given this, it was up to Mrs. Edwards to decide what she preferred and to act on what she took to be in her best interest.

Patrick says: But surely there was undeniable evidence that restricting Mrs. Edwards's liberty—in particular, forcing her to remain in the hospital—was in her best interest in this case. Being forced to stay in the hospital may have frustrated some of her preferences, but it may well have enhanced many of her other preferences and interests. For instance, if Mrs. Edwards was kept in the hospital, this would have frustrated her strong preference to go home, but it would also have furthered her interest in living. And by giving her a longer life, it would also have furthered other preferences she has—such as the preference for taking risks. One can't do that when one is dead. So it's not clear to me that we would oppose limitations on our liberty if we were to find ourselves in a situation relevantly similar to Mrs. Edwards's situation.

Warren says: Medical expertise gives us good hypotheses about a patient's future, not undeniable evidence. I do not deny, however, that the evidence was strong that Mrs. Edwards would suffer harm. To keep Mrs. Edwards in the hospital any longer against her will would have constituted a great incursion on her liberty. And I believe that in the original position, people would not agree to great incursions on the liberty of competent persons for their own good. We would want to have our competence tested and to be duly warned by the experts of the risks we were taking, but we would ultimately want to preserve our right to self-determination.

Doran says: I agree, Warren, that after due warning, competent people should have the right to self-determination. However, among other things, I question whether Mrs. Edwards was adequately warned. In the original position, I think people would agree to more consultations and psychological evaluations before allowing a person to take such great risks for so trivial a reason.

THEORY

An **act utilitarian** might consider the whole discussion wrong-headed. Any restriction on liberty would be automatically justified, on that view, if it maximized happiness. Very likely, in this instance, happiness would be greater for everyone affected if Mrs. Edwards had been prevented from becoming hypoxic and, as a result, demented.

However, it should be noted that in *On Liberty*, John Stuart Mill presents a complex utilitarian argument against any paternalistic interference in a competent person's voluntary choices. He argues that for several reasons, in the final analysis, competent people will be happier if left free to make their own voluntary decisions in matters that do not harm others.

Warren says: I think people in the original position are not going to want to surrender their autonomy unless absolutely necessary. They know that generally a person knows his or her own interests best. The warnings, delays, and competence evaluations were sufficient in Mrs. Edwards's case. It was time to let her make her own decisions.

Doran says: So, to sum up: In your view, people in the original position would want to give themselves a strong right to autonomy in order to protect their interests. This strong right to autonomy entails a strong presumption in favour of competent individuals making their own decisions, provided they do not violate others' autonomy. This is why Mrs. Edwards, if competent, would have the right to reject her doctors' and nurses' medical advice. The right is not absolute, however, since people in the original position would want to protect themselves from, for instance, their ill-considered rash decisions. Paternalistic restrictions are justified when the benefits are significant and the loss of liberty insignificant. And in situations where the loss of liberty is significant, warnings are still appropriate, but not prohibitions. Mrs. Edwards had sufficient warning, though, and so the decision to follow or to reject the doctor's advice was now properly hers to make.

Warren says: Yes. In this case, Mrs. Edwards's right to autonomy gave her the right to book out AMA, but staff members were right to delay and to try to dissuade her. They were also right to order a test of her competence. That done, they were right to let her go.

Patrick says: Well, I think people in the original position would agree to greater restrictions on their liberties when the choice to be made is clearly so dangerous and so at odds with their overall preferences. These greater restrictions seem to be in people's interest in the original position. But let's move on. Thus far we have been granting for the sake of argument that Mrs. Edwards was competent to make her health care decisions. I, however, think Mrs. Edwards was not competent to make her health care decisions, and this again leads me to think that the hospital erred in the moral duty to protect her from harming herself.

UP FOR DISCUSSION

Do you think that the hospital staff did enough to protect Mrs. Edwards from harming herself? Why or why not?

Doran says: I agree with you, Patrick, that people in the original position would agree to greater restrictions on their liberties when the choice to be made is clearly so dangerous and so at odds with their overall preferences. And I also think Mrs. Edwards was not competent to make her health care decisions. So why don't we hear Warren's defence of his premise (5), the premise which claims both that Mrs. Edwards was competent to make her health care decisions and that she gave a valid refusal of care.

Patrick says: Right, I have concerns about both of those. Let's start first with the issue of competence.

OBJECTIONS TO PREMISE (5)

Was Mrs. Edwards Competent?

Warren says: Okay, but let me first clarify what I mean when I say that Mrs. Edwards was competent. To say that someone is competent is to say that she has certain capacities or abilities. Individuals may be competent relative to some tasks, but not others. For instance, someone may be competent to drive a car, but not competent to fly a plane. When I say that Mrs. Edwards was competent, I'm saying that she was competent to make decisions about her health care. She may, however, have been incompetent in other areas, but these are not directly relevant to our present concerns.

BACKGROUND

Premise (5) states: Mrs. Edwards was a competent patient who was given access to information about her condition, but deliberately chose to ignore that information and to leave the hospital against the medical recommendations of her physician and nurses.

Medical professionals assess the capacity of a patient for rational self-determination with respect to his or her future medical care. The courts call a person competent in a different sense: to be competent means to have the legal authority to make those decisions. We are interested in the notion of competence as capacity rather than as authority.

Patrick says: That sounds right. Competence is a relation: people are competent relative to certain activities. But I have serious doubts about whether Mrs. Edwards was competent to make important decisions about her health care. My doubts stem in part from the fact that she wanted to live, but at the same time insisted on eating solid food rather than a soft diet. If the medical professionals were right, these preferences were blatantly inconsistent. If Mrs. Edwards ate solid food, it was quite likely that she'd choke and either die or suffer serious brain damage. So I have concerns about whether Mrs. Edwards had the capacity to understand her situation and to decide what to do about it. If she was not competent in this context, then the right to autonomy would not entail that Mrs. Edwards had a right to refuse treatment.

Warren says: I agree that if Mrs. Edwards was not competent to refuse treatment, then the hospital staff should not have accepted her refusal of treatment, but let's look carefully at what makes you doubt her competence in this respect. It is that she had blatantly inconsistent goals, and this shows that she did not adequately understand the nature of her condition and the consequences of her actions. I disagree, however, that her goals were blatantly inconsistent *to her*. They may have appeared so to the doctor and to others. She just didn't accept expert medical advice. Mrs. Edwards chose not to believe the experts, but surely that does not entail that she was incompetent.

Doran says: I agree that *to her* these goals were not blatantly inconsistent, but the doctor was obviously right that her goals were, *in fact*, blatantly inconsistent.

Patrick says: Right. Her goals were not inconsistent *to her*. But that's just the problem—she *should have* recognized that her goals were actually inconsistent. The mere fact that Mrs. Edwards chose not to believe her doctors does not, of course, show that she was incompetent. The problem is that she did not see what everyone else saw: that she could not eat solid food *and* avoid serious harm. It is not as if, for instance, the experts disagreed about the consequences of her eating solid food. Her belief that she could eat solid food, despite her condition, seemed entirely baseless—it flew in the face of all available evidence.

Warren says: That is only so with hindsight. At the time, the nature of her condition was not obvious. Physicians sometimes disagree about a diagnosis of MS or dysphagia. A layperson cannot be expected to just see that the diagnosis is correct.

Doran says: I think you miss the point. It's not about a diagnosis of MS. It's about the danger of choking on solid food. Surely any reasonable person would accept what the medical professionals say in this case, especially given that Mrs. Edwards had choked in the past. It was her refusal to accept what should've been obvious to any reasonable person that shows that she was in denial and not competent to refuse treatment. She *denied* that she was likely to choke if she ate solid foods; she *denied* that medical expertise was needed if she did choke; and she even *denied* that she had MS or that she was ill at all.

Patrick says: Well put, Doran. The concern about her competence stems from her denial of facts that any reasonable person would see as obvious. She refused to admit that she was ill or that choking was a probable and very serious threat to her health, and her denial of these things, given the available medical evidence, was baseless and therefore irrational.

Warren says: Yes, Mrs. Edwards had choked once in the past. Most of us have done that sort of thing. But that is not enough to convince a reasonable person that the medical professionals were right about a diagnosis of dysphagia. Make no mistake about it, this is a complex medical diagnosis, not something any reasonable layperson must understand. So it comes down to this: must any reasonable person accept what medical professionals say when the evidence is not clear to that person? I say, No.

> **UP FOR DISCUSSION**
> Do you think Mrs. Edwards was competent to make her own health care decisions? Why or why not?

The Gangrenous Foot Example

Doran says: Let me give you an actual case on which we can probably agree about incompetence to refuse treatment, so we can compare that to Mrs. Edwards's case. A homeless woman was taken to the hospital with a horrible infection in her foot, caused by frostbite. The foot had turned gangrenous. It needed to be amputated or she would die. The woman refused to admit it was gangrenous, however, and said she wanted to live and wanted to keep her foot. The doctors showed her the foot, but she never wanted to look, and when she did, she said it was just dirt, or that it was getting better, when plainly it was getting worse.

She was insensitive to clear and overwhelming evidence, and this led her to state two goals that were in blatant conflict (even though she did not realize this): "I want to live" and "I want to keep my foot."[1] Now, I agree that a competent person could say, "I would prefer to die rather than have my foot amputated, so I reject the medical advice." But this is different. Do you think this homeless woman was competent or incompetent?

Patrick says: I think she was quite clearly incompetent.

Warren says: I admit that, in this case, we have clear incompetence to refuse treatment. Once you see your foot washed and then try to pretend that the discoloration is from dirt, you really are in denial. Mrs. Edwards's denial was different. It was a denial of a complex medical diagnosis of dysphagia on evidence that she did not see and understand. Mrs. Edwards, moreover, had a successful career built partly on strong skepticism about expertise of others and on a damn-the-torpedoes attitude to danger. That was her preference as well, to live on the edge. She thought the doctors were exaggerating their own

[1] Thomas Grisso and Paul S. Appelbaum, *Assessing Competence to Consent to Treatment: A Guide for Physicians and Other Health Professionals* (New York: Oxford University Press, 1998), 42–43.

UP FOR DISCUSSION

Do you think Mrs. Edwards's denial of the risk of choking is a case that falls under the principle of denying facts that any reasonable person should see?

importance and the dangers. Her life experience gave her some evidence for this being so. She competently made a choice that was mistaken.

Denying the probability of her choking in the future is a matter of denying an expert prognosis, not a denial of facts obvious to any reasonable person. As for her saying she wasn't ill, that was a denial of the obvious, but perhaps exaggeration rather than incompetence. Patients often say "I'm fine," when this is pure hyperbole.

I think we agree on the principle that denying facts that any reasonable person should see is a sign of incompetence. However, I do not take her denials as indicating that she was incompetent in this way. She was refusing expert medical advice, but if we are compelled to accept the views of experts, our autonomy would be very severely restricted. We could never refuse treatment. In this case it was about a diagnosis of dysphagia and the prognosis, the medical expert's claim that Mrs. Edwards was in heightened danger of choking in future. This was not something that a reasonable person would have to accept as true.

Incompetence to Refuse Medical Care: Skepticism without Reason

Patrick says: It's not just what Mrs. Edwards believed, but *why* she believed it, that makes me doubt her competence. I agree with you that rejecting the advice of experts is not necessarily a sign of incompetence. But this is a case where *all* the experts seemed to agree on the dangers of eating solid food, given her condition. And, as far as I can see, Mrs. Edwards had no good reason at all to doubt what all the experts were telling her. If Mrs. Edwards was competent to make decisions about the treatment of her condition, she must have been capable of giving reasons in support of her decisions.

Warren says: I agree that doubt without reason is irrational and a sign of incompetence. That kind of baseless skepticism could make a person incompetent to refuse treatment. Strong skepticism and a strong preference for taking risks, however, had served Mrs. Edwards very well throughout her life, as we know from Chantal Nolet's descriptions. Her life experience was the basis of her skepticism about expert opinion.

Patrick says: I think it's one thing to doubt the experts when it comes to running a business, but quite another to doubt physicians, nurses, etc., about the gravity of one's condition. Moreover, this wasn't a situation in which Mrs. Edwards recognized the risks of eating solid food but chose to eat solid food anyway, because she had a preference for risky behaviour. If that were the case, I might agree that Mrs. Edwards was competent. In this case, however, she denied the risks, despite everyone's telling her that eating solid food was likely to seriously harm or kill her, and her denial was without reason.

Warren says: Are you incompetent if you don't agree with experts for no reason except that skepticism about expertise has served you well through your life? We let people choose prayer over chemotherapy, for instance. We don't call them incompetent, although we may think they are stubborn and mistaken.

UP FOR DISCUSSION

How would you characterize a reasonable degree of skepticism for patients in hospital care?

Patrick says: Well, I do have doubts about the competence of people who would choose prayer over chemotherapy. But, setting that issue aside, it seems to me that there's an important difference between people who choose prayer over chemotherapy and Mrs. Edwards's denial of obvious facts and refusal of treatment. The choice of prayer over chemotherapy makes sense, given other beliefs such people have—for example, the belief in God and His power to heal. I think these beliefs are mistaken, but they are beliefs reasonable people hold. And given these beliefs, the choice of prayer can, I suppose, make sense. Similarly, a person's preference for alternative treatments over conventional therapies isn't a sign of incompetence if that person has a reasonable network of beliefs supporting her choice. Mrs. Edwards's case seems different, however. There's no background set of reasonable beliefs from which her denial of what all the experts are telling her makes sense.

Warren says: The two cases aren't different. Mrs. Edwards's choice to reject the experts made sense in her world view, just as the religious person's choice to reject expertise makes sense in his or her world view. As I have explained already, Mrs. Edwards built a successful business, in part, by being domineering, independent, eccentric, and skeptical of expert claims. Her rejection of expert medical advice was part and parcel of the skepticism that had guided her well much of her life. Indeed, Mrs. Edwards's refusal was more rational than that of the religious believer. Mrs. Edwards had experience of the success of her views in this life—not in some promised unevidenced afterlife.

Patrick says: Okay. Perhaps, then, her skepticism was not entirely baseless, given her background beliefs and experiences. But I'm not sure her "world view" is one that a reasonable person could hold, so I still question her competence.

Doran says: Interesting. But even if her world view was unreasonable, Patrick, perhaps we can still judge her to be competent, provided that she was reasoning well from that perspective?

Warren says: That's right. We don't want to say that she was incompetent just because she has a set of beliefs that others regard as unreasonable. She was capable of understanding her situation. And she was capable of making health care decisions that were reasonable from her point of view. Surely, then, she was competent.

Patrick says: Warren, earlier you said that "we agree on the principle that denying facts that any reasonable person should see is a sign of incompetence." Is this claim consistent with your admitting that she has a world view that other people regard as unreasonable?

Warren says: Yes, some other people would find Mrs. Edwards's skepticism unreasonable, but not any reasonable person. The reasonable person test can help us with cases like watching your foot being washed and then claiming that the discoloration from gangrene is just dirt. It cannot help us with world views. If it could, we might rule out, say, Jehovah's Witnesses as competent. Given their world view, however, their rejection of blood transfusions is reasonable. Given Mrs. Edwards's world view, similarly, her rejection of medical expert diagnosis and prognosis was reasonable. We have to distinguish ordinary observables, like discoloured skin, from high-level principles, like skepticism of authorities, when we use the reasonable person test.

Patrick says: Surely, however, competence also requires that one's perspective or background beliefs be reasonable. If that's right, and Mrs. Edwards's background beliefs were not reasonable, as I suspect, then she was not competent.

Warren says: By background beliefs we may mean various things. If Mrs. Edwards had a belief that she was made of glass, then she would have an unreasonable belief in the background to which any reasonable person would object. Instead, she had a strong belief in the value of skepticism. Some pre-eminently reasonable people share this belief.

Patrick says: I'm not at all suggesting that it is unreasonable to be skeptical. I think it's quite reasonable to be skeptical about lots of

UP FOR DISCUSSION

Do you think that Mrs. Edwards's skepticism regarding the expert medical opinion that she was at great risk of death from choking is more analogous to holding a controversial world view or to holding an unreasonable view such as that one is made out of glass? Can one be incompetent because one holds unreasonable world views? For example, is a person incompetent if he believes that he should live on the streets because he has the view that buildings are frequently visited by devils seeking his death? If we say such a person is incompetent because of his strange views, can we deny that others are incompetent because of their unusual religious views—for instance, the view that medicines are unnecessary since God's will alone decides who will live and who will die?

things—the claims of psychics, for instance. It is clearly not reasonable, however, to be skeptical about one's condition when there is a consensus among medical experts, and when one has no evidence that they may be mistaken.

Competence and Psychiatric Evaluation

Warren says: Here is one additional reason why one ought to think Mrs. Edwards was competent. She received a psychiatric evaluation and was found to be competent. Surely, if one believes in a strong right to autonomy, one is going to want to let people exercise that autonomy if they have been found to be competent by a psychiatrist.

Doran says: Yes, it seems that a finding of competence by a psychiatrist should count as a reason in favour of thinking that a patient really is competent. But that presupposes that the evaluation was adequate. And there is reason to doubt the adequacy of Mrs. Edwards's evaluation.

Patrick says: I agree, Doran.

Warren says: Why would you question the adequacy of Mrs. Edwards's evaluation?

Doran says: The psychiatrist, apparently, did not take into account all the relevant facts about Mrs. Edwards's case. This is why, I suspect, Dr. Paladin believed that staff failed to adequately protect Mrs. Edwards when she was allowed to leave the hospital without further delay. Presumably the psychiatrist had access to Mrs. Edwards's chart, and this would have included her medical history and diagnosis, but presumably it did not include clear enough information about her hallucinations about Nettles the cat, nor enough details about her denial of her condition. Either that, or he failed to take account of these things. Given these problems in the evaluation, I think that the psychiatrist's findings were not, by themselves, a strong reason to believe Mrs. Edwards was competent.

Moreover, even if the psychiatric evaluation was done adequately, it would be a mistake to count the psychiatrist's finding of competence as conclusive. For, as we know, psychiatrists can err in such judgments; moreover, different psychiatrists can reach conflicting conclusions about a patient's competence. So, I would say that the psychiatrist's declaration of competence in

Mrs. Edwards's case was not enough to conclusively prove that she was indeed competent.

Patrick says: Again, I agree with you Doran. The psychiatric evaluation gives us *one* reason for thinking that Mrs. Edwards was competent. But the evaluation was incomplete, as just noted, and the psychiatrist's assessment of Mrs. Edwards was at odds with Dr. Paladin's doubts about Mrs. Edwards. Dr. Paladin, it seems, thought that Mrs. Edwards was *not* competent, and as her physician, she presumably had a broader and deeper understanding of Mrs. Edwards's physical and mental condition.

Warren says: I agree that a psychiatric evaluation, even when adequately performed, is not decisive proof of competence. But few judgments in medicine are decisive. They just have to be sufficiently decisive, like this psychiatric evaluation. I believe, however, that an adequate evaluation finding that a patient is competent to make health care decisions needs to be treated with a great deal of respect. In the original position, we would want to be allowed to exercise our strong right to autonomy if we were found competent, and we would not want to be under continual examination in the real world just because somebody disagreed with the earlier examinations.

Psychiatric evaluation is the best way we currently have of determining whether the patient can competently choose. So, I believe that, given a psychiatric evaluation that shows the patient is capable of deciding freely to accept and understand information or not accept it, the patient counts as competent to reject medical treatment. If one adequate psychiatric evaluation determines that the patient is competent in this sense, then that is all the proof the hospital staff should seek. Patients should not be under **double jeopardy** when it comes to evaluation of their competence.

Patrick says: But given the psychiatrist's lack of relevant information, he arguably wasn't in a position to decide whether Mrs. Edwards was capable of these things.

Doran says: That's right. If the psychiatric evaluation is a key reason for thinking that Mrs. Edwards was competent, then one had better be confident that the psychiatric evaluation was well done. But for the reasons I mentioned previously, I do not have this confidence.

Moreover, I think people in the original position will want to ensure that they really are competent when they are deciding to reject or accept medical treatment. They would thus want there to be an adequate, thorough evaluation. Given

DEFINITION

Double jeopardy is the name of a legal rule that prohibits being tried twice for the same crime on the same set of facts. Here, Warren is applying the term to health care, and saying that a patient should not be required to prove her competence twice.

the questions about the adequacy of Mrs. Edwards's evaluation, I therefore do not think people in the original position would object to a second, more thorough evaluation.

Patrick says: Right. I think that in the original position, people would accept a rule that required further testing and restrictions on liberty, if necessary, in situations like the ones under discussion. The psychiatrist said Mrs. Edwards was competent. Her physician—who had much more interaction with her—thought otherwise. Surely people in the original position would want further testing to ensure competence in such situations.

Warren says: How many evaluations must one have before one is deemed competent to refuse treatment? Dr. Paladin would never have been satisfied. Nurse Chantal Nolet, on the other hand, already was satisfied about Mrs. Edwards's competence. She cared deeply about her friend and knew her very well. Her opinion of Mrs. Edwards's competence and preferences weighs more heavily with me for that reason. Chantal was convinced that Mrs. Edwards was competent to refuse both expertise and treatment, and Chantal knew that Mrs. Edwards was running a risk by not listening to medical advice and ran that risk with relish.

Doran says: But how confident can one be, given that this is a "hard case"?

Warren says: I admit that Mrs. Edwards was on the cusp. That is what drives us to clarify our views about competence and autonomy. Perhaps the evaluation could have gone either way in a case like this. What we find by this debate, however, is that competence cannot be measured by the patient's willingness to accept a doctor's diagnosis or prognosis. If we always treat unwillingness as being in denial, we end the possibility of competent refusal of treatment.

Doran says: I agree with that.

Patrick says: I agree, too. We shouldn't *always* treat unwillingness as being in denial, and hence a sign of incompetence. But sometimes unwillingness does show incompetence, and I believe this is one of those times, for the reasons given.

Warren says: Well, perhaps that is a good stopping point. We seem to agree in theory, but not in the application to this particular case. I agree

> **THEORY**
>
> It is very important from the point of view of the ethics of care that there was this strong, caring relationship between the nurse, Chantal Nolet, and the patient, Mrs. Edwards. Chantal displayed the primary virtue of care in her relationship with Mrs. Edwards.
>
> The very closeness of the two is a problem from other perspectives. Some might worry that Chantal would not be impartial enough to treat all her patients with the same degree of care. Partiality might also blind her to things that an impartial observer would recognize in Mrs. Edwards.

UP FOR DISCUSSION

Warren argues for two points above: (1) an additional reason to think Mrs. Edwards was competent to make her own health care decisions was that she received a psychiatric evaluation, and was found to be competent; and (2) if one believes in a strong right to autonomy, one is going to want to let people exercise that right if they have been found to be competent by a psychiatrist.

Discuss these two points as they relate to Mrs. Edwards's case. Do you think that the fact that Mrs. Edwards was deemed competent by the hospital psychiatrist is a strong reason to think that she was, in fact, competent to make the decision to leave the hospital?

with you two that there are serious concerns about Mrs. Edwards's competence, but we just draw the line in different places.

Doran says: Agreed. You make a lot of good points about competence.

Patrick says: Let's move on now to consider a further issue. Besides the question of whether Mrs. Edwards was competent, there is the question whether her refusal of care was **valid.** For even if you managed to convince me that she was competent, I worry that her refusal of treatment was not valid, since she was not adequately informed.

Warren says: I believe that her refusal was valid.

Did Mrs. Edwards Give a Valid Refusal?

Patrick says: Well, it is generally agreed that a patient's consent or refusal is valid only if it is informed. And a patient's consent or refusal counts as informed only if the patient is given relevant information and understands that information. The patient may accept or reject the information provided. But in cases where the rejection is based on obviously false beliefs, as it appears to have been in Mrs. Edwards's case, it's hard to see how we can regard her refusal as *informed.*

Warren says: It's still valid—ignorant consent and refusal may well be valid.[2]

DEFINITION

The term **valid** has different meanings when we speak of valid arguments and valid consent. To say that a patient's decision to consent to or to refuse medical care is valid is to say that it is a legitimate reflection of the patient's free choice. What is necessary for consent or refusal to be valid is, of course, a matter of much debate.

For instance, suppose a patient says to a physician, "I don't understand the treatment you have explained, but I trust you. Go ahead." Deliberate ignorance does not render the patient's acceptance of treatment invalid. The flip side is that if a patient says, "I don't trust you, so I don't wish any further information or treatment," deliberate ignorance should not render the patient's refusal invalid.

---

[2] Warren's views on consent are influenced by Benjamin Freedman, "A Moral Theory of Informed Consent," *Hastings Center Report* 5, no. 4 (1975): 32–39, rept. in *Readings in Biomedical Ethics: A Canadian Focus*, 3rd ed., ed. Eike-Henner W. Kluge (Toronto: Pearson-Prentice Hall, 2005), 161.

Doran says: Well, I must say that your proposal seems right to me, but that it is an adventurous view. The literature on this subject emphasizes the need for freely informed consent to accept or reject treatment.[3] The idea seems to be that one's acceptance or refusal of medical treatment is not valid if one does not understand what various treatments are available, what the major risks are, etc.

THEORY

Because Patrick is using a common criterion for the validity of either acceptance or refusal of treatment, that it be informed, Warren's position is unorthodox and the onus is on him to provide strong reasons for rejecting the criterion.

Warren says: Yes, I realize that I am in a distinct minority here, but I think the majority is wrong. It seems to me to be false that a person must understand the relevant facts about her situation in order to make a valid choice, for a competent person might reasonably prefer not to know the facts. Let me be clear, though, that I believe the patient should be given access to the relevant medical information in an understandable form. The patient is not, however, required to accept or understand the information to give valid acceptance or refusal of treatment.

Patrick says: So you deny that consents and refusals must be informed to be valid?

Warren says: If being informed means retaining explanations, understanding, and accepting the relevant facts, then, yes, I'm denying that valid consents and refusals must be informed. On my view, none of these things is necessary for a valid consent or refusal.

Patrick says: None of these is required for valid consent or valid refusal? That seems mistaken. While I don't think it's necessary that a patient agree with her doctors and accept their advice and recommendations, it does seem plausible that valid consents and refusals must be informed at least in the sense that the patient has been provided with the relevant information about her condition and understands this information.

Warren says: The patient must have access to the relevant information in an understandable form. If, however, Dr. Paladin gave Mrs. Edwards a good pamphlet on dysphagia, Mrs. Edwards would not have to keep it or even read it. In my view, if the patient is capable of deciding freely to accept or reject information and is capable of understanding that information as well as capable of seeing obvious facts that any reasonable person would accept, the patient's rejection or acceptance of medical treatment counts as valid.

---

[3] See, for example, Tom L. Beauchamp and James F. Childress, *Principles of Biomedical Ethics,* 5th ed. (New York: Oxford University Press, 2001), chap. 3.

In Mrs. Edwards's case, I believe that she had adequate access to information, but she did not accept it, try to understand it, or believe it. Her decision was deliberately ignorant of the diagnosis and prognosis before she checked out of the hospital. She freely and deliberately chose not to follow medical expertise.

Doran says: That's a plausible outline of a view of valid consent (and valid refusal). If the purpose of obtaining patient consent is to make sure that the patient's right to self-determination (that is, autonomy) is respected, and if the patient freely says, "I don't want to know the details . . . ," then respect for autonomy might reasonably require not making the patient know the details. Given this, I guess I would like to clarify what is needed to be "capable of deciding freely to accept or reject information," and to be "capable of understanding that information."

Patrick says: It doesn't sound very plausible to me. But I'll reserve final judgment until Warren clarifies his view.

Warren says: Okay, so there are two main points which require clarification. The first is what I mean when I speak of being capable of deciding freely to accept or reject information. The second is what is meant by being capable of understanding that information as well as being capable of seeing obvious facts that any reasonable person would accept.

Let's take the first point first, and look at what we normally expect in a competent adult's free decisions and see if that helps to clarify things. Part of what it is for people to decide freely is that we think their decisions flow from themselves, not from someone or something else like a hypnotist or a brain disease. We think that those decisions reflect their preferences and that those preferences are not themselves induced in some way incompatible with that person's ownership of them. There are, of course, some deep questions about free will that are not answerable here, but I am looking for something more on the surface of our thinking about deciding freely.

> **TECHNIQUE**
>
> Often it is a good idea to seek clarification of a view before considering its truth or falsity.

Doran says: Okay, although it is somewhat vague, I am prepared to grant your claim about what is involved in deciding freely to accept or reject information. But what about your idea that patients must be capable of understanding information to give valid consent or refusal? Is the idea that patients are capable of understanding their alternatives, understanding their preferences, and judging in a reasonable way that a certain alternative will best promote their preferences?

Warren says: At some level I would accept that, but, as I have explained, it might be at the level of choosing which kind of expertise, if any, to accept rather than understanding the alternatives as the experts describe them.

Doran says: So, on your view, a competent person's consent or refusal is valid if she can freely choose some alternative based on her preferences, and where she makes this choice in light of her understanding of her situation and the alternatives. This may include accepting the physicians' and nurses' view of her situation, or it may include accepting her own view of the situation, provided that it is not a view that any reasonable person could see as false. Is that it?

Warren says: Yes.

Patrick says: But there's more to the view you proposed, Warren. The choice to refuse treatment can be valid even if the patient refuses to hear what the medical experts have to say about her condition. That is, she can choose to be ignorant about medical opinion, and still her refusal of treatment can be valid.

Warren says: Yes, that's my view: uninformed consent or refusal may be valid. Suppose you say to your doctor, "I am in pain. I don't want to hear all about my condition right now. I trust you. You've never steered me wrong. Go ahead with the operation." That would surely be valid consent. Similarly, refusal can be valid without the patient's accepting information as long as the information is available. As long as one is competent and freely chooses to ignore information, one may accept or refuse treatment validly.

> **UP FOR DISCUSSION**
>
> Warren says that it "would surely be valid consent" if a patient says to her doctor, "I am in pain. I don't want to hear all about my condition right now. I trust you. You've never steered me wrong. Go ahead with the operation." Do you agree? Why or why not?

Doran says: I think I agree with that—but, of course, we disagree on whether Mrs. Edwards satisfied this principle, because we disagree on whether she was competent.

Patrick says: I'm not sure I agree. Warren suggests that a valid consent or refusal requires the *capacity* to make free choices, and the capacity to understand the relevant information. I'm sure that in some sense Mrs. Edwards had the capacity to understand and appreciate what the experts told her about her condition and the dangers of eating solid food. But, in fact, she did *not* understand this: her arrogance, stubbornness, and foolishness prevented her from seeing the facts as everyone else saw them. For a refusal to count as valid, one needs more than the capacity to understand relevant information; it seems one needs an actual understanding of the information. How can my consent be valid if I don't even know what I'm consenting to?

BACKGROUND

"Some commentators have attempted to define *informed consent* by specifying the elements of the concept, in particular by dividing the elements into an *information* component and a *consent* component. The information component refers to disclosure of information and comprehension of what is disclosed. The consent component refers to both a voluntary decision and an authorization to proceed. Legal, regulatory, philosophical, medical, and psychological literatures tend to favor the following elements as the components of informed consent: (1) competence, (2) disclosure, (3) understanding, (4) voluntariness, and (5) consent."

Source: Tom L. Beauchamp and James F. Childress, *Principles of Medical Ethics*, 5th ed., p. 79.

UP FOR DISCUSSION

Must consent be fully informed to be valid? If not, to what degree, if any, must it be informed?

Warren says: I deny that one actually needs to understand the relevant information in order to give a valid refusal of medical treatment. What one needs is the ability to freely decide whether or not one wants to know the relevant information. As we have seen, it can be quite reasonable for a competent person not to want to know the details of his or her treatment options, especially if such knowledge will only do that person harm. Mrs. Edwards freely decided not to believe the experts' advice, yet her refusal was valid.

Doran says: Well, Warren, your view definitely challenges the prevailing view that valid consents and refusals must be informed, and you present a compelling case for your position. There are still lots of unanswered questions, but time is short, so why don't we move on now.

Warren says: Sure.

Patrick says: Why don't we turn to an examination of premise (7) in your argument, Warren, which states *If Mrs. Edwards was within her rights to refuse treatment, then the hospital was morally required to respect this choice.* I have some doubts about this premise.

Warren says: Let's hear your objection.

OBJECTIONS TO PREMISE (7)

Virtue Overpowers the Right to Refuse

Patrick says: Even if you can satisfy me that Mrs. Edwards was competent and adequately informed, I may part company with your premise (7). For even if Mrs. Edwards had the right to refuse treatment, it does not follow that the hospital staff was morally required to respect that decision. The right to refuse treatment is not absolute. In cases where exercising this right is likely to defeat a patient's chosen health care goals, it seems the hospital staff may be justified in restricting a patient's liberty. Mrs. Edwards presumably wanted to continue living. But because she was stubborn, foolish, reckless, and arrogant, she rejected the advice of her doctors and nurses and, as a result, was likely to die if she was dismissed. If Mrs. Edwards did not want to die, and her actions were very likely to kill her because they were based on mistaken beliefs, then perhaps the responsible, beneficent, and charitable thing to do was to force her to stay in the hospital. So Mrs. Edwards may have had a right to refuse treatment, but respecting this right may not have been the virtuous thing to do, all things considered.

BACKGROUND

The questions of competence, valid refusal of care, and whether the right to self-determination should win out over protecting the patient from harm and premature death are poignantly raised in the story of Donald (Dax) Cowart. Dax's case was made into two documentaries. These documentaries tell the story of a man who suffered third-degree burns to 68 percent of his body. Dax's recovery required that he submit to excruciatingly painful baths and treatments. Dax refused to consent to these treatments, yet they were performed against his will. He was held against his will for fourteen months. Eventually, Dax was able to leave the hospital and go on with his life. Although he now says that he is happy, he still insists that his wishes should have been respected and that he should have been allowed to die.

Warren says: That is a very interesting objection. You say even if the patient is competent and has a clear right, by way of autonomy, to refuse treatment, we might still be morally required to force treatment on that patient. The reason is that it would be virtuous to do so in cases like Mrs. Edwards's. On my theory, of course, if the patient has a right that is not outweighed by other rights or duties, then we must accept her refusal. Let me, however, try to meet you on your territory as you have often met me in my theoretical realm.

Accepting, for the sake of argument, what I take to be your view, that virtues may outweigh rights, I would have to question the responsibility and charity you see here. It is irresponsible to treat a patient as incompetent when that patient is known to be competent. This undermines not only the dignity of that patient but can lead to paternalism becoming entrenched to everyone's detriment. It is, by the same token, not charitable. We know that Mrs. Edwards would have been outraged to be treated in this way, and had already found ways around the soft diet restriction. It does not appear that attempting to force treatment would do any good. The only alternative the staff had was pursued thoroughly when Chantal did her best to educate Mrs. Edwards at home after her release. That was charitable, but applying force that was both impractical and an outrage to the patient's dignity would not, all things considered, have been virtuous.

Patrick says: Those are good points, and I recognize that there is much room for argument here as to what was the virtuous thing to do. But I'm not convinced that you've got things right. You suggest, for instance, that it is irresponsible to treat a patient as incompetent when that patient is known to be competent. Given this, it's not

THEORY

Recall that paternalism is interference in the liberty of another person for that person's good. Patrick is here arguing for what is often called **weak paternalism.** This is the view that interference with liberty is justified in order to prevent people from behaving in ways that are likely to defeat their goals. By contrast, **strong paternalism** is the view that we may legitimately prevent a person from attempting to realize irrational or mistaken goals. See Gerald Dworkin's entry "Paternalism" in the *Stanford Encyclopedia of Philosophy,* http://plato.stanford.edu/entries/paternalism/.

THEORY

Notice the opportunity to use care ethics in this situation. The caring thing to do might well differ from the requirements laid down by rights theories.

clear to me why you see seat belt laws, or virtually any other paternalistic interference with our liberty, as justified. Aren't these also irresponsible, since they involve treating competent people as if they were incompetent?

It seems to me that it is irresponsible *not* to restrict our liberty in cases where our freely chosen acts are based on clearly false beliefs and the acts are likely to undermine very important goals we have—like the goal to continue living!

Warren says: Beliefs that are clearly false to Dr. Paladin may not be clearly false to any reasonable person, so we cannot respect the dignity of Mrs. Edwards if we require her to accept Dr. Paladin's views because Dr. Paladin is an expert. Further, seat belt legislation and the like are different from forcing health care on someone. The latter is a much more important interference and so is not the kind of thing that should be forced on a competent person, but the former interference is so trivial, and the benefits so huge, that it is more easily justified on grounds of virtue. Kindness and caring for others, for instance, require that we ignore trivial liberties to prevent massive suffering that obviously results.

Patrick says: Well, I suppose that what I'm suggesting is that significant interference may be justified in cases where a person's actions are likely to undermine that person's freely chosen significant goals. If, for instance, people prefer to avoid injury, it may be legitimate to force people to wear seat belts. Similarly, if patients have a strong preference to continue living, then it may be permissible to prevent them from leaving the hospital if we are quite certain they'll engage in behaviours that are likely to kill them.

Doubt Justifies Delay

Doran says: Here for me is the concern. As you know, I have serious doubts about whether Mrs. Edwards was competent to make her decision to refuse treatment. This is especially so in Scene 4, after her choking incident in the hospital. She seemed very confused about where she was, and what she was saying—though I agree hers was a hard, borderline case. Given that it was a borderline case of competence, it seems to me that we should consider whether the hospital staff did all they ought to in order to enable Mrs. Edwards to make the right choice for herself.

For instance, I notice that there were a couple of patient-care conferences to discuss Mrs. Edwards's situation. This is good, but I think it would have been better if these conferences had been more inclusive, and had brought together Mrs. Edwards and her husband, as well as a mental health professional, to discuss with everyone what was important to Mrs. Edwards, as well as the medical history, the doctor's diagnosis, the risks of releasing her, the importance of getting a home nurse if she were to decide to leave the hospital, etc. A more inclusive group effort would have been best. I am not necessarily claiming that Mrs. Edwards ought to have been forced to stay in the hospital on a soft diet, but I am suggesting that it would have been better for the hospital staff to have taken a different approach toward Mrs. Edwards. A more caring approach toward Mrs. Edwards ought to have been followed. I believe such an approach would have had a better chance of respecting Mrs. Edwards's choices while protecting her from the gravest risks.

Warren says: Mr. Edwards, her husband, seemed to be totally under Mrs. Edwards's influence, so he would not have tried to dissuade her. Mrs. Edwards might have been included in such a conference, but enough was done in the actual event whether or not there was such a conference. The hospital staff got a psychiatric evaluation. The balance between protection of the vulnerable and respect for autonomy was achieved. As Chantal noted, Mrs. Edwards was not to be persuaded.

Doran says: Yes, I am not saying the hospital staff members were grossly negligent, or that they did nothing. But it is pretty clear from the get-go that they had grave concerns about Mrs. Edwards's competence, and about the risks she was willing to take for the sake of a chop. At the end, after Mrs. Edwards chokes and becomes hypoxic, the staff also seem to agree—for the most part—that they ought to have done more. I am trying to think about what that "more" ought to have been. I am suggesting that more efforts should have been made to talk with her and with her family about their concerns. Doing so may not have worked, but it should have been tried. They should also perhaps have gotten her to sign an AMA. Perhaps these extra meetings or conversations would have persuaded Mr. Edwards, if not Mrs. Edwards, to hire a home nurse.

Warren says: Mr. Edwards was not about to oppose Mrs. Edwards. One could always do more for almost any patient, but the staff has to balance that against neglect of other patients who are willing to be helped. As for signatures, that is a legal issue rather than a moral one. The staff members working with Mrs. Edwards all knew her mind plainly enough. To be treated as a child would be horrific for someone of her temperament. She did not become hypoxic for the sake of a chop but for the sake of her independence and personal dignity. It is doubtful that any different outcome could have been achieved with additional efforts.

Doran says: I think the hour or two of extra meetings to try to ensure that Mrs. Edwards knew the risks, to hear her wishes, and to persuade her to try to mitigate those risks would have been well worth their time. At the very least, it would have helped the medical team know that they did all they could. The signature is in a sense a legal issue, but it does have a moral point: namely, it helps the patient see the gravity of her choice. (I agree, though, that the moral issue is not one of actually signing an AMA document, but of understanding that one is going AMA. The extra meetings would just help underscore that fact.) You say they all "knew her mind plainly enough," but that seems wrong. Chantal, and apparently the psychiatrist, thought Mrs. Edwards was competent to make her health care decisions, but others on the team thought she was not competent and in denial. Lastly, to consult with her and her husband further was not "to treat her as a child"; it was simply the caring, responsible thing to do.

Warren says: In the coarse exigencies of day-to-day health care in a busy hospital, doing what is required is hard enough. Doing more for Mrs. Edwards would have been pointless from a practical point of view, and would have taken time away from other patients. They knew her mind insofar as they knew what she wanted and knew that there was no changing her mind. Delay was what Dr. Paladin hoped for—and a possible reappraisal of her mental status. That would, if successful, have treated her as a child, for if she could be declared incompetent she could perhaps have been forced to follow the treatment regime.

Remember, too, that Chantal did go to Mrs. Edwards's home and give her the whole nine yards of warnings. I'm content that enough was done to establish Mrs. Edwards's competence.

Doran says: Yes, Chantal was very caring, though some may wonder whether her past relationship with Mrs. Edwards clouded her judgment and constituted a conflict of interest. That is not my view, however.

Perhaps we could step back from the facts of Mrs. Edwards's case. Can we agree on a general principle, if not always on the application of that principle, about what hospital staff ought to do in cases where a patient of borderline competence makes a decision AMA that is likely to put her life in danger? Can we agree that we want the patient to have autonomy, but also to be protected from rash decisions that could be very harmful to herself or others?

Warren says: I think we are agreed on that. It is just that in this case we do not see the same balance point between protecting the vulnerable and

UP FOR DISCUSSION

In the drama, Chantal has herself transferred to take over the care of her friend Jillian Edwards. Is this morally laudatory since she is expressing gratitude and fulfilling a special obligation to a friend, or blameworthy as partiality not befitting a health care professional?

respecting autonomy. I am emphasizing autonomy a little more because I believe that, in the original position, we would see it as in our interest generally to be able to direct our own lives. This interest is so strong that we would prefer to err on the side of autonomy rather than that of protection.

Doran says: Yes, what we are just debating is this: How much protection should be given to patients to protect them from their rash choices?

I want to recommend that in potentially serious medical situations, the hospital staff should, among other steps, discuss (as a team) with the patient (and perhaps immediate family and/or caregivers) what the patient's wishes are, and explain to the patient what their recommendations are, so that an agreement can be struck, or failing that, so that steps can be suggested to patient and family to protect the patient somewhat in case she goes AMA. Here I think the insights of care ethics are to the point. We recognize the autonomy of competent patients, but we want to demonstrate concern that the patient exercises her autonomy safely and in an informed way.

> **UP FOR DISCUSSION**
> How would you describe the ideal balance between patient safety and patient autonomy?

Patrick says: Right. That is the kind of position I have been arguing for from my virtue ethics perspective. The right to autonomy is not absolute; it must be balanced against virtues such as compassion, charity, and beneficence. Even if Mrs. Edwards had a right to refuse medical care, it was very foolish of her to exercise this right, given the situation. The medical professionals working with Mrs. Edward recognized the foolishness of her decision to refuse care, and so more should have been done to prevent her from harming herself.

Warren says: The general suggestion seems fine to me. In cases like this, however, if one has to choose between hopeless attempts at persuasion of one adamantine patient and doing what will get results for other, more co-operative, patients, the choice is clear. One should attend to the other patients. Mrs. Edwards was so obdurate that no meeting to discuss her case was likely to be fruitful. She was a hard woman, and that made this a particularly hard case. Consequently, I come down on the side of the right to autonomy with some hesitation, not with total confidence.

Patrick says: Well, this looks like a good point to end our debate of this case. Warren, it looks like Doran and I remain unconvinced that it was morally permissible for the hospital staff to release Mrs. Edwards when they did.

Warren says: Yes, it seems my arguments have failed to persuade you.

Doran says: Right, but by critically examining your argument, I think we were able to shed much light on the difficulties involved in clarifying the concepts of autonomy, competence, and valid consent in a medical context.

SUMMARY

Here is a summary of the main questions, concepts, and arguments covered in this chapter:

- In this chapter, we debate the proposition *It was a moral error for the staff to allow Mrs. Edwards to discharge herself without further evaluation.* Warren denies the proposition; Doran and Patrick accept it.
- Warren defends his view by appealing to his favoured approach to ethics, social contract theory. He argues that in the original position people would want to protect their interests by insisting on a strong right to autonomy in the real world. This right to autonomy, while not absolute, would prevent others from significant paternalistic interferences in a competent person's liberty. Warren then argues that Mrs. Edwards was a competent person who made a valid refusal of care. To continue to hold her in the hospital against her will would be a significant paternalistic interference, and therefore the hospital staff did not err when they allowed her to discharge herself when they did.
- Defence of Warren's argument requires an examination of several difficult topics: "What is competence, and how is it related to autonomy?"; "When is paternalism justified?"; and "What is valid consent?"
- Warren thinks that only minor interferences in a competent person's liberty can be justified, whereas Doran and Patrick think that more substantial paternalistic interferences with competent persons can be justified.
- Warren argues that Mrs. Edwards was competent, but Patrick and Doran disagree.
- Warren advances an argument that valid consent need not be informed consent, and Patrick disagrees.
- Warren thinks that Mrs. Edwards's refusal of care was a valid refusal, although neither Doran nor Patrick thinks her refusal was valid.
- Patrick argues that even if Mrs. Edwards had a right to refuse care, it does not follow that the hospital staff should have allowed her to exercise that right, given that it could seriously harm her. The virtuous thing to do may have been to restrict Mrs. Edwards's liberty to prevent her from serious harm or death.
- Doran argues that more efforts were required to ensure that Mrs. Edwards and her family understood her circumstances and the consequences of her refusing care. Warren thinks that enough efforts were made, and further efforts would have been fruitless.

Review Questions

1. What is autonomy?
2. Why does Warren think that people in the original position would want to protect their right to autonomy in the real world?
3. What is paternalism?
4. Explain Warren's reason for rejecting paternalism in Mrs. Edwards's case. Explain why Doran and Patrick think that some paternalism is justified in Mrs. Edwards's case.
5. How is *competence* defined?
6. When it comes to health care decisions, what do Warren, Patrick, and Doran think is necessary to be a competent patient?
7. Why does Warren think Mrs. Edwards was competent to reject medical advice and to discharge herself from the hospital?
8. Why do Patrick and Doran think that Mrs. Edwards was not competent to reject medical advice and to discharge herself from the hospital?
9. Why, according to Warren, does valid refusal or acceptance of medical care not require that one understand the medical advice being given?
10. What does Patrick think is necessary for valid consent or refusal of medical care?
11. Explain Patrick's argument for the view that the hospital was not morally required to accept Mrs. Edwards's decision to discharge herself from the hospital, even if her decision was competent and adequately informed. What is Warren's response to this argument?
12. What concerns does Doran raise about the hospital staff's behaviour when it came to allowing Mrs. Edwards to leave the hospital? Explain Warren's reply to Doran on this point.

WWW.MCGRAWHILL.CA/OLC/SMOLKIN

CHAPTER 6

ABORTION

INTRODUCTION

The legal and moral status of **abortion** in Canada has been hotly debated for over a century, and abortion continues to be an emotional and divisive issue in Canadian society. In 1892, Canada's Parliament passed its first Criminal Code, which prohibited abortion (as well as the sale of contraceptives). This prohibition was relaxed in the late 1960s, when Pierre Trudeau's Liberal government permitted abortion in cases where pregnancy threatened the mother's life or health. In 1988, the Supreme Court of Canada struck down legal restrictions on abortion as unconstitutional. Chief Justice Brian Dickson stated: "Forcing a woman, by threat of criminal sanction to carry a fetus to term unless she meets certain criteria unrelated to her own priorities and aspirations, is a profound interference with a woman's body and thus a violation of her security of the person."[1] Although there is at present no law in Canada restricting abortion, many Canadians believe that some legal restrictions are called for, because they believe that abortion is a serious moral wrong, at least in certain circumstances.

In this chapter we cast a critical eye on arguments both for and against the moral permissibility of abortion. Our drama presents the case of Derek

_____
[1] *Morgentaler, Smolling and Scott v. The Queen* [1988] 1 SCR 30.

and Deb, a couple who run a successful business they have started on their own. It takes much effort to keep it going, but they have a good income from the business. Derek is 42 and Deb is 37, and they're expecting their first child. A series of routine blood and ultrasound tests determined that Deb is at high risk to have a fetus with **Down's syndrome.** As our drama begins, Deb and Derek have just received confirmation from **amniocentesis** that the fetus Deb is bearing does indeed have Down's. Deb is initially in favour of having the child, while Derek is very strongly in favour of aborting the fetus in order to protect their marriage and the business they have worked hard to build. In the end, Deb concedes and agrees to have an abortion.

Our debate focuses on the question whether it is morally permissible for Deb to have an abortion, given her circumstances. Her life is not endangered by the pregnancy, but she sees abortion as necessary in order to protect important relationships and projects. We agree that Deb's abortion is morally permissible, although it turns out that we have very different reasons in support of our common conclusion. Before we each present our own arguments, we examine several **conservative** arguments against abortion, arguments which imply that it would be morally wrong for Deb to have an abortion in her situation. We explain why we think these arguments are unsound. Patrick then argues that the moral status of abortion cannot be settled just by considering the issue of whose rights trump whose; instead, we must reflect on whether having an abortion is consistent with acting virtuously, where this includes more than respecting rights. Importantly, Patrick argues that even if the fetus has a right to life, it would still be morally permissible to abort it in certain situations, including Deb's. A virtuous person, Patrick goes on to argue, would view abortion as a morally difficult matter, an act that requires good reasons in order to be justified, reasons which are present in Deb's case. Doran argues that her sixteen-week-old fetus has at best a weak right to life—one that is not sufficient to trump Deb's right to control her body. Unlike Patrick, Doran thinks that early abortions (in normal circumstances) are morally permissible regardless of the pregnant woman's reasons. Warren reaches the conclusion that Deb's abortion is permissible by applying his social contract theory. He thinks that a woman's right to autonomy renders abortions at early stages (in normal circumstances) morally permissible in most cases.

DEFINITION

"**Down syndrome** [or **Down's syndrome**] is a genetic condition in which a person has 47 *chromosomes* instead of the usual 46. . . . In most cases, Down syndrome occurs when there is an extra copy of chromosome 21. This form of Down syndrome is called Trisomy 21. The extra chromosome causes problems with the way the body and brain develop. Down syndrome is the most common single cause of human birth defects.

"Physical development is often slower than normal. Most children with Down syndrome never reach their average adult height. Children may also have delayed mental and social development. According to the National Institute of Child Health and Human Development, most persons with Down syndrome have mild to moderate mental retardation."

Source: http://www.nlm.nih.gov/medlineplus/ency/article/000997.htm#Definition.

Amniocentesis is a prenatal diagnostic procedure performed in order to detect fetal abnormalities. A needle is used to remove a sample of the amniotic fluid surrounding the fetus. The amniotic fluid contains skin cells from the fetus, which are analyzed to determine potential problems with the fetus.

LEARNING OBJECTIVES

After completing this chapter, you should be able to:

- Explain and evaluate some important conservative arguments against abortion
- Distinguish Warren's and Patrick's views on the moral significance of the fact that a fetus is a potential person
- Understand Patrick's reasons for thinking that Deb's abortion is morally permissible
- Describe the reasons why Warren and Doran disagree with Patrick's argument
- Explain Doran's argument for the moral permissibility of Deb's abortion
- Discuss Patrick and Warren's reasons for rejecting Doran's argument
- Defend your own view on the morality of abortion, in general, and the morality of Deb's abortion, in particular

DRAMA

Please note: This case is based on various true stories, although names, places, and some uncontroversial elements of the case have been changed to preserve anonymity and confidentiality. Discussions of this and similar cases with health care professionals have also informed this fictional case. The drama merely raises issues. The philosophical arguments are to be found in the debate following the drama.

CHARACTERS

Deb: *37 years old, a businesswoman, married to Derek*
Derek: *42 years old, a businessman, married to Deb*

Deb: I can't believe it. I hoped right up to the last moment it would be okay.

Derek: Honey, we'll try again. Everything will work out next time. At least we know about this early.

Deb: It doesn't feel that way to me, Derek. Sixteen weeks this child has been growing inside me. I feel like I need to protect her.

Derek: It must be so hard for you, Deb. It's awful. But Deb, that's why we had the tests, so we wouldn't have a child with . . . problems. It's too hard to do. Look at Lawrence and Anne. They tried to tough it out and now I hear they're splitting up. It's too much. Everything changes. If we had a child like that, you couldn't work like you do now. We couldn't keep the house. Everything would be so different, but it doesn't have to be that way. We can try again. We can have a normal child. Deb, Deb—look at me. We can. That's why we had the tests, isn't it? Isn't it, Deb?

Deb: I guess. Still, it's different when it's real like this. When we were told to get the tests it was just something like a worry in the back of my mind. It wasn't going to happen to us. I don't know. Maybe I'm not as tough as I thought I was. Maybe I never really thought it through. It just isn't that easy. I care about her now, Derek. She wasn't real to me then.

Derek: Love, I know you're a sweet and caring woman. That's part of what I love about you. But you've got drive too. You're happy when you're creating our future in our company. You love our house and the kind of life we have now. We don't have to throw that all away. We don't have to. We have options. We can have it all, but not if we continue this pregnancy. Look, I talked to Lawrence yesterday, and he was really bitter. Anne is exhausted. The government help they thought they could get never seems to materialize. They've already burnt through all their savings. So Lawrence says to me, about his retarded son, he says, "You know it's not like he's ever going to understand all we've had to give up for him or appreciate it. I won't even ever be able to take him down to the park to hit a few balls. He can only take. He can't give back." I think of Lawrence and Anne struggling through a totally thankless life and it really gets me.

Deb: But maybe it won't be that bad. The doctor says there's a huge variation in Down's. Maybe she'll be really high functioning.

Derek: Sweetheart, I can see how you're torn by this. But think about what you're saying. High functioning! Is that what we want to hear about our kid? Deb, Deb, Deb. We want a daughter who will go to university some day, not just be at the upper end of retarded. I can't bear the thought of it.

Deb: But there are families with kids like this who are so loved and it isn't all bad, honey. We don't know what it might be like. She doesn't have any really severe physical things showing up on ultrasound. Maybe she won't be so badly off mentally, either. We don't know what we can do until we try.

Derek: Love is what moves you now, but I don't want a life of sacrifice just because of the feelings that move you for a while. You're the one who is always so bugged by uncertainty. You've stopped us from taking risks time and time again because things were too unpredictable. What's different now? Only that we are betting our whole way of life, and the odds are terrible. Don't do this to yourself. Don't to this to us, honey. Please don't.

Deb: Derek. Take it slow. We don't have to decide this minute.

Derek: You're right. We have to be careful and deliberate about this. Still, I want to talk about something else. Nobody would be patting us on the back saying how heroic we are for doing this. Look at Anne and Lawrence. They come in for some really tough criticism behind their backs. People say they got themselves into this. It's like they're letting the side down. They didn't have to have a child that would be a drain on them and everyone. You know we both felt they shouldn't have done it.

Deb: I feel guilty for that now. There are lots of ways kids give back to their parents, and they aren't all money or appreciation or winning a ball game.

Derek: Oh honey, don't feel guilty. No, babe, you were right when you said Anne shouldn't have gone through with it. It's not fair to the kid or anyone to have a kid like that when you can *avoid* it. Everybody pays. But these kids can't give back. It's like Lawrence says. They can only take. That's why we developed the tests. That's why we use the tests. It makes our society stronger if we are all individually healthier. You're always saying that in business we should not support the weak.

Deb: This is different!

Derek: Okay, I'm sorry. It's a bad comparison. But it still makes the world a better place if every individual is as healthy as we can make her. It's a better world if nobody needs to suffer and nobody needs to support these suffering, unhealthy children. You know it is. That's why society supports the whole medical thing with tests and ways of dealing with it when things go wrong.

Deb: Just call it what it is, abortion. We want to kill someone here.

Derek: Okay, it's abortion we're talking about, and that's not a bad thing. There's a fetus that could become someone, but it's not someone yet. Abortion gives us much better options than we would have. I just don't want you to blame yourself, honey. Some day we're going to be celebrating our child graduating, not celebrating her learning to feed herself when she should be graduating. We've planned our lives. We've had a real curve thrown at us, but we're not out yet. There's nothing wrong with abortion to do something good for ourselves and everybody. There's nothing wrong at all. We have a choice, and that's a good thing.

Deb: I'm not saying it has to be wrong, Derek, but it isn't wrong to have the child either. It may be a very good thing to do. Maybe it's a good thing just because she would be helpless and we are strong and can take care of her. Maybe that's not such a bad life.

Derek: It is for me, Deb. I can't do this. I look at Lawrence and I say "Not me." Maybe it's my weakness, but it's tough enough being a parent without that extra challenge. I want a normal child. I can't do this. Maybe it seems right for you now, but please, please think about what you would have to give up.

Deb: What are you saying, Derek? Won't you be there for me if I have this child?

Derek: Oh God, Deb! I don't know what I'm saying. I know I am scared. Deb, I don't want to do this. I really don't. I don't think it's right, not just wrong for us but plain wrong. Do you remember that deaf couple that deliberately had a deaf child? We were sure they shouldn't do that, weren't we? I'm still sure.

Deb: I can't do this alone, Derek. If you can't raise this child, we can't raise her. Even if you tried, you'd be resentful. You wouldn't be in it. It would be hopeless. I can't fight you on this, Derek. All I can do is cry.

DEBATE
Clarifying the Case and Identifying Relevant Facts

Doran says: Warren, why don't you begin with a very brief summary of the drama?

Warren says: Sure. Deb and Derek are trying to decide whether or not to abort given that their fetus has Down's. Derek is unwilling to take on the rigours of parenting a child with Down's. He considered another family's difficulties with raising a disabled child and is unwilling to live like that. Derek is also very concerned that their lifestyle would be drastically altered if they had a disabled child. Deb is willing to raise a child with Down's, but realizes that it will probably break up the marriage. In the end, she gives in, accepting abortion reluctantly.

Doran says: It is not just the marriage and their lifestyle—they have built a business, and it requires their constant concern, but Deb is uncertain, as she has bonded emotionally with the fetus growing inside her.

Warren says: Yes.

Patrick says: Warren, do we know how long Deb and Derek have been together, and how solid their relationship is?

Warren says: They have been together two years.

Patrick says: And we can assume that their relationship is solid?

Warren says: They have bought a house and built a business together. They are pretty solid, but cracks are showing over the abortion decision.

Doran says: I think we can assume their relationship is solid, but Derek is clearly telling Deb that he cannot stay in the relationship if they choose to have the disabled child. For him, that was understood from the start. He says that this is why they did genetic testing in the first place.

Patrick says: If they have the baby, is that the end of their business? They can't have both?

Warren says: Yes, it takes two people to manage the business. Derek could not do it if Deb was dealing with a child full-time indefinitely.

Patrick says: Could he not get someone else in to help? Or is Deb herself needed?

Warren says: Like most family businesses, it requires more work than a business partner would normally commit to. Derek can't see how to keep the business without Deb.

Patrick says: Does Deb agree at the end that having an abortion is the best thing to do, in order to preserve their marriage and business, or does she simply cave in to Derek?

Warren says: She agrees reluctantly. She just does not want to take on raising this child on her own and realizes that she can't count on Derek to help. At best he would be resentful, and the marriage might not survive.

Patrick says: But if Derek was okay with having the child, she would have not had an abortion?

Warren says: Right.

Patrick says: How far along in the pregnancy was Deb when the abortion was performed?

Warren says: At the end of the case it has not yet been performed. It is just after the amniocentesis at sixteen weeks.

Doran says: What is the level of fetal development at sixteen weeks?

DEFINITIONS

A **zygote** is a single diploid cell that results from the merging of a sperm and ovum through a process of fertilization. The developing organism, from the moment of conception until about the end of the eighth week, is called an **embryo.** From that point until birth it is called a **fetus.**

Warren says: At twelve to sixteen weeks from the last menstrual period, quickening occurs. The mother feels the **fetus** moving within her. This would likely influence Deb's feelings. At sixteen weeks the length is about eighteen centimetres, the brain structure has been complete since about twelve weeks.

Doran says: The fetus's development is in that middling range—it is not a **zygote** or an **embryo,** it has a brain and functioning nervous system, but it is certainly less conscious than a newborn, or even a fully formed fetus. It is incapable of surviving on its own, since vital organs, like lungs, are not yet formed.

Patrick says: Is the fetus unable to feel pain at that stage, sixteen weeks?

Warren says: We just do not know. Experts disagree. Because the fetus's brain structure is complete, it may be somewhat conscious, and so it may be able to feel pain. However, I doubt that it is conscious to any significant degree, and so I doubt it can feel pain at this stage of development.

Patrick says: Yes, of course, if it's not conscious, then it can't feel pain.

Warren says: Our own experience seems to assure that. (This is why we cannot feel pain when we are under anesthetic.) Of course, a low level of consciousness might be sufficient to feel pain. Physicians are sometimes uncertain enough about the ability of the fetus to feel pain that they will give a sixteen-week-old fetus a lethal injection prior to the abortion procedure.

UP FOR DISCUSSION

On what basis can one determine whether another individual is conscious? Using those criteria, how confident can we be that a sixteen-week-old-fetus is or is not conscious?

Doran says: So the fetus, at this stage of development, may be able to feel pain, and so would have to be at least somewhat conscious; however, the fetus at this stage may not be conscious (and so would not be able to feel pain), and it is almost certainly not self-aware.

Patrick says: If Deb does not abort, do we know, or have any reasonable idea of, how serious their child's mental disability will be?

Warren says: One cannot tell in advance. The Down's syndrome is evident, but it can be very severe or produce a high-functioning Down's child or anything in between.

Patrick says: So there's a range of possible disabilities. If their child was born with severe disabilities, couldn't they opt for adoption?

Warren says: Deb would not do this because she thinks it would be impossible for her to give up the child if she went through with the pregnancy. She may also have been concerned that her child would not be adopted, given that she believes it can be difficult to find homes for children with Down's and other disabilities.

Patrick says: Okay, I see. So, formally, it may be an option, but it's unrealistic to think Deb could do that.

Warren says: Yes.

BACKGROUND

According to a 2006 article in *Maclean's* magazine, there are approximately 150 families across North America who are on a waiting list to adopt a Down's syndrome child.

Source: Cathy Gulli, "A Demand for Down's: People Wanting to Adopt a Child with Down's Syndrome Are Finding There's a Waiting List," *Maclean's*, April 10, 2006, http://www.macleans.ca/article.jsp?content=20060410_124933_124933.

Doran says: Well, it would be hard for her to give up the child for adoption, and hard for her to have an abortion, and hard for her to keep the child. I would say that each of these was an option for Deb, though some of these choices would have been harder for her than others.

Warren says: Yes, I suppose Doran's right that it is a matter of what is the hardest choice.

Doran says: Okay, to sum up then, Deb gives in to Derek's pressures, the business needs her to survive, and they believe she cannot work in the business if they have a Down's child. Also, Derek does not want to forgo his lifestyle, and he believes that would be necessary if they were to raise a child with Down's. Their relationship probably won't survive if the child is born and raised by them, and their relationship may survive if there is an abortion. There is, moreover, reason to think they can try again, and that the resulting child would possibly be born healthy and without Down's.

Warren says: That about sums things up. They are at some risk of conceiving with Down's again, but it is not a foregone conclusion.

Patrick says: Right. This case, like the others, raises a number of difficult moral questions. Why don't we now decide which of these we want to debate.

MORAL ISSUES RAISED BY THE CASE

Doran says: Well, several ethical issues come to mind. Is it morally permissible for Deb to obtain an abortion under these circumstances? Does Derek act permissibly in pressuring his wife? Does Deb act virtuously when she gives in to Derek's ultimatum? I'd be interested in debating any of these questions.

Patrick says: Those are all interesting questions, but I think we should focus on the permissibility of Deb's having an abortion in this situation.

Warren says: Yes, I think that's a central question raised by the case.

Doran says: Okay, so the question we're debating is this: *Is it morally permissible for Deb to have an abortion in this situation?*

Patrick says: Yes, that's the question. What do you guys think?

Stating Our Positions

Doran says: I believe it is morally permissible for Deb to obtain an abortion. I believe this because I believe that the fetus, at this stage of development, does not have a significant moral right to life. The woman's right to control what happens in and to her body should prevail.

Warren says: I agree that it is morally permissible for Deb to have an abortion. My reason is that this is in accord with rules we would choose if we were in the original position. In the original position we would have a difficult choice. On the one hand, we would not want to be forced to use our bodies or other resources to bear, have, and raise a child who might present us with great difficulties and require heavy sacrifices. On the other hand, sympathy, among other considerations, would inhibit us from making rules that treat the fetus as having no value. I come down, ultimately, on the side of the right of the woman to choose.

UP FOR DISCUSSION

Opponents of abortion think that social contract theory stacks the deck against their view because people in the original position know they are rational beings. They cannot be fetuses. They cannot be the victims of abortion in the real world. Is this a reasonable objection to social contract theory? Can you think of a reply?

Patrick says: This is a very hard case, but I agree with you guys that it would be permissible for Deb to abort, though I agree for different reasons. From my virtue ethics perspective, I don't think the moral status of Deb's having an abortion can be settled just by looking at the rights possessed by the fetus and the mother (and father). For even if Deb has a right to control her body, abortion may still be wrong. And even if her fetus has a right to life, Deb's abortion may still be permissible. To determine whether Deb's having an abortion is wrong, we need to consider whether she is acting viciously or not in having the abortion. We need to consider, for instance, whether having an abortion would exhibit cruelty, selfishness, disrespect, etc. All things considered, I conclude—though somewhat tentatively—that having an abortion in this case would not be vicious, and hence, not wrong.

Warren says: Your approach sounds interesting, Patrick. Why don't we proceed as follows? Let's first consider some important arguments *against* the morality of abortion. Since none of us accepts these arguments, we should first raise them and explain why we think they fail. We can then turn to Patrick's virtue-based argument, and see whether or not we accept his argument as sound. If disagreement persists between us, perhaps we can also look at

UP FOR
DISCUSSION

What do you think? Is it permissible for Deb to have an abortion? Why or why not?

Doran's pro-choice argument on abortion, and see if it is any more conclusive.

Patrick says: Sure.

Doran says: That sounds like a good plan.

LEADING ARGUMENTS AGAINST THE MORALITY OF ABORTION

Doran says: Many conservatives—those who generally oppose abortion—claim that abortion is wrong in all, or virtually all, cases. This is because they believe that it involves the unjust or wrongful killing of the fetus.

Patrick says: Right. But conservatives have different, sometimes *quite* different, reasons for thinking this.

Warren says: Let's consider some of their reasons.

Noonan's Argument

Doran says: We cannot consider all of their arguments, but let's look at some of the most influential. For instance, John T. Noonan, in his widely read paper on abortion, argues as follows.[2]

TECHNIQUE

Students of logic will see that this is an argument in the broad sense, sometimes referred to as a derivation. An argument in the narrower sense has only one conclusion. Here a series of arguments is used to derive a final conclusion using earlier conclusions in the derivation as premises.

(1) Any being with human **genetic code** is a human.
(2) Fetuses receive human genetic code at conception.
(3) Therefore, fetuses are human at conception.
(4) Being human (i.e., having the right genetic code) is sufficient for having moral rights, including a right to life.
(5) So, fetuses have moral rights from conception.
(6) It is, presumptively, seriously immoral to kill a being that has moral rights.
(7) Therefore, abortion is, presumptively, seriously immoral from conception.

Warren says: Yes, that seems to be his argument, although your description of the argument contains premises that he does not explicitly state.

---

[2] John T. Noonan, Jr., "An Almost Absolute Value in History," in *The Morality of Abortion: Legal and Historical Perspectives,* ed. John T. Noonan, Jr. (Cambridge, MA: Harvard University Press, 1970).

For instance, he never explicitly states premise (4), that being genetically human is sufficient for having moral rights. However, it is quite clear that premise (4) is implicit in his argument. Noonan focuses much of his energy on supporting premise (1). Specifically, he gives a couple of reasons why he thinks that having a human genetic code is sufficient for something to be a human being. First, by maintaining that all who have human genetic code are human, he thinks we will guard against the tendency to discriminate against some on the basis of their abilities, or lack of abilities. Secondly, he thinks that genetic humanity—what we might now distinguish by human DNA—is morally significant since it is the material that is the "biological carrier of human wisdom."

Patrick says: And I take it he maintains that it is only *presumptively* seriously immoral to kill a human being because he wants to allow for the possibility that killing in self-defence, or perhaps applying the death penalty, may be morally permissible.

Doran says: Yes, that's right. He maintains that intentionally killing an innocent human being can *very* rarely be justified. When it comes to abortion, he appears willing to recognize its permissibility only when necessary to save the pregnant woman's life.[3]

Warren says: So he would certainly contend that it is wrong for Deb to have an abortion.

Patrick says: Right. This is an interesting argument, but I believe it fails.

Evaluating Premise (1) of Noonan's Argument

Patrick says: Premise (1), which states that any being with human genetic code is a human, looks especially suspicious. Non-humans can have human genetic code.

Doran says: I agree. Cattle are sometimes injected with human genetic code to make their milk more digestible, but the mere fact that they have this genetic code does not make them human. Likewise, pigs are sometimes injected with human DNA so they can

UP FOR DISCUSSION

Suppose a woman discovers that the child she is carrying has a serious disease such that the child's life is likely to contain much more pain than pleasure. Noonan's view seems to imply that having an abortion in this situation would be wrong. Do you agree? Why or why not?

---

[3] Actually, his view is unclear on this point: He grants the permissibility of abortion when the fetus cannot survive and the mother's life is threatened. However, he is less clear about whether abortion of a viable fetus would be morally permissible even to save the mother's life.

grow tissue that can be transplanted to humans, yet we would not call these pigs human.

Warren says: These counterexamples might not be persuasive. For Noonan might say that individuals that have *only* human DNA are human. The cattle and pigs you mentioned do not have all and *only* the human genetic code, so they need not be viewed as human on this interpretation of his premise.

Patrick says: Yes, I suppose that is the charitable way to interpret Noonan.

Doran says: But I don't think this interpretation of his premise will help his argument very much, for it, too, is vulnerable to clear counterexamples.

Warren says: That's true: some human cells have all, and only, human DNA, but we do not consider human cells to be human beings.

Doran says: I agree that it is implausible to think that the mere possession of all and only human DNA is sufficient for being human. To see this consider some analogies: Think of an acorn. It has the DNA of an oak tree, yet no one would consider an acorn to be an oak tree, merely in virtue of the fact that they share the same DNA. Likewise, imagine you come over for breakfast and I serve you an omelet. You say that the eggs are delicious. I, however, correct you. I point out that the eggs you're eating were fertilized. Thus, what you are eating are (three) chickens! Surely this would strike you as absurd. Similarly, it seems absurd to suggest that a one-celled organism could be a human being, merely because it happened to contain all and only human DNA. At best, such an organism has the potential to become a human being, but it is not one yet!

Patrick says: Right, and further, possessing all and only human DNA is not even *necessary* for being a human being. To see this, consider **xenotransplantation**—the transplantation of non-human organs into humans. If I received, say, a heart valve from a pig, then I would not have all and only human DNA. So the modified premise would then imply that I ceased to be human!

Warren says: It appears, then, that premise (1) in Noonan's argument, whichever way it is interpreted, is quite clearly false.

TECHNIQUE

Warren is employing a methodological principle called **the principle of charity.** This principle instructs us to interpret an author's claims and arguments in the best possible light. The general aim is to arrive at a fair and sympathetic understanding of the author's position in order to critically evaluate it. In this case, Noonan appears to be relying on a premise that is clearly false. The principle of charity requires that we try to find a more plausible understanding of his premise. Employing the principle here will help Warren, Doran, and Patrick avoid making weak criticisms that Noonan could easily escape by a more careful statement of the premise in question.

UP FOR DISCUSSION

Do you see a way of defending Noonan's claim that a being with human DNA is a human being? Can you think of other objections to this premise?

Evaluating Premise (4) of Noonan's Argument

Warren says: Interestingly, even if we grant Noonan's claim that one is in some sense human in virtue of possessing human genetic code, I think Noonan's argument is still in trouble, since premise (4) looks dubious.

Doran says: I agree. Premise (4) says that being human is sufficient for having rights. This is dubious because if we really think that human DNA is sufficient to make one human as is claimed in premise (1), then we would also have to say that having human DNA is sufficient for having rights. But that seems much too strong. As Warren noted previously, many human cells have all and only human DNA, but we do not grant individual human cells human rights. Similarly, the process of IVF (in-vitro fertilization) requires the creation and subsequent loss of many human fertilized ova, but it seems to be mistaken to regard this process as one that involves mass manslaughter.

BACKGROUND

Mary Anne Warren famously distinguishes genetic humanity from moral humanity. Genetic humanity, she argues, is based on one's species classification, but moral humanity is based on whether or not one is a rights holder. Mary Anne Warren then goes on to argue that it is a mistake to equate moral humanity with genetic humanity. The former, she argues, is neither necessary nor sufficient for the latter. On her view, a fertilized human ovum may be genetically human, but it is not morally human.

Source: Mary Anne Warren, "On the Moral and Legal Status of Abortion," in *Biomedical Ethics*, 4th ed., ed. Thomas A. Mappes and David DeGrazia, 434–40 (New York: *McGraw-Hill, 1996)., 434–40.*

UP FOR DISCUSSION

Do you think that the possession of human genetic code ought to give a being moral rights?

Marquis's Argument for the Wrongfulness of Abortion

Warren says: Given the many problems with claiming that the possession of human DNA is sufficient for being human, or being a rights holder, some conservatives on the abortion issue give rather different reasons for their opposition to abortion. One of the most interesting is an argument by Don Marquis.[4]

(1) It is, presumptively, seriously immoral to kill you and me because it deprives us of a future of value.

(2) In standard cases of abortion, abortion deprives the fetus of a future of value—a future like ours.

(3) Therefore, standard cases of abortion are, presumptively, seriously immoral.

The novelty of Marquis's argument is that he is not claiming that fetuses are human or that they have rights, and so forth;

---

[4] Don Marquis, "Why Abortion Is Immoral," *Journal of Philosophy* 86, no. 4 (1989): 183–202.

instead, he asks a different question. Why is it wrong to kill you or me? After identifying a principal reason why it is wrong to kill you or me, he then says that this reason also applies to the killing of fetuses—so it is wrong too, and for the same reason.

Marquis's view, in the end, is that once we have an identifiable being, then we have an individual with a future like ours. It is presumptively wrong to kill beings with futures like ours, so it is presumptively wrong to kill fetuses.[5]

UP FOR DISCUSSION

Would an act utilitarian agree with Marquis's account of why aborting a fetus in a normal pregnancy is morally wrong? Why or why not?

Doran says: So Marquis thinks it is wrong to kill us because it robs us of our valuable future. That is, it robs us of experiences, activities, etc., that we value now and would have come to enjoy in the future.

Warren says: Yes, that's the basic idea. And so he would say that Deb's abortion is morally wrong for the same reason that killing one of us is wrong—it robs one of a valuable future.

Evaluating Premise (2) of Marquis's Argument

Patrick says: When discussing this argument in class, my students often target premise (2). They reject the premise that, in standard cases of abortion, the fetus is deprived of a future of value. They suggest that children that are unwanted are not likely to have good futures. But this objection is rather weak.

UP FOR DISCUSSION

Do you agree that, in standard cases, abortion prevents the fetus from having a future of value?

Doran says: Yes, this objection seems wrong to me, or at least exaggerated. Often, indeed probably most of the time, even if a child is unwanted, it is doubtful that her future would be so bad that it would be not worth living! As a case in point, it is doubtful that if Deb were to continue with the pregnancy, her child's life would be so bad as to be not worth living. We would be unlikely to think, once the child was born, that it would be a blessing for the child if she were to die prematurely.

Evaluating Premise (1) of Marquis's Argument: The Contraception Objection

Warren says: Okay, then, if one is to reject Marquis's argument, it seems that one needs to question his first premise. Has he identified a reason

---

[5] In his analysis, Marquis excludes from consideration non-standard cases of pregnancy, such as pregnancy due to rape, pregnancy that endangers the woman's life, or cases of fetal abnormality. He simply takes no position on these non-standard cases.

that is sufficient for making killing someone immoral, namely, that it causes the individual the loss of a future like ours?

Doran says: There is reason to suspect not. First, if we accepted premise (1), it seems that it would imply that contraception is immoral, since it seems that contraception also prevents a future of value. Of course, contraception is not immoral, so premise (1) must be rejected.[6]

Warren says: Marquis, however, would deny that his premise entails that contraception is seriously immoral, for he would claim that prior to implantation, there is not yet an individual that exists who has a possible future of value. He never says it is wrong to prevent potential individuals from existing who will then have futures of value; rather, he says it is wrong to prevent individuals who already exist from having futures of value.

Patrick says: Well, to make this sort of reply, I think Marquis owes us an account of what constitutes an *individual* in the relevant sense. Sperm and ova are not individuals, on his view, but a zygote is? Why? This is not an easy question to answer.

Warren says: The response might be that the zygote will develop into a human being who could be a person unless it is prevented from doing so, while the sperm or ovum, left alone, will not do so. That, however, is weak.

Patrick says: Yes, it is weak. We use contraceptives to prevent sperm and ova from developing into human beings. And nobody would say, moreover, after reflecting on the care needed for a successful pregnancy, that the zygote is simply left alone for a human being to emerge.

Warren says: Yes, the enormous contribution of the mother seems typically forgotten in such arguments.

Patrick says: As you noted earlier, Warren, the novelty of Marquis's argument is, in part, that it does not rely on the premise that the fetus is a human, or a being with rights. But his notion of an "individual" is equally problematic.

UP FOR DISCUSSION

Do you think that the contraception objection succeeds?

---

[6] Notice the objection raised here would apply equally to artificial and natural forms of birth control. Even the rhythm method, favoured by the Catholic Church, would be seriously immoral, for, if successful, it too prevents an individual from having a future like ours.

Challenging the Logical Validity of Marquis's Argument: The Equivocation Objection

Doran says: Well, I agree with your points, but I want to add the following even stronger objection. As we have seen, Marquis argues:

(1) It is seriously immoral to cause the loss of a future of value.
(2) In standard cases, fetuses are caused the loss of a future of value when aborted.

(3) Therefore, in standard cases abortion is seriously immoral.

DEFINITIONS

To commit the **fallacy of equivocation** is to use a term in two different senses so as to make an **argument** which is not valid appear valid.

But one might object that this argument commits the **fallacy of equivocation.**[7] Specifically, the phrase "cause the loss" is ambiguous—it has more than one meaning.

To see this, consider some uses of the phrase "cause the loss of":

Case 1. Patrick and I run a race. Patrick loses because I outrun him. I *cause the loss of* something of value for Patrick, namely his winning of the trophy.

Case 2. Patrick and I run a race. Patrick loses because I tied his shoelaces together before the starting gun goes off. I *cause the loss of* something of value for Patrick, namely, his winning of the trophy.

Now, in the first and second cases, I caused the loss of something of value. But only in the second case is the cause of the loss morally problematic. Let's consider a couple more examples:

Case 1. I am *caused the loss of* much happiness because Patrick gets a job that I dearly wanted, after we both applied for it.

Case 2. I am *caused the loss of* much happiness because Patrick gets a job that I dearly wanted, after we both applied for it, but he got it because he sabotaged my resumé.

Case 1. Your landlord does not renew your lease, *causing you the loss of* your beloved apartment.

Case 2. Your landlord does not renew your lease, *causing you the loss of* your beloved apartment, even though she had promised you that she would renew your lease.

In each of these cases, a loss of something of value is caused. But only in Case 2 is the causing of the loss morally objectionable.

---

[7] This point is made by Walter Sinnott-Armstrong, "You Can't Lose What You Ain't Never Had," *Philosophical Studies* 96, no. 1 (1999): 59–72.

Thus we might distinguish *neutral losses* from *moral losses.* Both neutral losses and moral losses involve causing the loss of something of value. They differ only in that it is not wrong to cause neutral losses, while it is wrong to cause moral losses.

Warren says: So, Doran, what, in your view, makes it wrong to cause a moral loss and not wrong to cause a neutral loss?

Doran says: It appears that the moral loss involves a violation of the person's rights or involves some unfairness, while the neutral loss cases do not involve violations of the person's rights or any unfairness. This is confirmed by each of the cases above. It is not morally objectionable if I beat Patrick in a race, or if he beats me in a competition for a job, if we both fairly competed, but it becomes morally objectionable when one of us acts in ways that make the competition unfair. Similarly, the landlord's decision not to renew your lease seems only to be wrong in the second case, where she violates her duty to you to keep her promise to renew the lease.

UP FOR DISCUSSION

Natural advantages might be unfair, too, since it is a matter of luck whether one has good genes. For example, is it fair if Doran beats Patrick in a race because he has superior natural athletic ability?

Warren says: Okay, with this distinction between neutral losses and moral losses in mind, I'm sure you can generate problems for Marquis's argument.

Doran says: That's right. Premise (1), which states that it's wrong to cause the loss of a valuable future, is true only if a moral loss is intended. But then for the argument to be valid, premise (2), which states that abortion causes the fetus the loss of a valuable future, would also have to be read in as a moral loss. However, Marquis **begs the question** if he merely assumes that abortion causes a moral loss. He could only do that if he assumes that fetuses have a right to their futures, or that it was somehow unfair to the fetus to abort it, but Marquis never proves that such rights are violated or that it is somehow unfair. Indeed, it is precisely the issue of whether fetuses have rights that he hopes to avoid by giving his future-like-ours argument.

DEFINITION

To **beg the question** is to presuppose what you want to prove. See **circularity** in Chapter 1.

Patrick says: Of course, Marquis could instead argue that abortion causes a neutral loss. This would be true, in standard cases, but this, of course, wouldn't help his argument much.

Doran says: That's right, because if he used neutral loss in premise (2), he'd then have to use neutral loss in premise (1)—and that would

UP FOR DISCUSSION

What do you think of Marquis's argument? Do you agree that killing a fetus is wrong for the same reason that killing you or me is wrong?

make premise (1) false, for as we have seen, it is not wrong to cause merely neutral losses.

Thus, I think Marquis's argument fails because of the fallacy of equivocation. He uses the phrase "cause the loss of" with two very different meanings.

In order for his argument to succeed, he first needs to show that fetuses have a right to their futures, and then that this right is violated if the pregnant woman obtains an abortion, but these are precisely the issues that he had hoped to sidestep.

The Moral Significance of Potential

Warren says: Thus far, we have seen that both the conservative argument that a being with human DNA is a human being with human rights, that is, that a biologically human being is a human being in the moral sense, and the conservative argument that focuses on the *prima facie* wrongness of causing the loss of a future of value, are problematic. Others might try to argue that a human *person* begins at conception, and that all human persons are rights holders, but that argument will likely run into familiar problems. A single cell, or a clump of cells with human genetic code, is no more a person than an acorn is an oak tree. But more interesting are arguments that start from the seemingly incontrovertible premise that fetuses, even embryos and zygotes, are potential persons. Perhaps it could then be argued that one deserves some kind of moral consideration in virtue of this potential? Specifically, it might be argued that the potential to become a person gives the developing fetus *moral rights,* or, at the very least, that the potential to become a person gives the developing fetus *moral value.*[8]

Potential and Rights

Doran says: Let's first consider the argument that potential gives the fetus rights. I take it that it goes something like this:

(1) From conception onward we have a *potential person.*
(2) If one is a potential person, then one should get the basic rights of a person.
(3) Therefore, from conception onward, one should get the basic rights of a person.[9]

---

[8] For an excellent discussion of the moral significance of potentiality, see Joel Feinberg, "Abortion," in *Matters of Life and Death,* ed. Tom Regan (New York: Random House, 1980), 183–217.
[9] See, for example, Bertha Alvarez Manninen, "Revisiting the Argument from Fetal Potential," http://www.pubmedcentral.nih.gov/articlerender.fcgi?artid=1892780#B3.

Evaluating Premise (2)

Patrick says: Premise (2) is certainly suspect. The general principle which underlies premise (2) is this: *If x is a potential y, and y has rights R, then x now has rights R.* But such a principle is clearly false. If I am interested in buying your car and your car is for sale, then I am the potential owner of your car. But I do not get any rights to your car in virtue of that potential. My rights to your car will only exist once I am the *actual* owner. Likewise, some students who are reading this text might not be of legal drinking age, though they are potentially old enough to drink. But I doubt very much that they could persuade the bartender to pour them a pint on the basis of the potentiality argument! Arguing that "I have the potential to be old enough to have the right to consume alcohol, so I should get that right now" may get you thrown out of the bar, but it would be quite surprising if it got you a beer!

UP FOR DISCUSSION

Can you think of your own counter-example to this potentiality principle?

Doran says: Indeed, it seems that potential is just that, potential. It means one *might become* something else. When one becomes that other thing, it seems reasonable to get the rights of that thing. But there is no reason to grant something the rights of another thing merely because of its potential.

UP FOR DISCUSSION

Can you think of a case where the mere fact of potential gives one rights?

Potential and Value

Warren says: Well, the appeal to potentiality as a source of rights is unpersuasive, but the idea that the fetus has *value* because it is a potential person seems more promising. After all, persons are of great value, and fetuses, even fertilized ova, are potential persons; therefore, it is only reasonable to think they too have value even if not as great as persons' value. Such a judgment seems reasonable inasmuch as so many prospective parents recognize that a miscarriage is a tremendous loss, much worse than a mere failure to get pregnant in the first place.

Doran says: Such an argument *seems* plausible. But is it plausible upon reflection? Lumps of coal are potential diamonds, but lumps of coal do not get the value of diamonds. Sperm cells, perhaps, are potential persons, but we do not attach great value to sperm cells! So, why should a one-celled fertilized ovum, or even a developing fetus, get great value just because one day it could become something else that has great value?

Patrick says: I think Warren is right that the potential of something *can* increase its value. But before we examine why this may be so, it is important to clarify what might be meant by saying that the fetus is "valuable."

Doran says: Good. Much ink has been spilled on what is meant by "value." So we will just barely scratch the surface here. But some clarification is in order.

Patrick says: Philosophers commonly distinguish between **instrumental value** and **non-instrumental value**. To say that something has instrumental value is to say that it is valuable as a means to something else. Money, for instance, has instrumental value for most of us. It is valuable because it can get us some other things that we want or value.

Warren says: Right, money would not have value if we were living in a different sort of society, for example, one that relied on barter. It seems to have value merely because it happens to be useful, given the situation most of us find ourselves in.

Patrick says: Non-instrumental value is different. Put a little roughly, it is value that something has in itself or for its own sake, rather than as a means to some other end or ends. Some hold that pleasure, for instance, has non-instrumental value. The suggestion is that pleasure is good not as a means to something else, but for its own sake.

Doran says: And I suppose some things can have both instrumental and non-instrumental value. Children, for instance, might be valuable in and of themselves, and also as a means to other things, such as having someone to work the farm or to care for the parents when they are elderly.

Warren says: That sounds right.

Patrick says: Well, of course, much more could be said about the nature of value. There are, for instance, different kinds of non-instrumental value—for example, **intrinsic value** and **inherent value**. And it is not entirely clear what it means for something to have value in itself or for its own sake. But perhaps we have said enough for our present purposes, and we can just stick to our rough-and-ready distinction between instrumental and non-instrumental value.

Warren says: I will grant the rough-and-ready distinction to see where you go with it.

Doran says: Okay, so let's consider the kind of value fetuses are said to have in virtue of their potential. I suppose it is not controversial that fetuses can have instrumental value in virtue of their potential. If a pregnant woman wants to have a child, then the fetus would be valued as a means to this end. But I take it that this is not the kind of value that critics of abortion have in mind when they say the fetus has value. For them, the claim is the fetus has a kind of value in virtue of its potential, and this value exists even if the pregnant woman (or anyone else) does not value it instrumentally. Do you think the fetus can have value, even if it is not valued by anyone?

Warren says: On my view, something can have value even if nobody in the real world values it. That's because something can have value if those in the original position would value it. And I believe fetuses, in virtue of their potential, would generally be valued by those in the original position.

Patrick says: I too think that fetuses can have value in virtue of their potential, even if this value is not recognized by the pregnant woman or anyone, but I would support this position by appealing to considerations of virtue.

Doran says: Let's hear your arguments.

Warren's Reasons for Thinking the Fetus's Potential Can Give the Fetus Value

Warren says: In my view, something can have value if it is valued by those in the original position. I think, for a variety of reasons, that fetuses would be valued by people in the original position. For instance, people in the original position will see it as in their interest to keep their species or culture going, and so will value fetuses as a means to that. Also, they'd recognize the psychological fact that many people care greatly about having children that are biologically related to them. Thus, again, people in the original position will value fetuses as a means to this end.

Doran says: Interesting. So even if the pregnant woman does not want a child, her fetus can still have some value in some circumstances, because it would be valued by people in the original position. Further, on your view the fetus's value is, in a sense, instrumental value. That is, fetuses are valued as a means to other ends. But since these are ends that would be recognized by people in the original position, the fetus's instrumental value is, in a sense, **objective.**

DEFINITION

To say that some truth is **objective** is to say, roughly, that it is true independently of whether people happen to think, believe, or feel that it is true. For instance, if it is an objective truth that slavery is morally wrong, then it is true whether or not any anyone happens to believe that it is true or to desire it to be true. To say that some truth is subjective is to say that its truth is dependent on whether a person happens to think, believe, or feel it is true. For instance, it is plausible to assume that truths about which flavour of ice cream is best are subjective. If so, then, if I say, "Chocolate ice cream is better than vanilla," my claim will be true only if I really think chocolate is better than vanilla.

That is, value can exist even if no one in the real world recognizes it.

Warren says: Right. But I hasten to add that while people in the original position will recognize the value of the fetus in some circumstances, they will also recognize that it is in their interest to give people a strong right to reproductive liberty. This reproductive liberty will generally trump any value the fetus may have.

Doran says: What do you mean when you say that reproductive liberty will *generally* trump the fetus's value?

Warren says: Again, this is complicated, but here is the rough idea. As the fetus develops, parties in the original position are going to require ever better reasons to justify aborting it, at least in cases of healthy development. This is, in part, because people in the original position recognize that it is in their interests to respect and promote common human sympathy.[10] People sympathize with infants and others who are vulnerable. Since mature fetuses are so similar to newborn infants, they will be protected by parties in the original position, and abortion will be justified only in rare cases, such as cases of extreme hardship for the mother. When it comes to an embryo or immature fetus, however, the concern to respect our common sympathy for vulnerable humans is much less pressing, since the embryo or immature fetus is not that similar to a human infant. An immature embryo does not generate nearly as much sympathy as a newborn. The result is that people in the original position will favour protecting the interest in reproductive liberty in the cases of early pregnancy, and will therefore adopt a very permissive stance on early abortions.

Patrick says: Warren, you said that the fetus can have value, given that people in the original position will recognize the interests that people have in reproducing, continuing their species, and so forth. But I take it that people in the original position are not going to value fetuses that much, given our present circumstances. A population of 6.5 billion makes concern about the species' disappearing from lack

---

[10] For the origin of this contractarian position, see Jane English's use of an argument employing, in effect, the sympathy metarule in her "Abortion and the Concept of a Person," *Canadian Journal of Philosophy* 5, no. 2 (1975): 233–43. See also Warren's description of the sympathy metarule in our Chapter 3.

of reproduction a non-issue. Indeed, the current environmental problems facing the world would suggest that population *reduction* would be highly desirable, and insofar as fetuses go against the goal of population reduction, it seems that fetuses would have a certain amount of *negative* value as viewed from the original position. I wonder if your view might lead to a moral obligation to limit the number of children one has in certain circumstances—perhaps even a moral duty *to* abort.

Warren says: I agree that early fetuses in our present circumstances are going to have less value than early fetuses would have in a situation where one's species was on the brink of disappearance. The fact that the Earth's population levels are not sustainable will surely affect how people in the original position are going to view the value of fetuses. Nevertheless, people in the original position will still recognize that people in the real world have powerful drives to reproduce their genotype, and that it is therefore in their interest to protect fetuses. They will also generally want to protect people's liberty to make their own reproductive decisions. I grant your point, however, that, given the realities of our current environmental situation, it may be morally wrong to have more than one or two biological offspring. It would be in the interest of those in the original position to promote a sustainable population in the real world.

Doran says: So, how does all of this bear on Deb's situation?

Warren says: My arguments above imply that Deb's liberty trumps the value of the fetus in this case, given the immaturity of the fetus. So it's morally permissible for Deb to abort.

Patrick's Reasons for Thinking That Fetuses Have Value

Doran says: Patrick, why do you think the fetus can have value in virtue of its potential?

Patrick says: Well, the view I want to defend is not so much the view that the fetus has value *in virtue of its potential*—though potential is a relevant consideration. I want to defend the view that the fetus has value, period—at least past a certain point in its development. And I want to try to show that the fetus has this value even if the parents themselves do not want the child.

Doran says: Okay, what's your argument?

Patrick says: The argument depends on elements of my virtue-based theory that aren't yet fully worked out, but here's one way of getting at the rough idea. When a woman has a miscarriage beyond, say, the first month or two of pregnancy, it is typically—and rightfully, I believe—regarded as a loss that calls for certain responses and attitudes such as grief, mourning, etc.

Doran says: But you must admit that there are exceptions to this—for example, cases where the fetus has very serious, untreatable problems.

Patrick says: Yes, there are, of course, exceptions, like the kind of case you just mentioned. But even then, surely the loss of a human life makes feelings of grief appropriate.

Doran says: I'm not so sure I agree, but continue with your argument. We can consider objections once you've laid out your position.

Patrick says: In general, a miscarriage involves a loss that makes certain responses appropriate. We'd be shocked, for instance, if our attempts at consoling a woman who'd just experienced a miscarriage were met with the following response: "Oh, it's no big deal, I didn't want the child anyway. If I went full term, I would have had to cancel my holiday to Mexico."

Warren says: That seems right. But how does this help to support your view that the fetus has value, even if the mother doesn't want a child?

Patrick says: Well, the idea that the fetus has value helps to explain *why* we think a miscarriage normally calls for appropriate sorts of responses, and *why* we'd be shocked at the woman's response in the previous example. We are shocked because the mother who regards her miscarriage as no big deal *should* feel some sense of loss, since the miscarriage involved the loss of something that has value. And this must be a kind of non-instrumental value—a kind of value that the fetus has independently of its utility to her or how she happens to feel about the fetus.

This value can be demonstrated, I believe, by appeal to a certain conception of the good life. A good life for a human, I believe, consists in a variety of intrinsically, or as we've been saying, non-instrumentally, valuable projects, activities, relationships, etc. These include, for instance, meaningful work, creativity, service to others, pursuit of truth, athletic activities, aesthetic appreciation, and so on. As I said, these things are non-instrumentally valuable. They are valuable not as a means to a good life. They are, rather, *constitutive* of living a good life, and are therefore valuable for their own sake.

Warren says: A good life according to whom?

Doran says: Well, we can't really answer that question here. But, for now, we can just say that common sense strongly suggests that these are some of the things that can make a life go well. Please continue, Patrick.

Patrick says: Right, this isn't the time and place to explain and defend a theory of the good life—that's another book! Here I can only sketch the rough idea. I think that most of us would agree, upon reflection, that meaningful relationships, including having children, are a central component of a good life. Of course, I am not claiming that being a parent is *necessary* for a good life. One could certainly lead a good life by partaking in some combination of the other non-instrumental goods I just mentioned. But being a parent is certainly among the projects, relationships, and so on, that are constitutive of a good life.

If this is correct, I believe we can see why the loss of a fetus through miscarriage is typically and rightfully regarded as a loss of something that has a kind of non-instrumental value, and so why miscarriage normally calls for appropriate sorts of feelings. A miscarriage involves the loss of a human life, the life of being who plays an important role in meaningful relationships that are constitutive of a good life.

Doran says: Fair enough, but what if the mother didn't want the child? Or what if she already had several children, and did not want another?

Patrick says: I think we need to take things on a case-by-case basis. In the case of a mother who doesn't want the child, we need to look at the reasons why she doesn't want the child. Earlier I gave an example of a woman who wasn't upset by her miscarriage, because if she had gone full term, she'd have had to cancel her Mexican getaway. In this case, I believe that she *should* have had a much different attitude toward the loss of her fetus. This is why we would be shocked at her response. Her indifference reflects a callous, shallow, and ignorant character. These inappropriate attitudes toward the loss of her fetus's life likely stem, in large part, from an incorrect view what a good life involves.

Warren says: Yet, in spite of this moral inappropriateness, you do not want to say that everyone ought to want to be a parent?

Patrick says: No, I don't want to say that. But everyone ought to recognize parenthood as intrinsically valuable and thus that fetuses are valuable.

Suppose, for instance, that a woman who was involved in various worthwhile projects accidentally became pregnant and then suffered a miscarriage. She may feel both grief and relief, and both of these feelings would be appropriate in this case. Even if she did not want a child, she can and should still recognize parenthood as a non-instrumentally valuable activity. So, some feelings of loss seem appropriate. However, since she has other worthwhile projects she wants to pursue, at the same time her feelings of relief are quite understandable. The response is not, in this case, an indication of callousness, shallowness, and ignorance. It is not a case where she is indifferent to, or ignorant of, the value of the fetus and of parenthood. Rather, she sees this value but prefers to pursue other non-instrumentally valuable projects, activities, and relationships.

TECHNIQUE

Doran is employing an argument technique known as a **reductio ad absurdum.** He is attempting to show that Patrick's view cannot be correct because it has absurd implications.

Doran says: Okay, I think I see your view, though I don't agree with it. One concern I have is that your argument proves too much. For your view seems to imply that successful contraception should be viewed as an occasion for grief, since successful contraception, like miscarriage or abortion, seems to prevent an opportunity for participating in the non-instrumental good of parenting.

Patrick says: I don't think my view implies that. I don't see what prevents me from saying that a fetus (that is, a human being) is non-instrumentally valuable, yet denying that sperm and ova are non-instrumentally valuable. It is human beings who have value, because our relationships with them are constitutive of a good life. Our relationships with sperm and ova, however, are not a constitutive part of a good life. So there's no reason why I must say that successful contraception calls for feelings of grief.

Doran says: Well, I am not sure you can escape the *reductio* so easily. But let me set this aside, for my disagreement runs deeper than the point just discussed. I don't agree with you when you say that when a woman has a miscarriage, "it is typically—and rightfully, I believe—regarded as a loss that calls for certain responses and attitudes such as grief, mourning, etc." For it is not unusual for a woman to become pregnant by mistake, at a time when she does not want to have a child (or another child). In such situations, if a person were to miscarry shortly after learning that she was pregnant—say, by having a heavier than normal period—I see nothing wrong with her feeling intense relief.

Patrick says: Yes, feelings of relief would be quite understandable in that situation. But depending on when the miscarriage occurred, I also believe that there is still a loss involved that calls for an appropriate response. Though the woman is relieved not to be put in a tough position of having to choose between a child and, say, her career or other worthwhile projects, she ought to recognize that the loss of the fetus is the loss of something of value, for the reasons I've provided. So I think some feelings of loss are appropriate.

Doran says: I don't see why the fetus should be regarded *by her* as the loss of something of value. She can, or course, see it as the loss of something that *others* value. But since she doesn't want a child (at least at this time), why should *she* see the miscarriage as the loss of something of value?

Patrick says: That's a good question. Let me give an example that may help to illustrate and support my view. Consider, for instance, mountain-climbing. Personally, I'm not at all interested in climbing mountains, but at the same time I can recognize that this is a valuable pursuit—perhaps one kind of pursuit that is constitutive of living a good life, and therefore non-instrumentally valuable. The point I want to make is that even if I don't value mountain-climbing, I can still see it as a worthwhile activity. Similarly, then, what I want to say about the example of the woman you gave is that even if she doesn't value the child she was carrying, she should still recognize that her fetus has value, and that a miscarriage therefore involves the loss of something of value.

Doran says: I have no problems with your analogy *per se;* I just don't seem to share your intuitions on this point. If I don't value mountain-climbing, but others do, then I can agree that mountain-climbing is an activity that has value for others, but it would not have value for me. Likewise, if a woman who does not want a child becomes pregnant, I think she can properly say that the fetus does not have value for her, though a fetus would have value for another woman who wanted a child. And just as I think there is nothing inappropriate in my not feeling regret if I take some step to prevent myself from going mountain-climbing (say I go to the movies instead), I don't see anything inappropriate in a pregnant woman's not feeling regret if she does not want a child and she miscarries.

Patrick says: These are good points, Doran. You point out that if a woman who does not want a child becomes pregnant, the fetus she is carrying may not have value *for her.* I've been suggesting that the fetus has a kind non-instrumental value. I don't see these points as obviously incompatible. It seems one could recognize something as having non-instrumental value, even if that thing does not have value *for her.* Mountain-climbing, for instance, does not have value *for me,* but I still see it as a worthwhile activity. This discussion raises complex questions about the nature of value that we cannot hope to answer right now. Here, I've just tried to sketch the basic outline of the kind of argument that, I believe, can support the claim that fetuses have a kind of non-instrumental value. I realize, however, that my argument likely needs further refinement.

UP FOR DISCUSSION

Do you think fetuses have non-instrumental value? Why or why not?

Doran says: Fair enough. Let's suppose your argument is sound, and fetuses have value even if unwanted by the pregnant woman. I wonder, then, what does this view about the value of the fetus imply for the moral permissibility of abortion?

PATRICK'S VIRTUE-BASED ARGUMENT FOR WHY DEB ACTED PERMISSIBLY
Patrick's View That Abortion May Be Permissible Even If the Fetus Has Value

Patrick says: Whether an abortion is permissible or not, on my view, depends on more than just whether the fetus has value. That is one relevant factor, but not the only one. From my virtue ethics perspective, questions of right and wrong are settled by considering how the virtuous person would see things.[11] And this question directs us to consider whether a woman is acting virtuously or not in having an abortion. Since I think that the fetus is properly regarded as having some value, and that this value normally increases as the fetus develops and as the parents' emotional bonds with the fetus strengthen, then later-term abortions done for trivial reasons will usually be wrong. When abortion is done to protect and promote other worthwhile projects in one's life, then abortion may be permissible. I don't accept any general rules about when abortion is or is not permissible, however. Each case has to be decided on its own merits. In Deb's case, the particular case under discussion, I believe, somewhat tentatively, that abortion is permissible.

Doran says: Okay, although I don't agree with you about the value of the fetus, I understand why you want to say that abortion can be wrong, even if the fetus does not have rights. It can be wrong, on

---

[11] Readers interested in the application of virtue theory to the question of abortion should see Rosalind Hursthouse's "Virtue Theory and Abortion," *Philosophy & Public Affairs* 20, no. 3 (1991): 223–46. Patrick's argument owes much to Hursthouse's discussion of this issue.

your view, because the fetus has value, and a person should not destroy a thing of value for trivial reasons. I also assume, given your view that Deb acts permissibly when she obtains an abortion, that you believe the fetus does not have a right to life in virtue of this potential. Is that right?

Patrick's View That Abortion May Be Permissible Even If the Fetus Has a Right to Life

Patrick says: Well, it is true that I doubt that a fetus has a right to life. But I actually think that abortion can still be justified in many cases, including Deb's, even if the fetus does have a right to life. So I'd like to grant, just for the sake of argument, that the fetus has a right to life (or, in Marquis's case, I'd like to grant that a central reason why it is wrong to kill persons applies equally to fetuses). And I will try to show that even if this is true, it would still be morally permissible for Deb to have an abortion. I must admit, though, that my conclusions are rather tentative.

Doran says: That's a very bold strategy. It would be very powerful if you could show that it is not morally wrong for Deb to have an abortion even if conservatives are given their claim that the fetus has a right to life. Let's hear your argument.

Patrick says: Okay. One way of putting my argument is like this:

(1) It would be wrong for Deb to have an abortion in this situation if and only if virtuous persons would see Deb's having an abortion as wrong.
(2) Virtuous persons would not see Deb's having an abortion in this situation as wrong.
(3) Hence, it is not wrong for Deb to have an abortion in this situation.

Doran says: Can you offer some explanation and support for your premises?

Patrick says: Sure. The first premise follows from my view that an act is morally wrong (or prohibited) if and only if virtuous persons would perceive the action as morally wrong (or prohibited). Put briefly and roughly, perceiving an action as wrong is a matter of seeing the action as vicious (that is, as exhibiting vices), all things considered. So the idea is that Deb's having an abortion is wrong if and only if virtuous persons would see her action as vicious, all things considered.[12]

---

[12] See Chapter 3 for the details of Patrick's virtue theory.

Warren says: How about the second premise? Why do you think virtuous persons would not see Deb as acting viciously in this situation?

Patrick says: The difficulty of answering this question is what makes my position on this case somewhat tentative. We need to consider what virtues and vices Deb would be manifesting if she had an abortion in this situation. All things considered, she does not seem to be acting viciously; rather, I believe she is acting virtuously. Deb's reasons for having an abortion do not reveal her to be selfish, shallow, greedy, callous, and so on. Rather, her aborting in this situation arguably shows a reasonable concern to preserve and protect very important and worthwhile goods in her and Derek's life. If she has the child, it will likely destroy their marriage and the business they've built together. In short, the life she and Derek have worked hard to build would likely be ruined. Moreover, there's a near certainty that the child Deb is carrying will be mentally handicapped and some chance that this child will lead a very difficult life. Having an abortion in this situation therefore seems consistent with acting in accordance with many virtues including, for instance, love, friendship, prudence, industriousness, loyalty, and other virtues. I do recognize, however, that there is room to argue that having an abortion would exhibit certain vices. I've assumed, for instance, that the fetus has a right to life, so there's room to argue that having an abortion is seriously unjust. But, all things considered, I believe we have good reason for thinking that Deb is acting virtuously.

> **UP FOR**
> **DISCUSSION**
>
> Do you agree with Patrick's assessment of this case that Deb's having an abortion is virtuous, all things considered?

Deb's Alleged Lack of Integrity

Doran says: Given our different ethical perspectives, Warren and I would of course challenge your first premise. But let's set that issue aside and focus on the second premise. You claim Deb's act manifests the virtues of love, friendship, prudence, industriousness, loyalty, kindness, etc. This suggests her act is virtuous. But on the negative side, some people may quite reasonably say, as you noted, that her act is unjust, since it violates the fetus's right to life. Moreover, some may say her act manifests a number of other vices, including the vices of servility and lack of integrity. For she gives in to her husband's pressures and agrees to an abortion, even though she says that she loves the baby and wants to give birth to her. It surely seems that a reasonable person could conclude that Deb's decision to have the abortion in this case was not virtuous.

Patrick says: Well, since this is a hard case, it is a case about which reasonable people might disagree. But I think that, on careful consideration, Deb's abortion is not unjust. Let's set that issue aside for the moment, though, and focus on the question whether she exhibits a lack of integrity and independence. I do not believe she does. For notice that Deb is not acting contrary to any fundamental beliefs or principles she holds. It appears that she'd like to keep the child, but she also attaches significant value to her marriage and the business she and Derek have built. In the end, she judges that her marriage and business are more important to her than bringing this fetus to term, so she decides that having an abortion is the best thing to do in the situation. I don't see how that shows a lack of integrity or independence. She is acting prudently, lovingly, and responsibly.

> **UP FOR DISCUSSION**
>
> Do you think Deb's having an abortion in this situation demonstrates a lack of integrity? Do you think Derek is lacking in virtue? Give your reasons for your views.

Doran says: Perhaps you are right that Deb need not be viewed as lacking integrity, independence, or resolve, but there are other more serious objections that your argument faces.

The Right to Life Weighed against Deb's Virtues

Warren says: You have assumed, for the sake of argument, that the fetus has a right to life. But it is hard to see how Deb's reasons are sufficiently weighty to justify the killing of an individual with a right to life. Surely, in a case of conflict between saving one's lifestyle, business, and marriage, versus killing someone with a right to life, a virtuous person must choose to respect and protect the right to life. Deb's reasons are certainly not frivolous, but are they sufficient to permit killing an innocent human being? Surely that is not a way to act lovingly, as you put it earlier.

Doran says: I am with you on this one, Warren.

Patrick says: I believe the reasons are sufficient in this case. But it's important to note that I'm not endorsing a general rule that says it's morally okay to kill innocent individuals or humans to protect important goods in one's life. And I'm certainly not suggesting it is always okay to abort in order to save one's lifestyle. Among other things, we need to consider whether one's lifestyle is worth preserving. For instance, suppose that Deb became pregnant from a drunken one-night stand, and wanted to have an abortion, not to save her marriage and business, but to protect her "party hard" lifestyle. In this sort of situation, it might

UP FOR DISCUSSION

Do you think it would be morally wrong for a woman to have an abortion to preserve her "party hard" lifestyle? Why or why not?

well be vicious to have an abortion, since protecting a partying lifestyle is not in general a good enough reason to justify abortion. (However, that fact that "Partying Deb" may be an unfit mother perhaps provides a reason in support of abortion in this case.) But Deb's actual situation is very different from the one just imagined. She is having an abortion to save fundamental, worthwhile projects and relationships that are constitutive of living well.

Doran says: Are you saying it would be wrong for "Partying Deb" to have an abortion if the fetus has a right to life, because she lacks sufficiently strong reasons, but it would not be wrong for the Deb in our drama to have an abortion, even if the fetus has a right to life, for she has sufficiently strong reasons?

Patrick says: Yes, that's what I am saying.

Doran says: I suppose I can agree with you about "Partying Deb" *if* the fetus has a right to life. But what I don't see is why Deb has sufficiently strong reasons to abort, given your assumption that the fetus has a right to life.

Warren says: I agree. There is something odd about having prudential concerns outweigh moral ones. If we are assuming the fetus has a right to life, then it should not be deliberately killed without a strong moral justification. But concerns over Deb's continuing with her lifestyle, her business, and even her marriage, seem like concerns with her personal happiness, as opposed to moral justifications for killing.

Thomson and the Case of the Famous Violinist

Patrick says: To that I would say, first, that prudential concerns, that is, concerns about one's happiness and well-being, are moral concerns. Second, I would deny that the right to life always has the force that you two suggest. My denial of this premise rests on two main points, both of which purport to show that it does not follow from the fact that an innocent being has a right to life that it is always wrong to kill that being.

The first point is illustrated nicely by Judith Jarvis Thomson's renowned fanciful example of the famous violinist.[13] You are

---

[13] Judith Jarvis Thomson, "A Defense of Abortion," *Philosophy & Public Affairs* 1, no. 1 (1971): 47–66.

captured by a fanatic group that arranges to have you surgically attached to a famous, unconscious violinist, an innocent person whose life can only be saved by this form of attachment to you. You must stay attached for nine months until the violinist is able to function on his own, or the violinist will die. Thomson argues that you would have a right to detach yourself. The important point, for present purposes, is that the example shows, I believe, that even if the fetus has a right to life, it doesn't follow that abortion is always wrong, for the mother has a right to control her body.

Warren says: I'm not sure Thomson is of much help here insofar as you're trying to show that Deb's abortion is not wrong. Assuming Thomson's violinist analogy has merit, it shows only that abortion is permissible in cases of rape.

Doran says: I agree with Warren. Thomson uses the violinist analogy to argue that in cases of rape a woman has not given the fetus a right to use her body, so she may refuse to sustain its life without violating its right to life. Once you grant that the fetus has a right to life, I think it will be very difficult to avoid the conclusion that Deb's abortion is wrong. For, if we're to take the right to life seriously, we have to say that it is very wrong to kill beings who have this right, except in extremely rare circumstances. Thomson's examples involve such special circumstances—for example, rape and, elsewhere, self-defence and failed contraception—but Deb's situation is different.

Patrick says: I agree that Deb's case is different from Thomson's examples, and that Thomson's arguments do not show that Deb's abortion is permissible. What they do show, however, is that the right to life is not an absolute right not to be killed. In some cases, as Thomson argues, the fetus's right to life does not entail a right to use the mother's body. When the woman aborts the fetus, in such cases, she is not violating its rights, so killing the fetus is not unjust.

Doran says: So you're just using Thomson's examples to establish exceptions to a general rule?

Patrick says: Yes, that's right. My view is that it is, of course, normally seriously wrong to kill beings who have a right to life. But there are

TECHNIQUE

Health care professionals may wonder why anyone takes this science fiction example seriously. The point is not that this is an example of something currently medically possible or likely to happen at any time in the future. The example, instead, helps us to see that if people other than pregnant women had some human being physically dependent upon them, they might view their rights rather differently than many tend, traditionally, to view the rights of pregnant women. The example is designed to put the shoe on the other foot and shake some people out of complacent acceptance of moral tradition.

exceptions to this rule. In some cases, exercising a right to control one's body can justify killing innocent persons. In other cases, I believe, virtue may require—or at least permit—killing an innocent person or other being with a right to life. That is what I think justifies abortion in Deb's case. Aborting the fetus manifests a number of virtues that contribute to Deb's (and Derek's) well-being.

This leads me to my second point. I don't think the permissibility of Deb's abortion, and the question of abortion more generally, can be settled simply by looking at the rights possessed by the relevant parties. In addition to looking at rights and questions of justice, we need to consider other virtues and vices that are relevant in cases of abortion.

UP FOR DISCUSSION

Can you imagine a situation in which acting virtuously requires us to violate others' rights? Explain your answer.

Doran says: I agree that sometimes rights can be overridden by other considerations—a right to have a debt repaid, for instance, can be overridden in cases of extreme necessity. So a virtuous person might not repay a loan if she needs that money to buy medicine for her ailing child. But the right to life protects a much more important interest than does the right to be repaid a debt, and so it is going to take a much greater reason to override it. Self-defence, or defence of another, may be sufficient to override such a right, but I don't think the kinds of reasons that Deb has are sufficiently strong to justify killing the fetus, if we assume it has a significant right to life.

Patrick says: A couple of points in reply. First, although I've granted, for the sake of argument, that the fetus has a right to life, I confess to being a little unclear as to what exactly I've granted. That is, it's not entirely clear how we should understand the notion of a right to life. I suppose that to say that an individual has a right to life is to say, roughly, that the individual has a valid claim not to be killed.[14] But even if everyone has an equal right to life, it doesn't follow that everyone has an equal claim to life. This is because the strength of one's claim to life depends on more than just the right to life.

Warren says: I think I see the point you're trying to make, Patrick. Maybe this simple formulation will help. We can suppose that a right to life contributes considerable weight to one's claim to life. There are other factors, however, that can add to or subtract from this weight, thereby making one's claim stronger or weaker.

---

[14] Joel Feinberg, *Social Philosophy* (Englewood Cliffs, NJ: Prentice Hall, 1973), 64–67.

Patrick says: Yes, that's the basic idea. For instance, a 5-year-old, who has not yet lived a full life, has a greater claim to life than a 95-year-old who has lived a long and rewarding life. So age is one of the things that can affect one's claim to life. It doesn't much matter, however, whether you agree with these examples. The point is that even if we grant that everyone has an equal right to life, it doesn't follow that everyone has an equally strong claim against being killed. If we were to work through various examples, I think most of us would agree with this point.

Second, notice that I am not arguing that the fetus's right to life is violated (or overridden) in this case. What I'm arguing, rather, is that the fetus's right to life is not violated, since the *fetus's* right does not entail a claim against being killed that requires Deb to abandon very important and worthwhile relationships and projects in her life.

Perhaps conservatives will say I've given up the assumption that the fetus has a right to life. But that's not what I'm doing. I'm assuming that the fetus has a right to life, and so it has a legitimate claim not to be killed. What I'm suggesting, though, is that this claim can be made stronger or weaker, depending on various facts about the individual, her relations to others, and other particulars of her situation. The strength of one's claim to life must therefore be determined on a case-by-case basis.

Doran says: Your argument is very interesting, Patrick. And perhaps I can agree with you that the claim against killing a person can be stronger or weaker, even if the person has a (full and equal) right to life. But it seems to me that more must be said to justify your claim that a sixteen-week-old fetus's claim to life is not sufficiently strong to require the kinds of sacrifices Deb would have to make in order to keep the child. Why does the fetus's right to life create such a *weak* claim against being killed? We do not ordinarily think that considerations like the sincere desire to preserve one's marriage and one's business are sufficiently strong reasons to justify killing someone with a right to life. So why think that "the *fetus's* right to life does not entail a right that requires Deb to abandon very important and worthwhile relationships and projects in her life"? Are there any analogies or other sorts of considerations that you can give to defend your claim?

Patrick says: Well, as I've suggested, I believe the claim against being killed can be weaker or stronger, depending on such things as one's biological and social development, one's relationships, and so on. For instance, I would not likely be justified in killing *you* to protect important goods in my life. But your circumstances, and my relationship to you, are very different from the fetus's circumstances and Deb's relationship to it. You are a rational, self-conscious, autonomous being. You are a husband, parent, friend, colleague, and so on. So you have significant meaningful relationships with others. You are a philosopher with important work-related projects. You have a conception of what a good life is and you are trying to live that life. Given all these facts, protecting important goods in my life is pretty clearly not a good enough reason for killing you.

Doran says: Good!

Patrick says: But now compare this with the fetus. Deb's fetus is just sixteen weeks old. It is not a rational, self-conscious, autonomous being. It has no meaningful projects, relationships, etc., that it is aware of, no concept of the kind of life it wants to live, and so on. The fetus has relatively little to lose if it dies—though, as I've said, the death of the fetus is still the loss of something of value. And given that I've assumed that the fetus has a right to life, Deb's abortion would involve the loss of a being with such a right. So I do think that Deb's abortion should not be taken lightly, and that some grief and sorrow over the loss of the fetus's life is called for. Still, even if the fetus, like you and me, has a right to life, it seems that its claim not to be killed is considerably weaker than the claim against killing you or me.

Doran says: All right, I think I have a better grasp of your argument now. Your argument turns on the premise that even if it is granted that the fetus has a right to life—a valid claim not to be killed—it cannot plausibly be thought to have a claim not to be killed that is as strong as the claim possessed by the typical person. Given this, it is reasonable to think, at least in some situations, that its claim against being killed does not entail that people forgo important and worthwhile goods in life when there is a conflict between those goods and the life of the fetus. However, I suppose this argument would entail that if the fetus has a valid claim not to be killed, and/or if the fetus is (as you claim) valuable, then abortions will sometimes be morally wrong.

Patrick says: Yes, certainly. I'm not at all suggesting that abortion is always permissible. If Deb wanted to have an abortion, not to protect her business and marriage, but rather to protect holiday plans that she and Derek had made, then I would say that her abortion is seriously wrong. Of if Deb had wanted a late-term abortion to save her marriage and business, then abortion would likely be wrong. The permissibility of an abortion, on my view, must be decided on a case-by-case basis.

Doran says: Still, if we grant that the fetus has a full right to life, I do not see how it can be okay to kill it, given Deb's circumstances. I believe a full right to life would trump considerations like preserving one's business and marriage.

Patrick says: I believe I've made a reasonable case that it would be morally permissible for Deb to have an abortion. As I said before, Deb's decision seems consistent with acting virtuously, all things considered. Her pregnancy is not the result of irresponsible, thoughtless, or reckless behaviour. And her reasons for having an abortion do not reveal her to be selfish, shallow, greedy, callous, and so on. Rather, her aborting in this situation arguably shows a reasonable concern to preserve and protect very important and worthwhile goods in her and Derek's life. As I said, my conclusions in this case are somewhat tentative. And this is a hard case, so there's room for reasonable people to disagree.

UP FOR DISCUSSION

What do you think? Is it permissible for Deb to obtain an abortion in her circumstances, if we assume the fetus has a full and equal right to life?

Warren says: It is clear, though, you have not convinced Doran. So, I am curious: Why do you think nonetheless, Doran, that Deb's decision to abort is morally permissible?

DORAN'S ARGUMENT THAT DEB'S DECISION TO ABORT WAS MORALLY PERMISSIBLE

Doran says: You are right, Warren. I am not persuaded by Patrick's argument, though I agree with his conclusion that Deb acted permissibly. My argument for thinking she may permissibly obtain an abortion is the following:

(1) A fetus does not have a significant right to life at sixteen weeks' gestation.

(2) A woman has a moral right to control what happens in and to her body, provided she does not violate anyone else's (significant) rights.

(3) In Deb's case, her decision would not violate anyone else's (significant) rights.

(4) Therefore, Deb has a moral right to obtain an abortion.

Warren says: Well, clearly premise (1) would not be accepted by everyone. What reason can you give in support of this premise?

Patrick says: We need clarification of the notion of strength of rights as well.

Doran says: I believe the reason why a sixteen-week fetus does not have a significant right to life can most helpfully be explained if we ask a more general question: "In general, what gives something a right to life?" If we can answer this question, then we can apply it to fetuses and determine whether or not they have a right to life. In thinking about what gives something a right to life, we will eventually see the need to consider the question of whether or not rights to life can vary in their strength.[15]

The Rationality Criterion for a Right to Life

Doran says: Let's consider some obvious candidates for the basis of a right to life. One view says that one gets a right to life in virtue of being rational.[16] What is meant by "rational" varies, but the key idea is that you have the abilities to consciously set goals for yourself, and to come up with a particular life plan, that you are self-aware, have reasonably sophisticated problem-solving abilities and communication skills, etc. Of course, a normal adult human being is a paradigmatic example of a rational being, and so a normal adult human being would, on this view, be a paradigmatic example of someone who has a right to life.

Patrick says: It seems right that being rational is *sufficient* for a right to life, but some may wonder if it is *necessary*. For if rationality were necessary for a right to life, many humans would not have a right to life.

---

[15] The arguments advanced by Doran on the morality of abortion are closely based on L. Wayne Sumner, "A Third Way," in *The Problem of Abortion*, 2nd ed., ed. Joel Feinberg (Belmont, CA: Wadsworth Publishing, 1984), 71–93.

[16] Many ethical theories see a necessary connection between the possession of moral rights and being rational. For example, Kant argues that all and only rational beings have dignity and are proper objects of moral respect, while social contract theorists see morality as a kind of agreement that holds between rational agents. When it comes to the abortion issue, Mary Anne Warren appears to endorse the view that full moral rights require the possession of rationality. See her "On the Moral and Legal Status of Abortion," reprinted in *Biomedical Ethics*, 4th ed., ed. Thomas A. Mappes and David DeGrazia (New York: McGraw-Hill, 1996), 434–40.

Warren says: Indeed, not only fetuses, but human infants and the severely cognitively impaired would, on the proposed criterion, lack a right to life.

Doran says: Agreed. A rationality criterion would also presumably exclude non-human animals, yet many believe that we have a duty not to kill them, unless there is sufficient justification. Although there is much more to be said by those who support rationality as necessary for a right to life, I think we ultimately have to conclude that the proposed criterion is too restrictive.

So, let's consider an alternative criterion. Some have suggested that a right to life should be given to all who are alive. If you are alive, you have a fundamental interest in living, and the right to life protects that fundamental interest.[17]

The Life Criterion

Patrick says: The claim that all living things have a right to life is very counterintuitive. Bacteria are alive, but we do not think we are violating their rights when we take an antibiotic. Similarly, weeding a garden does not seem to be morally problematic, yet it would be, on this view, since weeds are alive and they're being killed.

Doran says: I completely agree. Being alive is much too broad a criterion for a right to life. Moreover, I think we can *explain* why such a criterion is too broad. Rights protect interests—I agree with that—but to have an interest in the relevant sense requires that one be able to take an interest, or to have a point of view that one values or can value. Merely living things, however, like bacteria and weeds, do not have these kinds of interests, and so cannot be said to have rights.

Warren says: Well, I am not sure that I agree with you on your analysis of interests and a right to life.

Patrick says: Right, many would question this analysis. There's a clear sense in which plants, for example, have interests—it is in their interests to receive adequate sunlight, nutrition, protection from the elements, and so on. But your point, I take it, is that plants do not have interests *in the relevant sense,*

> **TECHNIQUE**
>
> Notice that the rationality criterion and the life criterion of moral rights are rejected by using counterexamples. Further, notice that an explanation is also provided for why these principles err. Whenever possible, one should go beyond the mere appeal to a counterexample to reject a moral principle, and one should try to provide an explanation for why the principle in question is false. For, ideally, one wants to discover not just that a particular principle is false, but also why it is mistaken.

[17] Paul Taylor, "The Ethics of Respect for Nature," *Environmental Ethics* 3, no. 3 (1981): 197–218.

since they are not conscious, and so do not have a point of view from which it matters to them how their lives are going.

Doran says: Yes, that's right.

Warren says: This is an interesting issue, but let's leave it aside for now, and instead, let's hear what Doran thinks is the appropriate criterion of a right to life.

The Sentience Criterion

Doran says: I believe that a necessary and sufficient condition for one to have a right to life is that one be sentient. By sentient, I mean that one is a conscious creature, capable of feeling pleasure and pain, and so who can meaningfully be said to be benefited or harmed. If a being can feel, then it has interests that ought to be respected. And the reason these interests should be respected is because it makes a difference directly to those sentient individuals.

Warren says: It makes a difference directly to non-sentient beings when they are harmed as well. Both sentient and non-sentient beings may be unaware of the difference it makes.

Doran says: Of course, in a sense, it makes a difference to a non-sentient being if it is harmed. If a weed is poisoned, its life span will be shortened, just as if a dog's throat is slit, its life span will be shortened. But surely there is a clear and important difference between these two sorts of cases. The clearest difference between them is that the one can suffer and enjoy, while the other can't. The *animal* cares not to be cut up in a way that a weed does not. That one is conscious has clear and important moral significance.

Patrick says: I agree, Doran, that being sentient is morally significant for the reasons just mentioned. But I have doubts about sentience as a criterion for a right to life. Why do you think your view is more plausible than the other criteria for a right to life that we've considered and rejected?

Doran says: My sentience-based view does not imply that taking antibiotics or weeding one's garden are morally objectionable, since we can assume that bacteria and weeds are not sentient. And it does imply that mentally challenged humans and newborn human infants have a right to life, since they are sentient.

Further, I believe that a sentience-based view ties in with a plausible conception of the proper role of morality—morality ought to be concerned with enhancing well-being or happiness, and with protecting the vulnerable from suffering or injuries to their well-being. A sentience criterion of rights tells us that all and only beings that can suffer and or enjoy have a well-being, and that sentient beings are therefore to be protected from unwarranted harms. The newborn infant, for instance, can suffer and/or enjoy—it therefore has interests or a well-being that ought to be protected by morality.

Warren says: Well, what about fetuses, then? As fetuses mature, they too become sentient. So wouldn't that mean they'd also have a right to life, according to your view? In Deb's case, she had her abortion sometime after sixteen weeks—at a time when the fetus may well have been sentient. On your view, then, her fetus may well have had a right to life, so shouldn't your view be that her abortion was (probably) immoral?

Patrick says: Another question, probably related to Warren's, is this: Do all sentient creatures have an equal right to life?

Doran says: Good questions! To answer them, I need to fill in some more details of my view.

The Addition of Rationality to Sentience

Doran says: Although I think sentience is necessary and sufficient for a right to life, I believe that it is reasonable to think that the magnitude of the right to life varies according to the level of sentience. In general, we think that adult human beings have a full right to life, since they are what we may call fully sentient, in virtue of their rationality. Not only do they have various interests in not suffering and in having their instinctive drives satisfied, they also are capable of valuing their own lives, and they are equipped with the ability to form preferences, including the preference not to be killed. Further, rational beings can imagine their future and consider various possibilities that non-rational beings cannot. This, in turn, expands the number of things they can dread, and desire.

Also, rational beings can be greatly affected by the success and failures of their loved ones, they can take pleasure in their children's accomplishments, worry about their parents' health, be concerned about the fate of their planet, and wonder about what will happen after their death. These, plus whatever is directly happening to them, are all things that they can take pleasure or pain in. All of this adds to a rational being's level of sentience, to the dimensions by which such a life can go better or worse, and helps explain why we believe it is especially awful (normally speaking) to kill a rational being. These facts make it reasonable to think that normal adult humans are much more aware than non-rational beings, and this helps explain why they have particularly strong rights to life.

Warren says: None of the increases in sentience which you mention, Doran, require rationality. They require instead the ability to imagine one's future. Whether one does this in rational or irrational ways, one can have greatly increased sentience. The pains and pleasures of anticipation are among the most keen.

Patrick says: Good point, Warren. It seems that irrationality, and various kinds of serious psychological disorders, can enhance sentience. Think about a psychotic individual suffering from delusions.

Doran says: You guys are probably right. There are various ways one can become fully sentient—a robust (though irrational) imagination may be one way. Another way to become fully sentient is by having the psychological capacities of a typical adult human being—capacities that include rationality, imagination, empathy, etc.

It must be admitted, though, that most other mammals are sentient, though not as fully sentient as typical humans. They lack many, if not all, the abilities I just mentioned. This means they have a significant, but not a full, right to life. Again, this matches what most of us believe on reflection: namely, that killing a non-human animal is not something to be taken lightly. It requires a justification, though this justification is more easily met than the justification required for killing a being with a full right to life.

Patrick says: Okay, so I see now why you hold that sentient creatures have a right to life, and why this right can be stronger or weaker. Returning now to Warren's earlier question, what does your view imply about the rights of the fetus?

Doran says: Embryos and early fetuses are clearly not sentient, though later fetuses probably are sentient. I believe this to be the case primarily because I think that sentience (in human beings) requires a certain neurological base—one that is absent in the first parts of pregnancy, gradually emerges later in pregnancy, and is more developed by birth. Because sentience emerges gradually sometime in the middle months of pregnancy, fetuses begin to acquire a right to life at that time; however, because they are never fully sentient, the magnitude of that right to life remains only partial.

Patrick says: So what does your view imply about the permissibility of abortion?

Doran says: What this means for the morality of abortion is that early abortions do not involve the destruction of a being with a right to life. A pregnant woman is completely within her rights to have an abortion, during this period, for any reason. As the fetus develops and begins to be able to feel pleasure and pain, then it acquires a right to life that deserves to be respected. Nevertheless, this right is not of full magnitude, and thus can be more easily overridden in cases of conflict. Thus, if a woman's life or health is in danger, or if continuing with the pregnancy would otherwise set back her important interests to a significant degree, then it would be within her rights to obtain an abortion. Finally, as the fetus matures and becomes more developed psychologically, it earns a more robust right to life, one that will be increasingly difficult to override.

Warren says: What about Deb's case in particular?

Doran says: Turning to Deb's case, she is carrying a fetus that is perhaps sentient, though minimally so. The right to life of Deb's fetus, then, would be minimal—if it exists at all—at sixteen weeks. As the fetus's level of sentience develops, the strength of its right to life increases. She therefore acts permissibly when deciding to opt for an abortion at sixteen weeks, for she has sufficient reason to override the nascent right of her developing fetus.

Patrick says: Interesting. But I'm not sure I agree with your claim that in the early stages (prior to sentience) a pregnant woman may have an abortion for *any* reason. This seems too liberal a view to me. Even if the fetus is not sentient, it is a developing human being with the potential to become a sentient, rational being. Aborting such a being for trivial reasons would seem to be rather shallow and callous to me. In such cases, it might be wrong.

UP FOR DISCUSSION

Do you think that it is morally permissible for a woman to obtain an early abortion for any reason? Why or why not?

Objections to Doran's Sentience-Based Criterion of a Right to Life

Is Sentience Sufficient for a Right to Life?

Patrick says: I see how being sentient gives an individual an interest in seeking pleasure and avoiding pain. But how does sentience give one a right to life? Some sentient beings are not self-aware, and have no concept of themselves as beings with a past and a future. It is plausible to suppose that such beings have a right not to suffer unnecessarily, but it's not clear why we should think these (minimally) sentient beings have a right to life.

Doran says: Good question. I don't think that self-awareness and having a concept of oneself with a past and a future are necessary for a right to life, since I think newborn infants have a right to life, even though they probably lack these characteristics. As a thought experiment, consider a newborn infant that has some medical condition that will painlessly kill her in four months' time. Until the time of her death, the infant is expected to be happy and comfortable. It seems clear to me that such an infant has not only a right not to suffer, but also a right not to be killed. And a sentience criterion explains why. Though this baby will never be rational, and though it is doubtful that she is self-aware, she can still feel pleasure and pain, and so she has "a well-being." To kill her would go against her well-being, and so is *prima facie* wrong to do.

Patrick says: You earlier rejected the life criterion for a right to life on the ground that beings who are alive, but not sentient, can't *care* about whether their interests are being satisfied. Now, minimally sentient creatures do care about whether they suffer, so again I see why you would think they have a right not to suffer. But since minimally sentient beings don't conceive of themselves as distinct living beings with a past and future, it seems they can't care whether they live or die. So merely being sentient does not seem sufficient to me to get a right to life.

Doran says: You raise a challenging objection, Patrick. I suppose my answer is that there is a distinction between what is necessary for a being to have interests, and so rights, and what determines the particular interests (or rights) of a being that is a rights holder. I argued that in order to have interests (and so rights) at all, it is necessary for a being to be able to be benefited or harmed in a way that matters to it (and this will require that the being be sentient or aware). However, the determination of the particular interests of an individual is a separate matter. It is in my dogs' interests not to run in front of a passing truck, but they may not know it is in their interests. Likewise, it may be in an infant's interest not to be painlessly killed, though the infant won't know that.

Is Sentience Necessary for a Right to Life?

Warren says: While Patrick has questioned whether sentience is sufficient for a right to life, others will question whether sentience is necessary. A person in a temporary coma is not sentient, but such a person surely has a right to life.

Doran says: You raise a tricky issue. For obviously I think that a person in a temporary coma still has a right to life, even if this person lacks awareness. My response to this objection is to say that a person who falls into a temporary coma is still a sentient being, and thus still has interests that warrant protection, even if this person cannot access this capacity while in a coma. If I fall into a temporary coma (or otherwise become temporarily unconscious) later this evening, for instance, it seems clear that I will still have interests. It would still make sense to say, Doran has an interest and a right not to be killed because Doran values spending time with family, enjoys thinking about philosophy, and, if he is going to make a reasonable recovery, he prefers not to be killed. Thus, I think I can say that the coma objection does not work as a counterexample to my claim that sentience is necessary for having a right to life; for I believe that a sentient being who falls into a temporary state of unconsciousness retains his or her identity as a sentient being.

UP FOR DISCUSSION

If Doran argues that a person who falls into a temporary coma is still a sentient being, can he consistently say that a pre-conscious fetus is not a sentient being? Why or why not?

Warren says: Note the difference if the coma is permanent. Does this not show that what is really functioning here is the potential of a being to have a certain kind of future?

Doran says: Well, my views on the rights of the permanently comatose are complicated, and we lack the space to go into that here. So let me just address your question about potential. I do not think potential for further psychological development is what gives a sentient being a right to life. For I believe that many sentient beings clearly have significant rights to life, even if they are not fully sentient, and even if they do not have the potential to become fully sentient. Consider the case of the terminally ill infant discussed previously, or the case of a significantly mentally challenged human being. I would say they have significant rights to life, even if they lack the potential for significant psychological development.

The Objection That More Rational Individuals Will Have Stronger Rights to Life Than Less Rational Individuals

Warren says: According to your view, a right to life becomes weaker as rationality declines. Wouldn't that have the unacceptable implication that humans who were more rational would have greater rights to life than those who were less rational?

Patrick says: Right. So a brilliant scientist would have a greater right to life than the average soccer mom or dad?

Doran says: No, this objection is based on a misunderstanding of my view. I am not saying that the more rational one is, the greater one's right to life. Rather, I think that a right to life is a threshold concept. This means that once one has the ability to form preferences about continued existence, and once one is self-aware, one meets the threshold for having a full and equal right to life. This is because, once one has these characteristics, one is a person, with a sense of who one is. This is equally the case even if one person is less rational, or self-aware, or imaginative than some other person. Thus, it is not an implication of my view that the average person has a weaker right to life than the brilliant scientist, even if the average person is less rational than the brilliant scientist.

What does follow from my view, however, is that a sentient individual who is not fully sentient has a weaker right to life than a fully sentient being. Killing a normal adult human being is normally worse than killing a normal dog or cat, in part, because the former has a stronger right to life than the latter. And killing a normal dog or cat is normally worse than killing a fish or a chicken, again, in part, because the former has a stronger right to life than the latter. This appears to accord quite well with most people's moral common sense.

UP FOR DISCUSSION

Does Doran's view imply that an adult chimpanzee has more of a right to life than a newborn infant? If so, how strong an objection would that be to his view?

Patrick says: That seems right. But I think your view runs afoul of common sense when we consider the rights of infants and non-human animals.

Warren says: I agree. Doran's view also runs into problems when we consider the rights of severely mentally disabled humans.

Doran says: Okay, let me take these objections in turn, beginning with Warren's case.

The Objection That Rational Individuals Will Have Stronger Rights to Life Than Will Non-rational Individuals

Warren says: Isn't one of the conservatives' objections to the view that rights depend on degrees of sentience that it does not accord a full right to life to all humans? Specifically, severely mentally challenged humans would have a weaker right to life than you or I. This sounds like an objectionable form of *ableism*.

Doran says: Yes, you have identified a principal objection to my view. My reply may not be fully satisfactory, but here goes. First, it is important to note that most mentally challenged humans are sufficiently sentient to have a full right to life. Most mentally challenged humans are capable of significant levels of understanding, have developed linguistic skills, are capable of participating in loving relationships, and so forth. Now, depending where the threshold for full rights to life is set, it can reasonably be maintained that most cognitively impaired humans surpass this threshold and so would have full rights.

Patrick says: But there are of course humans who are so mentally impaired that they are only barely sentient.

Doran says: Yes, it is true that some humans are so badly off that they are only minimally sentient, less than many typical non-human mammals. Here, consistency requires that I accept that they do not have a full right to life.

Patrick says: But surely it can be just as wrong (and in some cases, maybe even more wrong) to kill a severely mentally disabled human than to kill another human without the mental disability.

Doran says: First of all, earlier you admitted that a plausible view must recognize that claims to life of some humans can be stronger than claims to life of other humans. Secondly, and this is very important, it is consistent with my view to claim that non-rational humans warrant great, perhaps full, moral protection. It is just that a right to life won't be the reason for this moral protection. For example, one reason to extend special moral protection to the mentally disabled is that we tend to believe that we should give special moral concern to those human beings who are especially disadvantaged through no fault of their own. Also, another reason to protect the severely mentally

UP FOR DISCUSSION

What do you think gives someone a right to life? What would your answer imply about the morality of abortion and the killing of non-human animals?

disabled from harm is that other humans tend to care a great deal about them. Thus, even if I concede that the severely mentally challenged don't have a full moral right to life, I believe that they should receive strong moral protections because of a combination of their rights and other morally important factors.

Patrick says: Okay, fair enough. And I suppose that you'd want to say something similar regarding infants. Infants are not rational, and so they are not fully sentient. So on your view they do not have a full right to life. But still, they deserve full moral protection, for the reasons you just mentioned. Is that your view?

Doran says: Yes, the remarks I just made in connection with the severely mentally disabled hold also in the case of infants. In such cases, the beings in question lack a full right to life, but they may be granted full moral protection

Warren says: I agree with your policy, but for other theoretical reasons. Using my social contract theory, I would support your view requiring strong protection of the mentally challenged by pointing to the **sympathy metarule.** If we could steel ourselves to killing the severely mentally challenged, we would not have sufficient sympathy to make us follow our rules against killing of innocents. People with ordinary human sympathies abhor such killing. Rules permitting such killing would therefore be contrary to the sympathy metarule. By the same token, I would support your approach of gradually increasing the rights of the fetus as it develops, because human sympathy for the fetus gradually increases as it gains more and more similarities of various kinds to a newborn. [18]

THEORY

The **sympathy metarule** governing choices of rules in the original position says: Choose rules that people with ordinary human sympathies could follow.

The Objection That Rational Non-humans Will Have Stronger Rights to Life Than Will Non-rational Humans

Patrick says: Though I suspect I know how you will reply, there's one last objection to your view that is worth considering. The objection is that your view implies that a mature adult chimpanzee, for instance, will have a greater right to life than an infant. This will strike many as highly counter-intuitive.

Doran says: Well, if we assume that a chimp is fully sentient, but a newborn infant is not, then, on my view, a chimp does have a greater right to life than a newborn human. And I admit that this is not likely

---

[18] English, "Abortion and the Concept of a Person."

to accord with people's intuitions, but this is not necessarily a problem with my view.

Patrick says: Why not? Most people would hold that an infant has a much stronger right to life than a chimpanzee.

Doran says: Even if the chimp has a greater right to life than the infant, there can be equally powerful (perhaps greater) reasons for not treating the human infant worse than the chimp. After all, since infants are sentient, they do have some significant rights on my view. Moreover, there are often very strong reasons against mistreating infants, based on the harmful effects this will have on other humans.

Patrick says: That seems right. But if we ignore the effect that killing has on others, then, on your view, it is morally worse to kill an adult chimpanzee than it is to kill an infant. Killing the infant is made worse than killing the chimpanzee, on your view, only by the fact that more humans will be harmed by killing the infant. But I'm not sure this is the correct explanation for why killing an infant is morally worse than killing a chimpanzee.

Doran says: I agree that on this point, my view parts company with most people's intuitions. But I am not sure that I should be too concerned about that. For, first, I think that any view of what gives someone rights is likely to run afoul of some of our intuitions, and second, I think that our moral intuitions when applied to other species are likely to be particularly biased, and hence unreliable.

I believe that the view of rights that I have defended is motivated by a plausible rationale, and that it is able to explain many of our deepest convictions about who and what has a right to life. Given this, I have more confidence in my analysis of the right to life than I do in our intuitions when it comes to the strength of the rights of newborn humans versus mature non-human primates. I repeat that on my view, it is, in itself, a morally serious matter to kill a newborn infant, for such an infant has a right to life. That my view implies that (in very isolated cases) it is an even more serious moral matter to kill a non-human of greater psychological abilities is an implication that I can live with.

> **THEORY**
>
> Note here that Doran is arguing that his views on the nature of moral rights and his moral judgments about particular cases are in **reflective equilibrium.** For more on this concept, see Chapter 1.

Reductio ad Vegetarianism?

Patrick says: Another concern many people have—though I'm not among them—is that your view, Doran, seems to imply that most of us are morally required to become vegetarians. I think the virtue ethics perspective suggests that most of us ought to be vegetarian, too. I don't see this as a problem with my view, and neither should you, I think.

Warren says: As a vegetarian, I don't consider this a powerful objection either, but meat lovers will want to know how you respond.

Doran says: Right. I think it is interesting that my rather permissive position on abortion turns out to be rather strict when it comes to the killing of non-human animals. On my view, non-human animals that are sentient have a right to life, and therefore ought not to be killed or harmed without just cause. Now, insofar as most of us do not have a compelling reason for eating meat—survival, health, etc.—and since most rearing and slaughtering of animals for food goes against the animals' most compelling interests, it follows that it is morally wrong for most of us to eat meat. There will be exceptions, of course, based on health or necessity, though I expect that for most people reading this book these exceptions will not apply, and a vegetarian diet would be morally required.

Warren says: Although I agree with this implication of your view, many will consider it a reduction of the view to absurdity. I guess you just have to bite the bullet and accept what we believe to be the right answer in spite of the views of many meat eaters.

Patrick says: I agree with you two that most of us ought to be vegetarian. But I don't base this on animals' having a right to life. I'm not sure they have any such right. But it is clear that animals have a serious interest in avoiding suffering. It's also true that most of us don't need to eat meat; we eat meat because it is convenient and we learn to enjoy its taste. The bottom line for me is that it is terribly cruel, callous, insensitive, and selfish to inflict tremendous suffering on animals simply for the fleeting pleasure one derives from eating them.

UP FOR DISCUSSION

How might Doran's and Patrick's views diverge when it comes to such questions as abortion on demand for first-trimester pregnancies? In the final analysis, do you think Deb's abortion is morally permissible? Why or why not?

Doran says: It must be admitted, though, that the question of what we owe to non-human animals would be a debate in its own right. So let's save a careful examination of this issue for another time.

SUMMARY

Here is a summary of the main questions, concepts, and arguments covered in this chapter:

- Conservative arguments against the general moral permissibility of abortion are critically examined and rejected.
- Patrick provides a virtue-based argument for the permissibility of Deb's abortion, while Doran and Warren state their objections.
- Doran considers various criteria for having a right to life and argues that Deb's abortion was permissible. Warren largely agrees with Doran's views, although for very different reasons.
- Ultimately, Patrick, Doran, and Warren agree, for different moral reasons, on allowing abortion in the first trimester but requiring ever stronger justification as the pregnancy continues. Both Doran and Warren employ rights-based arguments.
- Patrick, in contrast, objects to general rules concerning abortion and insists instead on a principle of particularity: each case must be judged on its own merits for virtue. Nonetheless, a fetus's claim to life will generally increase as it develops and as the mother and father bond with it. So Patrick agrees that late-term abortions will usually require stronger justification than early-term abortions.

Review Questions

1. Why does Noonan believe that the fetus is a human being from the moment of conception?
2. Why do Doran, Warren, and Patrick reject premise (1) in Noonan's argument?
3. What is the distinction between being a human being in the biological sense and being a person?
4. Why does Marquis believe that abortion is (typically) wrong?
5. Doran objects that Marquis's argument is unsound, because it commits the fallacy of equivocation. What is this objection?
6. Warren and Patrick argue that the fetus has value. What are their arguments?
7. What is Patrick's argument for the view that Deb's abortion is morally permissible?
8. Why do Doran and Warren object to Patrick's argument?
9. What is Doran's argument for the claim that Deb's abortion is morally permissible?
10. What, according to Doran, is required for a being to possess a full right to life?

CHAPTER 7

C-SECTION BY CHOICE

INTRODUCTION

In this chapter, we examine moral issues raised by the practice of **Caesarean section by choice (CSBC). Caesarean section, or C-section,** is the delivery of a fetus by surgical incision through the abdominal wall and uterus. While this method of delivery is commonly done for medical reasons, CSBC is C-section that is not medically indicated but rather chosen by the mother. CSBC has become popular of late among celebrities; in recent years, Madonna, Victoria Beckham, Britney Spears, and many other actors and musicians have chosen to have C-sections for non-medical reasons. The phenomenon is not just limited to stars, however, as statistics show more and more women opting for CSBC.

BACKGROUND

Legend has it that the C-section is so named because Julius Caesar was born that way.

Our drama focuses on Wendy, a woman who elects to have a C-section for a variety of non-medical reasons; these include convenience, preservation of her figure, and avoidance of pain. Wendy's doctor, Dr. Tan, refuses to provide her with a CSBC, because she believes the risks outweigh the benefits. Wendy then turns to a different physician, Dr. Tabor, who agrees to provide a CSBC. Although Dr. Tabor acknowledges that CSBC carries risks, she judges that it is very important to respect her patients' health care choices.

In the debate below, we focus on the question of whether Wendy's having a CSBC is morally permissible. The more general issue is whether it is morally permissible for any woman to have a CSBC. This debate pits the mother's right to **autonomy** against her duties to prevent harm to the baby, to herself, and to others. We also briefly consider the question whether a policy that permits CSBC is justifiable in a publicly funded system of health care. These matters are complicated by disagreement among experts about the risks and benefits of CSBC.

DEFINITION

Autonomy is used to refer generally to self-determination. Here, a right to autonomy means the right of the patient to choose her course of care without undue interference.

Doran argues that in the absence of clear and convincing evidence that CSBC poses significant harms to others, we ought to respect Wendy's autonomy. Since we are lacking such evidence, Doran therefore contends that Wendy's having a CSBC is morally permissible. Patrick and Warren agree that in general, we ought to respect individual autonomy. But they argue that even if the evidence is not conclusive, it does indicate that CSBC may involve risks of very serious harms to the child and to others, and that the duty to avoid unnecessary risks trumps Wendy's right to autonomy. The debate focuses on harms to the baby and the mother, and touches upon harms to others. Doran is not convinced that these risks are great enough to make Wendy's choice wrong. Patrick and Warren, by contrast, think that while some cases of CSBC are morally permissible, Wendy's CSBC is wrong. Patrick and Warren agree on much in this debate; however, they disagree on some of the likely harms of CSBC. In general, Warren thinks the harms of CSBC are likely to be greater and more varied than does Patrick.

LEARNING OBJECTIVES

After completing this chapter, you should be able to:

- Define *autonomy* and discuss the limits on the right to autonomy
- Explain why the ethical debate over CSBC is complicated by the fact that experts disagree about the risks and benefits of CSBC
- State Doran's autonomy-based argument for the permissibility of CSBC
- Understand Warren's good reason requirement, and what it implies for CSBC
- Outline Patrick's reasons for thinking that CSBC is wrong in Wendy's case, although not in all cases
- Explain why Doran rejects Warren's and Patrick's arguments that CSBC is wrong in Wendy's case
- Recognize how a general policy that permits CSBC may be wrong, even if Wendy's CSBC is not wrong

DRAMA

This case is based on various true stories, although names, places, and some uncontroversial elements of the case have been changed to preserve anonymity and confidentiality. Discussions of this and similar cases with health care professionals have also informed this fictional case. The drama merely raises issues. The philosophical arguments are to be found in the debate following the drama.

CHARACTERS

Wendy: *an expectant mother and fitness trainer*
Dr. Tan: *Wendy's family physician*
Dr. Tabor: *another family-practice physician Wendy visits*
Helena: *Wendy's friend*

Scene 1

Wendy consults her family physician to ask for a C-section for non-medical reasons.

Wendy: Dr. Tan, if it's good enough for Britney Spears and half of Hollywood, it's good enough for me. I want a C-section. Let's set one up. All joking aside though, Dr. Tan, I have considered this carefully, and C-section is what I really want.

Dr. Tan: But Wendy, there is no medical reason at all for you to have a C-section. We don't just do them on request.

Wendy: I'm not taking "No" for an answer, Dr. Tan. My body is my main business advertising. I can't afford to have less than the best, and I need predictability. I've got to schedule this, not wait for it to happen. I'm in business for myself.

Dr. Tan: What makes you think that a C-section is better?

Wendy: In my business, body aesthetics are crucial. My body is my main advertisement for my services to women. Clearly, if all the stars do it and look so good shortly after giving birth, it's the way to go. I know a number of trainers like me who have gone this route with excellent results.

Dr. Tan: There is no aesthetic advantage to this procedure, in spite of what you have heard, Wendy, and it is much harder on your body. The Hollywood crowd gets on lots of harmful bandwagons.

Wendy: Well, it just makes sense in other ways as well. Why should I go through the pain of labour and the uncertainty of scheduling when I can plan the time and day and avoid the pain? I'm a business woman. I like predictability.

Dr. Tan: Pain? A C-section is abdominal surgery. This is serious stuff. Recovering from a cut like that is not straightforward at all. The popularity of C-section has too much to do with fashion.

Wendy: Look, I promised my boyfriend I'd do this. Everybody knows it's better for sex if you don't stretch yourself out of shape.

Dr. Tan: That's a myth. Sexual function is not hampered by natural birth or improved by C-section.

Wendy: Yeah, tell Harry that.

Dr. Tan: Would you be willing to undergo dangerous surgery and avoid a wonderful natural process just because Harry is misinformed?

Wendy: Wonderful? What's wonderful about groaning in agony for hours?

Dr. Tan: If only you could know what it is really like. Most women who give birth naturally have a deep and significant experience—life-changing, in some cases.

Wendy: It was for my mom. She couldn't walk past a washroom for the rest of her life after having us kids. Then there was her **prolapse.**

DEFINITION

A **prolapse** is a falling or sinking down of part of the body. Here it refers to a downward displacement of the uterus.

Dr. Tan: It doesn't have to be that way. You can avoid stress incontinence and pelvic prolapse. In fact, there are exercises that are effective for lowering the risk of these problems. You, as a fitness trainer, should appreciate that. It might even form part of your business to help others do the training.

Wendy: I'm into achieving excellent health, not just prevention of illness. Vaginal delivery is full of dangers that can be avoided.

Dr. Tan: Wendy, you mustn't look at pregnancy as an illness. Many of my patients say that childbirth is one of the best things that ever happened to them. Talk to women who have experienced immense joy at giving birth naturally.

Wendy: Sorry, Dr. Tan. It's not like I really want to dismiss natural birth. Even if it is best for me, though, it may not be for my baby. Natural birth puts a baby through a lot more stress than a C-section. You know what's going to happen in a C-section, not like when things can go wrong and you use forceps and all that. I mean—it's so much safer for my baby. My friend Anastasia nearly lost her baby to **asphyxia** after a long and difficult labour. With C-section, you don't have to worry about that sort of thing.

DEFINITION

Asphyxia is a deadly condition caused by oxygen deprivation.

Dr. Tan: The evidence is, on balance, against that view, Wendy. C-section may be a life-saver when there is serious fetal distress, but in a healthy pregnancy it is not safer than natural childbirth. In fact, children born by C-section are more likely to end up in the special-care nursery than children born naturally. Respiratory problems at birth and asthma in later life are greater risks with

C-section. C-section babies are also less likely to be breastfed. Natural birth is better for your baby.

Wendy: Look, there are just too many pressures on me to do this. I want a C-section. "My body, my choice," right? If I can decide whether or not to procreate, I can decide how to give birth. My girlfriend from Brazil says everybody there gets a C-section if they can afford it. Please just set this up for me, Dr. Tan. Please.

Dr. Tan: I need a medical reason to do a C-section.

Wendy: Psychological stress counts as a reason for abortion, doesn't it? Why not say that is the reason? Let's just get this done.

Dr. Tan: I'm sorry, Wendy. You've been my patient for a long time, and I want to do my best for you. In this case, that amounts to giving you all the information you need to see what the best choice is for you and your baby. I can't give you what you want or are being pressured to request. I can give you lots of information that I think will persuade you that natural birth is the best course for you and your baby. Take these pamphlets home and please go over them carefully. I'll answer all your questions.

Wendy: Okay, thanks.

Scene 2

Wendy is at the office of a different physician, Dr. Tabor, to see if she will give her a C-section.

Wendy: Dr. Tabor, I *really* want a C-section.

Dr. Tabor: Well, I appreciate the reasons you have given. Physicians may very well disagree on this difficult issue, so there is nothing untoward at all about another physician refusing you even if I do not.

Wendy: So you're going to give me a C-section?

Dr. Tabor: Yes, if you still want one after you are fully informed. I accept a very strong right to patient autonomy.

Wendy: Dr. Tabor, I am informed to death. I read all this stuff my other doctor gave me and heard other opinions that favour C-section much more.

Dr. Tabor: Well, you must realize that physicians have been at odds about how to interpret the data you have been considering. Like Dr. Tan, I think the safest course is to try for vaginal delivery.

Wendy: But are you still going to let me have a C-section?

Dr. Tabor: While I favour natural birth in your case, I will accept your decision for C-section or natural birth once I am sure you are aware of the basic facts. I believe it's up to you once you know for sure what you are getting into. Let's go over the risks again, shall we?

Wendy: Good. Okay, let's.

Scene 3

Wendy discusses her decision with her friend, Helena.

Wendy: Helena, you're going to be proud of me. I really took control. My doctor didn't want to give me C-section on demand, so I found somebody else who will do it.

Helena: Well, of course I'm glad you're sticking up for what you want. You know I'll always support you, so please don't take this the wrong way, Wendy, but why do you want a C-section?

Wendy: Oh, lots of reasons. The thing is that I know the risks and decided to take them. It's my body, my choice.

Helena: I certainly agree with the general idea, of course, but I worry that our choices are being constructed by others.

Wendy: What?

Helena: Well, I choose things sometimes and then wonder if the choice really came from me.

Wendy: Like what?

Helena: Like getting my tubes tied. I had all sorts of good reasons, but when it was done I couldn't help thinking they were other people's reasons, like Jim's and my doctor's, but not my reasons.

Wendy: Oh, Helena. I'm sorry. I didn't know how you felt.

Helena: But this isn't about me. It's about you. I think that we women are often at the receiving end of huge social pressures that make us choose things. The way we dress, the way we make ourselves up, the way we live seem to me sometimes to be chosen for us by others. Some of our freedom is an illusion.

Wendy: Honestly, Helena, I don't think this is like that. I want a C-section for myself. Okay, so tell me. Who do you think would be making me choose this, and how?

Helena: Sorry, Wendy, but you need to know that C-section on demand is a political issue. It's about physicians taking control of birth, taking it away from women.

Wendy: Hold it, Helena. How do you figure that? If we are doing the demanding, how are they in control?

Helena: Women weren't behind the C-section on demand thing, physicians were. There was no massive uprising of women demanding the procedure. Even now, most women go for vaginal birth if they've got the full story. Physicians want to talk you into a C-section when they want it. It reduces their medico-legal risk. If something goes wrong with the birth they can say, "I did everything I could," while with vaginal birth they can always be asked, "Why didn't you do a C-section?" The vast majority of births are good. The bad ones are lawsuits. C-section also serves physicians' convenience. Why hang around for eight hours or get woken in the middle of the night to attend labour when you can schedule it to fit your day? The fact is that it's major abdominal surgery for you instead of a joyful natural process.

Wendy: Do you know how hard I had to fight to get this? Nobody is telling me to do it, quite the opposite.

Helena: Wendy, honey, I'm on your side. Think about it, though. Lately it's been made glamorous since all of these stars are having it done. That's how they sell us everything.

Wendy: Don't worry. That has no real effect on me.

Helena: Maybe not, but still, Wendy, I just hope you know whether you really want a C-section. Ask yourself about the pressures from the media, from your boyfriend, and from other women who have been sold this bill of goods and want to justify themselves. There's a powerful social system constructing women's choices. Giving birth was a hugely empowering achievement for me. C-section is just surgery empowering surgeons.

Wendy: No, it just gives me another option that I can choose or not. I know you want to help me, Helena, but you're mistaken. Nobody is manipulating me. I know what I'm doing.

DEBATE
Clarifying the Case and Identifying Relevant Facts

Patrick says: Right off the top we need to be clear about what exactly counts as CSBC. I know some planned C-sections are considered elective even though they are required for good medical reasons.

Warren says: That's right, some women may have medical conditions that make C-section a reasonable option, and they may elect in advance to go that route. But CSBC is different. CSBC is defined as "Caesarean delivery in the absence of medical indications."[1] The choice is that of the mother.

Patrick says: Does this happen much?

Warren says: CSBC is more and more common, although exact figures are hard to come by.[2] In spite of this, problems with C-sections generally make many physicians cautious. There is a long list of complications that are statistically more common for planned C-sections than for vaginal birth.[3] There is also the problem that women who have had a prior C-section are at an increased risk of complications leading to **hysterectomy** or even maternal mortality in their next pregnancy, however they deliver.[4] These statistics do not, however, contrast CSBC with normal vaginal delivery as we might want.

> **DEFINITION**
>
> A **hysterectomy** is an operation in which the uterus (the womb) is removed.

Doran says: It would not be helpful to look at studies that compare spontaneous vaginal births to C-sections. This is a potentially misleading comparison for our purposes, since one would expect that there are bound to be more problems in the C-section deliveries simply because they are likely to involve more problematic pregnancies to begin with. For our purposes, what we really need are studies that compare only healthy pregnancies, where some of these women opt for vaginal birth and some opt for CSBC. Are there such studies, and if not, is it reasonable to believe that CSBC is as safe as vaginal birth?

Warren says: Here is the best I could come up with in the literature to answer that. Unfortunately, there does not seem to exist a study comparing the risks and benefits for mother and child specifically of CSBC with normal vaginal birth. That would help guide ethical

---

[1] Jan E. Christilaw, "Cesarean Section by Choice: Constructing a Reproductive Rights Framework for the Debate," *International Journal of Gynecology and Obstetrics* 94, no. 3 (2006): 262–68. Readers may be interested to know that Dr. Christilaw is married to Warren. Dr. Christilaw has not, however, reviewed this debate, nor are the opinions and arguments expressed by Warren necessarily shared by her.

[2] T. Lavender, G. J. Hofmeyr, J. P. Neilson, C. Kingdon, and G. M. L. Gyte, "Caesarean Section for Non-medical Reasons at Term," *Cochrane Database of Systematic Reviews* 2006, issue 3, art. no.: CD004660, doi: 10.1002/14651858.CD004660.pub2. p.1.

For a carefully referenced discussion, see British Columbia Perinatal Health Program, *Caesarean Birth Task Force Report 2008* (Vancouver: BCPHP, 2008), 54–55.

[3] See, for example, National Collaborating Centre for Women's and Children's Health, *Caesarean Section*, National Institute for Clinical Excellence Guideline 13 (London: RCOG Press, 2004), 22.

[4] Lawrence Leeman, "Patient-Choice Cesarean Delivery," *American Family Physician* 72, no. 4 (2005): 697, 700, 705.

debate.[5] Absent such a study we have at least a very thorough evidence-based literature survey from highly qualified researchers that tells us that spontaneous vaginal birth is probably safer.[6] Another survey concludes that there simply is no recommendation one can make for practice on the basis of the available evidence.[7] The first literature survey takes what is known about the dangers of C-section in general over vaginal birth in general as data from which we can extrapolate. The second adopts strict criteria for the kind of study that would compare CSBC to spontaneous vaginal birth, and rules out all existing studies. At the same time, this survey warns that new, unexpected long-term risks of C-section continue to be reported.[8]

Doran says: It seems to be a moral failing that there are no adequate studies.

Warren says: It would be hard to justify a methodologically complex, extremely expensive study for a procedure that is not medically required. Consider, moreover, the ethics of undertaking an experiment where women would receive surgery in the absence of a medical indication.[9] Try to get that past a research ethics board! We don't have the exact factual information we want, and we are not likely to get it soon.

TECHNIQUE

Sound ethical reasoning requires not only a careful use of moral principles but also sensitivity to relevant empirical matters. Deciding whether CSBC is morally permissible will involve consideration of how safe or harmful it is thought to be. This turns out to be a question which experts do not answer with one voice. We must, therefore, ask what is morally required under conditions of uncertainty.

Doran says: I don't know how problematic that study would be, since there appear to be plenty of volunteers already for CSBC—we could then compare those already willing participants with spontaneous natural births. At any rate, we do not have those studies to guide us.

Patrick says: Well, don't the professional organizations advise practitioners on what to do in the light of the less-than-robust evidence?

Warren says: Yes, many accept the view expressed by FIGO (the International Federation of Gynecology and Obstetrics). Let me read you FIGO's position: "At present there is no hard evidence on the relative risks and benefits of term Caesarean

---

[5] Lavender et al., "Caesarean Section for Non-medical Reasons at Term."

[6] These researchers say that "available data, although not robust, suggest that overall maternal and perinatal mortality, and short- and long-term maternal and neonatal morbidity favor vaginal delivery." See Joseph R. Wax, Angelina Cartin, Michael G. Pinette, and Jacquelyn Blackstone, "Patient Choice Cesarean: An Evidence-Based Review," *Obstetrical & Gynecological Survey* 59, no. 8 (2004): 601–16.

[7] Lavender et al., "Caesarean Section for Non-medical Reasons at Term."

[8] Ibid., 3.

[9] Ibid., 7.

delivery for non-medical reasons, as compared with vaginal delivery. However, available evidence suggests that normal vaginal delivery is safer in the short and long term for both mother and child. Surgery on the uterus also has implications for later pregnancies and deliveries. In addition, there is also a natural concern at introducing an artificial method of delivery in place of the natural process without medical justification. . . . At present, because hard evidence of net benefit does not exist, performing Caesarean section for non-medical reasons is ethically not justified."[10] This position is not, however, universally accepted.

Doran says: Right. I heard that the **NIH** has taken the position that they can neither support nor oppose CSBC, given the lack of evidence of its risks and benefits compared with planned vaginal births.[11]

DEFINITION

The **NIH** (the National Institutes of Health) is the primary federal agency for conducting and supporting medical research in the United States.

Warren says: Yes, that's right, Doran.

Doran says: I've brought along a recent statement on CSBC from the NIH; before we go any further, we should look carefully at its exact conclusions:

"The incidence of cesarean delivery without medical or obstetric indications is increasing in the United States, and a component of this increase is cesarean delivery on maternal request. Given the tools available, the magnitude of this component is difficult to quantify.

There is insufficient evidence to evaluate fully the benefits and risks of cesarean delivery on maternal request as compared to planned vaginal delivery, and more research is needed.

Until quality evidence becomes available, any decision to perform a cesarean delivery on maternal request should be carefully individualized and consistent with ethical principles.

Given that the risks of placenta previa and accreta rise with each cesarean delivery, cesarean delivery on maternal request is not recommended for women desiring several children.

Cesarean delivery on maternal request should not be performed prior to 39 weeks of gestation or without verification of lung maturity, because of the significant danger of neonatal respiratory complications.

---

[10] FIGO Committee for the Ethical Aspects of Reproduction and Women's Health, *Recommendations on Ethical Issues in Obstetrics and Gynecology* (London: FIGO, 2006).

[11] US Department of Health and Human Services, "Panel Finds Insufficient Evidence to Recommend For or Against Maternal-Request Caesarean Delivery," *NIH News,* 29 March 2006, http://www.nih.gov/news/pr/mar2006/od-29.htm.

Maternal request for cesarean delivery should not be motivated by unavailability of effective pain management. Efforts must be made to assure availability of pain management services for all women.

NIH or another appropriate Federal agency should establish and maintain a Web site to provide up-to-date information on the benefits and risks of all modes of delivery."[12]

BACKGROUND

Warren had the privilege of attending a multidisciplinary health care conference in 2008, "Cesarean Birth in BC: A Consensus Conference." Participants expressed sharp and passionate disagreement about risks and benefits of C-section. Nonetheless, a consensus statement resulted from the debate.

Source: British Columbia Perinatal Health Program, *Caesarean Birth Task Force Report 2008.*

Patrick says: Interesting. It may be that there is not so much a disagreement about data between NIH and FIGO. The disagreement may be rather about how to interpret and use the data. FIGO's advice is compatible with this: if you don't know what the risks and benefits of CSBC are, and since you don't have to take the risks, don't take them. NIH, on the other hand, seems to say if you can't prove CSBC is riskier, let it be an option. Such advice may be seen as both medical and ethical.

Warren says: We should note, moreover, that this statement does not appear to represent the only view endorsed by the US medical establishment. According to a widely reprinted news article, "U.S. health officials are trying to cut the Caesarean delivery rate in half, bringing it down to 15 percent by 2010." The article quotes two prominent medical doctors who say that there is a growing body of evidence that suggests that C-sections are less safe than normal vaginal births; one of them says that the increased use of C-section goes against the basic rule of medicine, "Do no harm."[13] One of the doctors, the former director of women's and children's health for the World Health Organization (WHO), reiterates what the WHO has long been saying, that maternal mortality goes up if the C-section rate in a country drops below 10 percent or rises above 15 percent.[14] It seems reasonable to expect rates to rise with CSBC.[15]

---

[12] National Institutes of Health, *NIH State-of-the-Science Conference Statement: Cesarean Delivery on Maternal Request,* 27–29 March 2006, http://consensus.nih.gov/2006/2006CesareanSOS027 Statementhtml.htm.

[13] HealthDay © 2007, "Soaring C-section Rate Troubles Doctors," 13 July 2007, http://www.washingtonpost.com/wp-dyn/content/article/2007/07/13/AR2007071301423.html.

[14] World Health Organization, *Recommendations, Joint Interregional Conference on Appropriate Technology for Birth, Fortaleza, Brazil, 22–26 April 1985.*

[15] "Caesarean birth rates in Canada have increased by 45% in the last decade, from 18.2% in 1995–1996 to 26.3% in 2005–2006" (British Columbia Perinatal Health Program, *Caesarean Birth Task Force Report 2008,* 3).

Many individual choices may add up to one big social problem of increased maternal mortality or at least **morbidity**. It is a reasonable hypothesis that that may be happening here and now because of CSBC. Again, it is uncertain, partly because increased maternal age and body mass index may make the WHO figure too low. Both of those things increase the need for C-sections to save lives.

BACKGROUND

Recall that the right to autonomy, in the present context, refers to the right of the patient to choose her course of care without undue interference. It is important to note, however, that choosing a course of treatment does not imply getting it, for one's choice may conflict with, for example, the rights and interests of others. Thus, even though Wendy has chosen to have a C-section, it does not necessarily follow that she ought to be given one.

Patrick says: Well, let's see what light we can shed on the ethics of CSBC, in the light of these conflicting guidelines.

MORAL ISSUES RAISED BY THE CASE

Doran says: The drama certainly raises a lot of thorny moral problems related to CSBC. There are questions about the ethics of Wendy's particular decision to choose a C-section; there are questions of professional ethics, such as whether it is unethical for a health care professional to grant Wendy's request for CSBC; further still, one might wonder whether the medical system should provide (and pay for) Wendy's CSBC given that it is not medically indicated and health care resources are scarce.

And, of course, beyond the specifics of Wendy's case, one should consider whether CSBC is, *in general,* a morally permissible choice for women to make, for health care professionals to accede to, and for the health care system to provide.

Warren says: Further to this last point, there are concerns about the ills attendant on CSBC as a social policy—a policy that might harm women as a group.

Patrick says: Well, we obviously cannot consider all of these questions, so let's proceed systematically and focus on the more central questions. *I propose that we begin by considering the moral permissibility of Wendy's decision to opt for CSBC, and the permissibility of CSBC more generally.* Later, we can turn to other moral questions if time permits.

THEORY

Feminist author Carol Gilligan might find the whole discussion here misguided. Instead of trying to arrive "at an objectively fair or just resolution to which all rational persons could agree, the responsibility conception focuses instead on the limitations of any particular resolution and describes the conflicts that remain." Moral judgments will be more contextual and dependent on relationships, according to an ethics of care. A care-based approach would be reluctant to consider the morality of CSBC in general. Instead, each individual case of CSBC needs to be considered on its own terms, and solutions need to be arrived at by bringing together the interested parties.

Source: Carol Gilligan, In a Different Voice: Psychological Theory and Women's Development (Cambridge, MA: Harvard University Press, 1982), 6–22.

Warren says: Okay, let's get started. Doran, why don't you begin by stating your view about the moral permissibility of Wendy's having a CSBC?

Stating Our Positions

Doran says: This is a tough case, and I am not sure what to think. Perhaps the easiest thing to argue would be that Wendy's decision to go for CSBC is wrong, given that the risks to self and baby appear to be greater with C-section than vaginal delivery, and given that the reasons Wendy has for opting for CSBC seem less than compelling. But I want to try to argue for a different conclusion. Thus, my tentative conclusion will be that while Wendy's is not the best decision, it is not morally wrong, either. From my deontological pluralist view, respect for individual liberty, and the absence of clear, conclusive evidence of serious enough harm to others, incline me to view her choice as morally permissible.

Patrick says: I agree with you, Doran, that we ought, in general, to respect autonomy. And this entails that we should often permit people to make choices and act in ways that are not best, provided that the risk of harm (to others, in particular) is not too great.

Though we don't know for certain, the available evidence does suggest that CSBC *may* put mother and child at greater risk of serious harm than vaginal delivery. The risk, in absolute terms, may be relatively small, but the possible harms are serious. Given this, I believe it would be rather foolish, reckless, and irresponsible to opt for CSBC unless one has good reasons for having one. When we look at Wendy's situation, I'm not convinced that her reasons are good enough to justify CSBC. So, all things considered, I think CSBC is wrong in Wendy's case.

Warren says: This is a vexed issue, all right. I find it very troubling to sort out my views, but I will side with Patrick here. Although a very strong right to autonomy would be supported in the original position, even if Wendy's decision is autonomous it would be a morally wrong decision. Her choosing C-section is wrong because she is needlessly taking unknown risks for no clear benefit. She is gambling with her child's life and health as well as with her own life and well-being. As parents we ought not to take such chances with ourselves for our dependents' sake, and we certainly shouldn't risk harming our kids for no good reason.

At the same time, however, I recognize that women's rights to control their own bodies with respect to reproduction are often wrongly restricted. Those who oppose these rights often assert instead the rights of the unborn child. I wish to strongly differentiate my view from the position of, for instance, the anti-choice movement in the abortion debate. Here I am concerned with possible harms to a wanted, born child.

Patrick says: Nice point, Warren. I, too, would differentiate my view about this case from an anti-choice position regarding abortion. Although I believe that Wendy's having a CSBC is wrong, I'm not arguing that the alleged rights of the unborn child trump a woman's right to have a CSBC or an abortion.[16]

Warren says: Doran, why don't you give us your argument for thinking CSBC is a permissible choice for Wendy, and see if you can get Patrick and me to change our minds?

DORAN'S ARGUMENT FOR WHY WENDY'S DECISION IS MORALLY PERMISSIBLE

Doran says: I'll give it a shot, with the reminder that I am not at all sure that my view is the correct one. I am prepared to advance an argument for my view, but it may well be the case that you guys end up showing me the error of my ways.

Let me begin by outlining my reasoning. The details can be filled in later as we debate.

(1) The autonomous decisions of competent patients are, **presumptively, morally permissible.**

(2) Wendy is a competent patient who exercises her right to autonomy when she opts for CSBC.

(3) Therefore, Wendy's decision for CSBC is, presumptively, morally permissible.

(4) This presumption ought to be respected unless it is seriously wrong in other respects—e.g., it seriously harms others, or is unfair, or violates the rights of others, etc.

(5) Wendy's choice is not seriously wrong in these other respects.

(6) Therefore, her CSBC is morally permissible.

> **UP FOR DISCUSSION**
>
> What are your initial thoughts about the moral permissibility of Wendy's CSBC? Explain your reasons.

> **TECHNIQUE**
>
> Notice how philosophy differs from what is commonly known as "debate." In a debate, one typically takes a position and then defends it at all costs, regardless of whether one agrees with the position defended. However, in philosophy the goal is to find the truth through the careful use of reason. Accordingly, if it turns out that the arguments against are stronger than the arguments for, then one should be willing to revise or jettison one's original views and embrace the strongest arguments.

> **TECHNIQUE**
>
> Doran puts his argument in **standard form,** numbering the premises and conclusion and stripping the argument down to the essentials. This allows easy reference to individual premises. It also enhances the clarity of the argument and allows readers to focus their evaluation.

---

[16] We consider the morality of abortion in Chapter 6.

Many of these premises will require a detailed defence—but that is an outline of the argument that I hope to show is sound.

Warren says: Well, I don't think you will have to do much to defend premise (1), since it is not controversial as long as you mean that the right to autonomy should, other things being equal, be respected in patients' decisions that affect mainly themselves, or other competent persons with their consent. Of course, Wendy's is not one of those cases where other things are equal. Others are seriously affected in Wendy's case. I accept your premise (1) on my interpretation, and I will bring up considerations about people other than Wendy later.

For the sake of argument, let us accept premise (2) as well. Like Wendy's friend Helena, I have some concerns about subtle social coercion or coercion from her partner undermining Wendy's autonomy, but we do not really know enough about these things in Wendy's case to know whether she is being coerced. Let's focus, then, on the question of harm to the child and mother.

Patrick says: I too have concerns about Wendy's autonomy. She is informed, in the sense that her doctor tells her about the risks and the uncertainty surrounding CSBC, but she stubbornly refuses to accept what her doctor is saying. Wendy's tone throughout the drama suggests to me that she has already decided to have a CSBC, and that she could not be persuaded otherwise. This leads me to have some doubt about her ability to make an informed and, hence, autonomous choice. I'm willing to go along, however, with the assumption that she is autonomous and focus on the question of harm.

TECHNIQUE

To accept a premise for the sake of argument is not to accept it as true. It is just to accept it for the present purposes to focus on a different part of the argument. The premise may still be rejected later on.

UP FOR DISCUSSION

Given the concerns expressed by Warren and Patrick, do you think that Wendy's choice is autonomous? Why or why not? (For a more involved discussion of the concept of autonomy see Chapter 5.)

DO POTENTIAL HARMS MAKE WENDY'S AUTONOMOUS CHOICE WRONG?

Patrick says: Let's see, Doran, whether you can give a sound argument for your claim in premise (5), that the possibly harmful effects of Wendy's (autonomous) choice are not sufficient to show that her freely chosen act is wrong. This is probably the most controversial premise of your argument, and so it is the one on which we should focus most of our attention.

Warren says: Yes, I must say that this premise surprised me, since most experts agree that CSBC puts one's baby at greater risk of respiratory problems and of not gaining the benefits of breastfeeding. Much worse, but much less common, things can happen as well, like serious accidental surgical cuts to the baby or even the death of the baby. Surely it is wrong to assume these greater risks of unknown probability, risks of harms to others, without a good reason to do so. Also, CSBC might wrong others in more insidious ways. For instance, CSBC might strain the medical system, or unfairly use up scarce medical resources. Also, there is the concern that CSBC will needlessly **medicalize** what is a safe natural process, significantly changing the culture of birth for the worse. CSBC, if accepted, would needlessly give the medical establishment effective control over birth. These harms would affect everyone, but especially women.

> **DEFINITION**
>
> To **medicalize** an event in a patient's life is to intervene to a great extent medically rather than letting the event proceed naturally. There is much debate, however, about what it means for an event to proceed naturally.

Patrick says: I am inclined to agree with you, Warren, that Doran's premise (5) is false. However, I am not sure that CSBC is likely to have all of the insidious harms that you suggest. I'm also rather skeptical of the idea that CSBC medicalizes an otherwise natural process. After all, some uncomplicated vaginal births in hospitals are highly medicalized procedures and so not very natural.

> **UP FOR DISCUSSION**
>
> What is a "natural" birth? Are "natural" births always morally better than "unnatural" births? Explain your answer.

Harms to the Baby

Doran says: Okay, let's start with a discussion of possible harms to the child, and then later we can consider whether CSBC harms others besides the child.

Warren says: Doran, in general, do you agree that CSBC is worse for the baby than vaginal delivery? And do you accept that vaginal delivery is medically the best choice for Wendy's baby?

Doran says: In deciding this issue, things are complicated by our limited knowledge about the risks of CSBC to the baby when compared to vaginal delivery. I'm not sure I agree that all of these risks are relevant, because of their extreme rarity, and because there are horror stories with respect to vaginal delivery as well. I am willing to grant that the evidence appears to be quite clear that CSBC probably poses some greater risks to the baby than vaginal delivery poses, at least in standard cases. (Probably respiratory issues are the biggest concern, followed by failure to breastfeed successfully.) Other things being equal, therefore, I am willing to grant that it would be *better* for the baby if mothers in general, and Wendy in this instance, opted for vaginal birth over CSBC. But the question is whether it would be *wrong* for her to opt for CSBC.

Warren says: I think it would be wrong. People in the original position would bias their decisions in favour of protecting the vulnerable. This is because they realize that they may themselves be vulnerable in the real world, at some point. Further, people in the original position are going to want to protect themselves from needless, serious harm. Thus, they will adopt a principle that says: "Do not take unnecessary risks of seriously harming others unless there is a good reason." We can call this latter principle the *good reason requirement*. Now, Wendy's CSBC violates this principle, since she does not have a good reason to expose her baby to the needless, serious harm posed by C-section. At least she has not expressed a good reason. There is no business advantage, in spite of what Wendy argues, since it is a medical fact that it will take her much longer to heal from a C-section. Being unable to conduct one's business tends to be a very serious business disadvantage which is hard to outweigh. She appears in the case to be mistakenly assuming that recovery from C-section is quicker. There is, moreover, no medical reason to expect a difference in the appearance of Wendy's body either, except that Wendy will have a scar. C-sections do not prevent stretch marks, as is sometimes supposed. Therefore, it is hard to understand the supposed aesthetic superiority of a C-section in Wendy's view. There is a great deal of pain associated with recovering from major abdominal surgery, while the pain of labour Wendy wishes to avoid can be minimized with medical pain control. She will have learned that sexual function is not improved with C-section and neither stress-incontinence nor prolapse is a necessary consequence of vaginal birth. Wendy becomes informed about the realities by the time she visits Dr. Tabor. Following the good reason requirement, Wendy should not take even low risks of serious harm to her child.

Doran says: Can you say a little bit more about what a good reason is in this context?

Warren says: We want people to be able to have reasons that would justify taking risks. Presumably, the greater the risks, the stronger the reasons one will require. There will, of course, be disputes about what will count as a good enough reason. For me the idea would be that a good enough reason would be one that justifies the risks even if the worst harms were to come to pass.

Patrick says: I suppose I agree with the good reason requirement, at least insofar as we're talking about parents and their children. But even then, there may be exceptions. In general, though, it does seem reckless and irresponsible for parents to put their children at risk of very serious harm, even if the harms are improbable, unless they have good reason to do so. And, as Warren just noted, Wendy does not seem to have good reasons for wanting a CSBC.

Doran says: I don't agree with the good reason requirement. People do not need to justify their choices with "good" reasons, when those choices are very unlikely to harm others. Since the probability of Wendy's CSBC harming others is extremely low, she does not need to have good reasons for a CSBC. Alternatively, I suppose I could agree with the good reason requirement and still hold that Wendy's reasons for having a CSBC are good enough. In that case, the good reason requirement would be trivially true, since virtually any reason would count as good enough when the probability of harming others is really low.

I believe I can show, moreover, that Wendy's CSBC is morally permissible, and that the good reason requirement is therefore false (or trivially true), by comparing it to other cases where parents act permissibly when they needlessly take real but somewhat unknown risks of harm with their children for no very good reason. Consistency requires that if we view these parental decisions as morally permissible, then we should not condemn CSBC on the grounds of the risk of harm it exposes the baby to. Let's start with this case. Consider parents who for reasons of convenience visit fast food restaurants to purchase cheeseburgers, soft drinks, and fries for their kids on a regular basis—say two times per week.

TECHNIQUE

Here Warren and Patrick illustrate the two ways one can reject an argument by analogy. One can argue, as Warren does, that there are relevant differences between the analogy (eating too much fast food) and the case under consideration (CSBC). Or, one can argue, as Patrick does, that even if the analogy is relevantly similar to the case under consideration, both are objectionable in the same way. Doran intends the fast food analogy to illustrate a case of permissible behaviour, but Patrick thinks that such behaviour is, in fact, impermissible.

UP FOR
DISCUSSION

Do you think it is morally wrong for parents, for convenience, to take their kids for junk food a couple of times per week, given that this risks inducing obesity? If you think this is not wrong, do you think this example disproves the good reason requirement? Is this case analogous to the risks posed by CSBC?

Warren says: I don't think that this is a good analogy. Are the risks of obesity comparable to the risks Wendy is running for her child? We just don't know, but I suspect that the risks of CSBC could be much worse if planned C-section is any indication.[17] Further, obesity and other ill effects from a poor diet are things a child can overcome with help. CSBC can cause problems to both the mother and the baby which cannot be eradicated.

Patrick: I also have doubts about whether this is a good analogy. In any case, even if it is a good analogy, I don't think it will help your argument, Doran, because it is surely wrong for parents to feed their children junk food on a regular basis, assuming more healthful foods are available. The virtuous parent would obviously show an appropriate level of concern for the health and well-being of his or her children. Giving your child fast food twice a week is rather irresponsible, given the long-term harms, if other options are available. A good parent would not regularly put convenience ahead of the child's health.

Warren says: I too think it is wrong of a parent to induce obesity and risk diseases associated with obesity in a child just because it is convenient.

Doran says: Well, then, consider a different analogy, one that clearly involves taking risks of possible harms to the parent and the child that are serious and possibly permanent. Parents routinely drive their children a kilometre or two to elementary school when they could have walked instead. Let's suppose evidence suggests that the risks of injury when driving are

---

[17] See, for instance, Hernandez-Dias et al., who mention a sevenfold increase in life-threatening persistent pulmonary hypertension of the newborn (a serious respiratory illness). Sonia Hernandez-Diaz, Linda J. Van Marter, Martha M. Werler, Carol Louik, and Allen A. Mitchell, "Risk Factors for Persistent Pulmonary Hypertension of the Newborn," *Pediatrics* 120, no. 2 (2007): e272–82.

    MacDorman et al. report neonatal mortality rates with no indicated risk at 1.77 per 1000 live births compared to vaginal births with a rate of 0.62. Marian F. MacDorman, Eugene Declercq, Fay Menaker, and Michael H. Malloy, "Infant and Neonatal Mortality for Primary Cesarean and Vaginal Births to Women with 'No Indicated Risk,' United States, 1998–2001 Birth Cohorts," *Birth* 33, no. 3 (2006): 175–82.

    See also Shiliang Liu, Robert M. Liston, K. S. Joseph, Maureen Heaman, Reg Sauve, and Michael S. Kramer, for the Maternal Health Study Group of the Canadian Perinatal Surveillance System, "Maternal Mortality and Severe Morbidity Associated with Low-Risk Planned Cesarean Delivery versus Planned Vaginal Delivery at Term," *CMAJ* 176, no. 4 (2007): 455–60.

greater than when one walks to school. Would it be morally wrong to drive merely because of the increased risk it poses to the child?

Warren says: That's a more persuasive example since, as you pointed out, driving, like CSBC, can result in death and injury immediately both to the infant and to the parent. I would say driving is wrong for parents who have a good alternative, though I suspect that many would not. For example, if I chose to drive my child to school just because I prefer not to walk, I would consider myself in the wrong. I would be needlessly endangering the vulnerable child in my care, on your assumption that driving really is more dangerous.

Patrick says: Yes, this is a better analogy, but again, I'm not sure it helps your case, Doran. Most parents, or at least many of them, have a good reason for driving their children to school. In most or many cases, it may be the only way to get their children to school in a timely manner. But if walking is a genuine option, and it's less risky than driving, then surely that is what parents ought to do.

Doran says: Well, you two may have that reaction, but I bet many of our readers won't. Common sense, they might argue, suggests that it is not morally wrong to drive one's kid to school, even if walking would be better. I side with common sense on this point.

> **UP FOR DISCUSSION**
>
> Do you agree with Patrick's claims that "most parents, or at least many of them, have a good reason for driving their children to school" and that "if walking is a genuine option, and it's less risky than driving, then surely that is what parents ought to do"? Why or why not?

Warren says: I too would bet that many readers won't think driving is wrong, but that is because they do not accept the hypothesis of the case. They believe their children are safer in their SUV than they are when crossing the road in front of somebody else's. SUVs have been successfully advertised as bastions of security. Actually, almost any car encases us in metal and gives us a sense of being well protected. If parents were really convinced that walking was safer, the psychological reaction might be different.

Patrick says: I'm not so sure about that, Warren. Unfortunately, I think many parents, in their day-to-day choices, put greater weight on convenience than the health and safety of their children. We all seem to do this to a greater or lesser extent, even when we recognize that it is wrong.

Doran says: People in our society do things routinely in their automobiles when they could have easily walked instead—driving to a new restaurant rather than going to one closer to home; driving to the store instead of walking or ordering something online; driving to church rather than walking; and so on. Perhaps such needless automobile trips are wrong because of the environmental damage they cause. But that's not relevant to the issue we are debating. Our present concern is with the level of permissible risk. And I believe that common sense tells us both that such automobile trips are riskier than walking, and that the added risk to the car's occupants is such that it is not enough to make such car trips wrong.

Patrick says: The added risk to the occupants of the car does not by itself make these various car trips wrong. But the added risk and the absence of good reasons for taking the risk do make the car trips wrong. It is surely irresponsible, selfish, and reckless to put others at risk of serious harm when one has no good reason for doing so. If common sense disagrees, as you suggest, Doran, then so much the worse for common sense.

UP FOR DISCUSSION

Consider the case of a mother who chooses not to breastfeed her newborn. Suppose that her reasons for not breastfeeding are roughly similar to Wendy's reasons for not wanting to undergo vaginal birth. Also, suppose that breastfeeding is generally believed to be best for the baby. Do you think that it would be morally wrong for this mother not to breastfeed? In what ways is this similar to CSBC? In what ways is this different? Do these similarities and differences affect moral permissibility?

Doran says: Let's move on and see whether this next case will persuade you. This case may be the most analogous to CSBC since it too involves decisions surrounding childbirth. Let's suppose we had a parent who favoured home birth (because her peers are doing it, she likes the idea, etc.), and let's stipulate—though I am not saying this is true—that the risks to the child of home birth are unclear but appear to be slightly greater than the risks of births in a hospital. Let's also say that some physicians are comfortable with the idea of home births, though the majority of physicians oppose it. I guess your view would be that you don't think it would be morally permissible for the mom to choose home birth, but that is not my reaction. I believe that if it can be shown that home births are safe in the vast majority of cases, then women should have that option, even if it is not the safest choice.

Patrick says: If the risks of a home birth are comparable to those of CSBC, and if a woman's reasons for wanting a home birth are as shallow as Wendy's appear to be for wanting a CSBC, then I would also say that the home birth is wrong. I suspect that in many cases, however, the reasons behind home birth are much better. A hospital birth might genuinely conflict with deeply held values. In that case, the risks may be permissible.

Warren says: This home birth example is a good challenge. I agree with Patrick: if the features of home birth were similar to CSBC, then I would count home birth as wrong. Some unsafe home birth practices *are* wrong. If, however, one has a registered midwife with proper equipment and backup, the features are rather different from CSBC. There can be considerable safety and signal advantages. In those cases the parents are not taking an unknown risk with terrible worst-case scenarios for little reason. I do not see a strong enough analogy here, since the reasons for home birth are, as Patrick pointed out, likely to be better than Wendy's reasons for CSBC.

> **UP FOR DISCUSSION**
>
> What is your reaction to the home birth analogy? Is it sufficiently analogous to influence your views about CSBC? How?

Doran says: Well, it seems to me, though not to you two, that these analogies suggest that there are lots of situations where parents put their children at some small increased risk of serious harm for reasons that are not always very compelling, and where most people would not think that these parents are doing wrong. And if that is so, then most people should not oppose Wendy's CSBC on the grounds that it puts her child at some small increased risk of serious harm.

> **UP FOR DISCUSSION**
>
> See if you can come up with a case that is analogous to Wendy's CSBC. What does this analogy reveal about the moral permissibility of Wendy's CSBC?

Further, and beyond an appeal to consistency, what I chiefly think is motivating my position is the belief that we ought to allow people freedom, and to limit it only when there is clear evidence that their actions pose a substantially greater risk of seriously harming or significantly wronging others. In cases where the increased risks of significant harm to others are really small, then I think it is mistaken to condemn such choices as morally wrong. The fact of the matter is that in Canada, the actual risk of serious harms to infants in healthy pregnancies is very small, both for vaginal delivery *and* for CSBC. Infant mortality rates in Canada are among the lowest in the world—and a lot of infant mortality that does exist is attributable to low birth weight and to congenital problems—but these are not relevant to the issue under consideration.[18] A general respect for liberty should therefore permit these choices, given that the likelihood of significant harm is so small. If we respect liberty, we must not require people to choose the very best.

---

[18] C. Robin Walker, "Infant Mortality in the U.S. and Canada," *Ob.Gyn. News,* 1 April 2005, http://findarticles.com/p/articles/mi_m0CYD/is_/ai_n27856064.

So what does this tell us about your good reason requirement, Warren? Again, it could be that the good reason requirement is true, but in cases like these, where risks of serious harms are really small, that almost anything counts as a good enough reason to justify the action. But what I'm more inclined to say is that the requirement to have a good reason whenever one puts someone else at greater than necessary risk of serious harm is false, and that this good reason requirement should only come into play when risks of significant harm to others become sufficiently likely. I believe this because I think respect for people's freedom means that we should not constantly require of them that they have good reasons for their choices, when those choices carry little real risk of harm to others.

UP FOR DISCUSSION

Suppose a slightly intoxicated parent runs an errand in his automobile with his child in the back seat. Given that his route has very little traffic, and given that he is only slightly impaired, he knows that his risk of crashing and significantly harming others is very low. What are the similarities and differences of this to CSBC? How do these affect permissibility?

Warren says: Common sense does not approve taking risks of catastrophe without a good reason. I do not think your examples show otherwise. Note, moreover, that it is not enough that the increased risk of harm to others be low to make it reasonable to take the risk. A reasonable person would not take unnecessary risks that include utterly unacceptable consequences of unknown probability for little benefit. When we justify choices on the basis of liberty, they must be choices that exercise a reasonable standard of care. This is especially the case when we are dealing with the most vulnerable in our society, like children. CSBC, in Wendy's case, does not demonstrate a reasonable standard of care, and thus is ruled out by the good reason requirement.

Patrick says: I agree, Warren, insofar as we are talking about parents taking risks with their children. It seems intuitively clear that a virtuous parent would not put his or her child at risk of serious harm, even when the probability of harm is low, without having a sufficiently good reason for taking this risk. Wendy's reasons for wanting a CSBC are not strong enough to justify the possible harms to her child. So her choice to have a C-section is wrong—it's irresponsible, selfish, shallow, reckless, and so forth.

What Doran's analogies suggest, then, is not that Wendy's CSBC is permissible; rather, they suggest that many other choices that parents make might also be wrong. In all of these cases, parents are behaving recklessly and irresponsibly: they are putting their children at a small risk of great harm for no good reason.

Doran says: As I have tried to explain, I believe that the right to autonomy will not be sufficiently respected if we accept Warren's principle that people should not take unnecessary risks of serious harm affecting others without a good reason. Too many things that we routinely choose for trivial reasons would fall into your category of putting others at greater risk of unknown harm, and so would be rendered immoral on your principle.

Patrick says: But that, of course, doesn't show that the principle is false. It may be, as I've suggested, that many things that parents routinely do are in fact morally wrong.

Doran says: That's true, Patrick. Interestingly, though, it does show that it may be wrong for people to condemn Wendy for CSBC and not to condemn other much more common behaviours. So, even if my arguments fail to persuade people of the permissibility of CSBC, they may persuade people to re-evaluate the permissibility of other actions where parents put their children at risk for unknown benefit.

UP FOR DISCUSSION

Do you accept the good reason requirement? If the probability of harm is low, what would count as a good reason for putting one's child at slightly increased risk? Did Wendy have a good enough reason for CSBC to justify the possible harms to her child?

Harms to the Mother

Patrick says: Thus far we have considered whether Wendy's CSBC is wrong because of the risks it poses to her baby, but we also should consider the related issue of whether Wendy is wrong to choose a CSBC because of the increased risks of harm to herself posed by the procedure.

Warren says: Yes, let's consider those risks. While there is no study that tells us exactly what we want to know about the risks of CSBC, there's a major Canadian cohort study of planned primary Caesarean section for **breech** presentation. The women in this study are healthy. They have no special risks aside from breech. This low-risk population showed a risk three times greater than women giving birth vaginally of serious problems like cardiac arrest, major infection, anaesthetic complications, venous **thromboembolism,** and bleeding that required hysterectomy.[19]

DEFINITION

Breech means buttocks, and breech presentation is the presentation of the buttocks or feet in labour, which entails more risk than presentation of the head. A **thromboembolism** is the obstruction of a blood vessel with particles carried by the blood from another site.

Doran says: It's noteworthy that the maternal mortality was the same for this group as for the vaginal group, and the rate is *extremely low* in Canada for all births.[20]

---

[19] Liu et al., "Maternal Mortality and Severe Morbidity."
[20] Ibid.

Warren says: That's right. Data from maternal registries in Britain and the US, however, do show a higher rate for C-section generally than for vaginal birth generally.[21]

Patrick says: But here in Canada risks to the mother of this procedure are generally low in absolute terms, are they not?

Warren says: Yes. In Canada we are blessed with such rarity of maternal mortality that the absolute risk is slight. Still, I have a report here that says, "Although the absolute difference is small, the risks of severe maternal morbidity associated with planned Cesarean delivery are higher than those associated with planned vaginal delivery. These risks should be considered by women contemplating an elective Cesarean delivery and by their physicians."[22] We also have to consider risks to the mother incurred in future pregnancies. Risks go up with the number of C-sections, and vaginal birth after C-section presents its own difficulties for the mother as well.

Doran says: Well, I will grant that there may be increased risks to the mother from CSBC. Choosing CSBC may, therefore, be imprudent, but is it morally wrong for a woman to make this choice? Is there a duty to oneself that is sufficiently strong that it should outweigh a woman's freedom of choice?

Patrick says: I would say there are duties to oneself, since living virtuously—living a flourishing life—requires that one show appropriate concern for one's mental and physical health. A virtuous person is not only courageous, honest, and trustworthy, for instance; he or she is also not reckless, intemperate, and gluttonous. But I want to tread carefully here, to avoid saying that people must be saints. A virtuous person would take appropriate care of her body, but this doesn't mean she can never indulge herself or take risks. Again, I don't think there's a general rule that would correctly state the appropriate level of concern for oneself; instead, it must be addressed on a case-by-case basis. I doubt that the risk to self in this case is weighty enough on its own to show that Wendy's CSBC is wrong. But the risks to self, when added to the risks to the baby (and perhaps others), give us good reason, I think, for holding that Wendy's CSBC is wrong.

---

[21] National Collaborating Centre for Women's and Children's Health, *Caesarean Section.*

[22] Liu et al., "Maternal Mortality and Severe Morbidity."

Doran says: I am inclined to agree with you that there are moral duties to self—what we often call *self-regarding duties*—though I would tend to follow Kant and say that there are certain things that one ought not to do to oneself because they would fail to show proper respect for one's own rational or autonomous nature. For example, I think a case could be made that sniffing glue, or taking crack cocaine, are not only imprudent, they are also immoral, since they directly assault one's ability to operate as an autonomous being. But I doubt that merely taking risks that are involved in CSBC are sufficient to make the act a violation of a self-regarding duty. The parent is still, almost certainly, likely to recover and to be able to function autonomously. So, while the choice may be rather foolish from the perspective of health, I tend not to think it is wrong on grounds of harm to self.

Warren says: Whatever duties are accepted in the original position would have to be duties that will serve our interests in the real world. Certainly something like W. D. Ross's duty of self-improvement, a duty to make ourselves better in respect of knowledge, virtue, and happiness, is in our interest.[23] This must, nonetheless, be balanced against a strong right to autonomy which is crucial to our self-interest. I think that the risks of CSBC might be small enough to justify the mother's taking them on the grounds that the right to autonomy would outweigh the duty of self-improvement if the mother alone were seriously affected by CSBC. That, however, is impossible, since if the mother is harmed by CSBC, then almost certainly so will her baby be harmed, and all others who care about them.

THEORY

W. D. Ross is a pre-eminent ethical intuitionist. Although Warren is a contractarian and not an intuitionist, he thinks some of Ross's rules would appeal to a majority in the original position.

UP FOR DISCUSSION

Can a person have duties to himself or herself? What duties would they include? Would they count as reasons against Wendy's CSBC?

Patrick says: So it seems we all agree that the harms to Wendy herself are not, by themselves, sufficiently weighty to show that choosing CSBC is wrong. The wrongness depends importantly on other factors, in particular on harms to the baby.

Warren says: And to others.

Doran says: What harms to others do you have in mind, Warren?

---

[23] Ross, *The Right and the Good*, 21.

Harms to Others besides the Baby and the Mother

Warren says: CSBC may cause various sorts of harms to others besides the mother and the infant. These harms are more at the level of a policy that allows for CSBC than for any individual CSBC. So let's focus on that.

UP FOR DISCUSSION

A Brazilian study claims that three-quarters of CSBC mothers surveyed said that the choice was not really theirs but that of their doctors or their partners. In a society where there is evidence that CSBC undermines women's autonomy, should CSBC be allowed? Does this affect the permissibility of CSBC in other societies? How, in general, do strong social pressures to accept medically unnecessary procedures affect their permissibility?

Source: See D. P. Béhague, C. G. Victora, and F. C. Barros, "Consumer Demand for Caesarean Sections in Brazil: Informed Decision Making, Patient Choice, or Social Inequality? A Population Based Birth Cohort Study Linking Ethnographic and Epidemiological Methods," *British Medical Journal* 324, no. 7343 (2002): 942–45.

UP FOR DISCUSSION

In opposing the position that CSBC enhances women's autonomy, Véronique Bergeron claims that informed consent cannot be meaningfully exercised unless women are made aware of the sexist underpinnings of the medical model of childbirth and its influence on the ethical reasoning of the American College of Obstetricians and Gynecologists. Are there moral implications of such a position for Wendy's CSBC? What, if any, evidence of harms to women's autonomy generally would be sufficient to deny the permissibility of CSBC as a policy?

Source: See Véronique Bergeron, "The Ethics of Cesarean Section on Maternal Request: A Feminist Critique of the American College of Obstetricians and Gynecologists' Position on Patient-Choice Surgery," *Bioethics* 21, no. 9 (2007): 478–87.

Patrick says: Okay, what harms to others do you see resulting from a policy that allows women the option of CSBC?

Warren says: There are harms both to the medical system and to women in general. Since our time is almost up, and since the whole question of whether CSBC harms women is very tricky, let me focus on the relatively straightforward issue of harms to the medical system.

Patrick says: Do you have in mind financial burdens to our medical system that could result if we had a policy permitting CSBC?

Warren says: Yes. I have here a recent study which says that Caesarean delivery costs 60 percent more than vaginal birth, and that $36,640,000 could be saved each year in Canada just by reducing Caesarean delivery from 26 percent to 20 percent of live births.[24] In a public health care system that is strapped for cash, this is an unjustified expense for a medically unnecessary procedure. That money could be used, for instance, to lessen the excessive wait times for some medically necessary procedures.

Doran says: There seems to be something right about your point that we should not burden an already stressed public medical system with unnecessary, costly medical procedures. Although I wonder whether our public system offers other unnecessary,

---

[24] British Columbia Perinatal Health Program, *Caesarean Birth Task Force Report 2008.*

costly medical procedures. If so, then there may be a fairness requirement that allows for publicly funded CSBC as well.

Patrick says: Right. It's not at all clear to me that a publicly funded system of health care should provide only medically necessary procedures. And I wonder whether we can sharply distinguish procedures that are medically necessary from those that are not. Intuitively, the distinction seems clear. But suppose, for instance, that a pregnant woman prefers a home birth to a hospital birth because the latter conflicts with deeply held religious beliefs or values. Would the possible psychological harms of a hospital birth make the home birth medically necessary? If not, should it still be funded in a public system like the one we have in Canada?

Doran says: Those are good questions, but we cannot adequately address them in the remaining time. So I suggest we set them aside, and focus on Warren's claim that a policy permitting CSBC would add an additional, and unnecessary, burden to our health care system.

Patrick says: That's fine by me.

Doran says: Even if you are right, Warren, that we should not burden an already stressed public medical system with unnecessary, costly medical procedures, I am not sure we can apply the dollar amounts you just cited to CSBC, for surely some of the reasons that make C-section more expensive do not apply to CSBC. For instance, C-section in general is probably done on women who have more health problems than women who deliver vaginally, but that factor would not apply to CSBC. Also, there are undoubtedly added costs with emergency C-sections that happen in the middle of the night, but those would not apply to CSBC procedures, since they would be scheduled procedures.

Notice, further, that even if CSBC is more costly than vaginal delivery, this concern can be dealt with without stopping women

UP FOR DISCUSSION

What counts as an unnecessary, costly medical procedure? Can you think of unnecessary, costly medical procedures that our public health care system provides? Consider these procedures: vasectomies; providing "artificial blood" or "bloodless surgery" to replace blood transfusions for Jehovah's Witnesses; using obstetricians for births that could be safely delivered by less costly midwives. Are any of these procedures medically unnecessary? If the public health care system provides these procedures, does that mean we should offer CSBC, too? If we decide not to offer CSBC as part of publicly funded health care, then should we decide not to offer similarly costly and unnecessary procedures?

from having the option of CSBC. There may be a way to fund them privately, for instance, without harming the public health care system.

Patrick says: Well, a private system for CSBC might still end up harming the public health care system. Re-hospitalization is more common for C-section than for natural birth, and so complications arising from these private instances of CSBC may eventually cut into the public system.

Doran says: That's true. I grant that it may take some work to get a system including CSBC which would not harm the public health care system, but I think we can see that it is at least a live possibility. Costs do not provide a reason, in principle, for the impermissibility of CSBC as a practice. But they may provide a reason against providing CSBC in the public system, if it turns out to be more costly than vaginal delivery.

Patrick says: The issue of allowing private CSBC gets tricky. There would be concerns about allowing access to CSBC only to the relatively wealthy, for instance, and that, of course, raises questions of fairness.

Doran says: Good point, Patrick. Whether it would be unfair or not to offer CSBC only on a private-payer basis raises the whole complicated issue of the morality of offering private health care alongside a public health care system. This is a very interesting topic, but is best saved for a separate debate.[25]

Patrick says: Agreed.

Warren says: Well, it looks as though you two aren't convinced either that CSBC is more expensive than vaginal delivery, or that it would be wrong to adopt a policy permitting CSBC even if it could be shown that it is more expensive. I have more arguments up my sleeve, but they'll have to wait for another day.

UP FOR DISCUSSION

Is it unfair to offer CSBC only to women who can afford to pay for it? If so, how strong a reason would that provide to oppose a policy which allowed private CSBC?

UP FOR DISCUSSION

There are many medically unnecessary procedures that physicians do not offer. Do you think this one ought to be offered? Why or why not? What distinguishes it?

UP FOR DISCUSSION

In the final analysis, do you think that Wendy's CSBC is morally wrong? In general, is CSBC wrong? Why or why not? Have your views or reasons changed in the light of this debate? If so, how?

---

[25] See our discussion of two-tier health care in Chapter 8.

SUMMARY

Here is a summary of the main questions, concepts, and arguments covered in this chapter:

- The main questions explored are *Is it morally permissible for Wendy to have a CSBC? Is it morally permissible for women in general to have CSBC?*
- CSBC is defined as a C-section that is not medically necessary, but rather chosen by the mother for non-medical reasons.
- *Autonomy* is defined as self-determination. The right to autonomy refers to a person's right to make her own decisions, including the right to choose her course of care without undue interference.
- The available evidence suggests that CSBC may carry greater risk to the child and mother than planned vaginal births. However, the data regarding the risks and benefits of CSBC are not conclusive, and the correct interpretation is a matter of some dispute.
- Doran argues for a strong presumption in favour of respecting the autonomous choices of patients. This presumption ought to be respected unless it is seriously wrong in other respects. Doran argues that Wendy's CSBC was autonomously chosen and was not seriously wrong in other respects. Although he admits that CSBC poses greater risks to the mother and baby than vaginal birth, he does not think these risks are great enough to override a woman's right to autonomy. He concludes, therefore, that it was morally permissible for Wendy to have a CSBC.
- Patrick argues that CSBC is permissible in some cases, but given the possible risk of very serious harms to the child, it is permissible only in cases where one has sufficiently good non-medical reasons for choosing a C-section delivery. Wendy does not have sufficiently good reason; her choice for a C-section manifests various vices and is therefore morally wrong.
- Warren agrees with Patrick's conclusion that Wendy's CSBC is morally wrong, but he agrees for different reasons. Persons in the original position would support a strong right to autonomy; at the same time, however, they would not approve of parents' subjecting their children to serious risk without any clear benefit. Since Wendy's having a CSBC would put her child at risk of serious harms, CSBC is wrong in her case.
- The questions of whether a policy that permits CSBC would be justified in a public system of health care like the one we have in Canada, and the permissibility of CSBC if it is performed and paid for privately, are briefly considered.

Review Questions

1. What does *autonomy* mean?
2. What are the possible benefits and risks of CSBC?
3. Why is the ethical debate over CSBC complicated by the fact that experts disagree about the benefits and risks of CSBC?
4. What is Doran's autonomy-based argument for the permissibility of CSBC?
5. Why do Warren and Patrick hold that Doran's argument is unsound?
6. Explain Warren's *good reason requirement*. What does he think it implies regarding the permissibility of Wendy's CSBC and CSBC in general?
7. Why does Doran reject the good reason requirement?
8. Patrick contends that it would be morally wrong for Wendy to have a CSBC. Why? Does he believe that CSBC is always wrong? Why or why not?
9. Why does Doran reject Warren's and Patrick's arguments that CSBC is wrong in Wendy's case?
10. Why might a general policy that permits CSBC be wrong, even if Wendy's CSBC is not wrong?

WWW.MCGRAWHILL.CA/OLC/SMOLKIN

CHAPTER 8

TWO-TIER HEALTH CARE

INTRODUCTION

Up until the late 1940s, health care in Canada was paid for privately. Access to medical services was based on one's ability to pay for it. In 1947, however, the government of Saskatchewan introduced the first provincial public health insurance plan that covered hospital services. Other provinces soon followed Saskatchewan's lead, and by the early 1970s, all the provinces provided universal public health insurance for both hospital and physician services. Although the administration of these services is the responsibility of the provinces, they receive funding from the federal government. In 1984, Parliament passed the *Canada Health Act,* which specifies criteria the provinces must meet in order to receive federal funding. Among other requirements, the provinces must provide "comprehensive" and "universal" care to all insured residents.

While Canada's public and universal health care system is the envy of many, it is not without its critics. In recent years, the system has come under fire for increasingly long waits for diagnostic procedures and other services. As we write this chapter, patients requiring **magnetic resonance imaging (MRI),** for instance, must wait from four to six

DEFINITION

MRI stands for **magnetic resonance imaging,** a technique for scanning for muscle and joint injuries. Both the scans and the machines that perform the scan are referred to as MRIs.

months. Over the past several years, private medical clinics offering MRI services have been popping up around the country. Those who can afford the roughly $900 fee for a straightforward MRI can now receive one within days in the private sector. Many see this move toward a blended private/public, or **two-tier, health care** system as a positive development, one that will help to take some of the pressure off of the public system and thereby benefit everyone, while others worry that a blended system will erode the public system.

Our drama focuses on Sanders and Ben, two talented high-school hockey players who have the potential to achieve their dream of playing in the Juniors, which may lead to the NHL with its promise of riches and fame. Unfortunately, both players are injured and need MRIs to determine the nature of their injuries and the best course of treatment. Sanders is lucky: he comes from a wealthy family that can afford to buy him a private MRI. Ben, however, comes from a family of modest means. His family cannot afford a private MRI, and Ben is too independent and proud to accept an offer from his team to pay for one. Because Sanders can afford a private MRI and Ben cannot, Sanders can return to the ice much sooner than Ben, and thereby improve his prospects of making the NHL.

The general issue raised by our drama is whether a two-tier system of health care in Canada is morally acceptable. The more specific question we focus on is whether a two-tier system of MRI in Canada is morally acceptable. At the heart of this question is a conflict between liberty, on the one hand, and fairness and equality, on the other hand. Advocates of two-tier MRI argue that people should be free to purchase private medical services if they have the desire and means to do so. Critics argue, however, that it is unfair that the wealthy have access to faster and perhaps better care than the less wealthy. Respect for equality, among other values, requires equal access to care. A further issue raised by our drama, and explored in our debate, is whether it is morally appropriate for people to use the private health care system if the system itself is not permissible.

In this debate, there is significant agreement among Doran, Warren, and Patrick on the question whether two-tier MRI is morally permissible. They agree that it is permissible in Canada, provided that certain conditions are met. Although there are differences in their views about what the relevant conditions are, there is agreement that private MRI is permissible only if it does not undermine the public health care system and the provision of other important social goods (for example, education, social and economic opportunity). These are *necessary* conditions; the authors argue that further conditions must be met in order to show that private MRI is morally permissible in Canada. Warren, for one, is skeptical of the claim that private MRI in Canada can satisfy these conditions, and so he thinks that private MRI is likely not morally permissible in Canada.

LEARNING OBJECTIVES

After completing this chapter, you should be able to:

- Explain the libertarian argument against taxation to support public health care
- Understand why libertarians think that people should have a right to purchase private health care
- Discuss two egalitarian arguments against two-tier medicine (against adding private to public medicine)
- State objections to these egalitarian arguments
- Describe Warren's, Patrick's, and Doran's views on when two-tier MRI is justified
- Explain why Warren and Patrick think it is permissible for Canadians to access two-tier MRI even if the government should not allow private medicine, and explain Doran's argument to the contrary

DRAMA

Please note: This case is based on various true stories, although names, places, and some uncontroversial elements of the case have been changed to preserve anonymity and confidentiality. Discussions of this and similar cases with health care professionals have also informed this fictional case. The drama merely raises issues. The philosophical arguments are to be found in the debate following the drama.

CHARACTERS

Coach: *the coach of a high-school-age hockey team*
  Art: *a former player on Coach's team*

The scene is a family restaurant where Coach sits looking glum as he eats breakfast. A former player of his, Art, walks in.

Art: Hey, Coach! It's been a long time.

Coach: Art, my man! Where've you been?

Art: Uganda. I've been setting up a computer system for Makerere University on a CIDA project.

Coach: Hell, not much ice time there, I'll bet.

Art: Yeah, hockey is not a concept there. Hell, cold is not a concept. Hey, I hear you're coaching the Arrows now.

Coach: Yeah.

Art: You don't sound overjoyed, Coach. What's up?

Coach: Don't get me wrong. I love the job. It's just player injuries that are weighing on my mind. You see, I've got this line we call the Sandbag Line that has been doing all the scoring. Ben Begin and Sanders Carter are what really make it cook. Sanders is right wing. Ben is left, and they click like magic. Ben sets up the play and Sanders pops it in.

Art: Who got hurt?

Coach: That's the hell of it. Both are hurt. Ben took a bad hit in the last game of this season and his knee is bad, but they don't know for sure what it is. They need to do an MRI. They told him he's got at least a three-month wait for that!

Art: Geez, that's hard. At least he finished the season. But man, three months is a lifetime when you're that age.

Coach: God, yes. A kid like that laid up through the summer. Ouch! So that injury was four weeks ago. The thing is, will he be diagnosed and treated in time to start next season? I'm really pulling for this kid. He's got heart. His family hasn't got two nickels to rub together, and since he's been old enough he's always worked and helped out with the costs. Hockey is expensive. His family scrimped and saved to put him in hockey and keep him there until he was old enough to handle most of the costs by taking part-time jobs. His family can't help any more. They've got younger kids to look after. Ben just keeps plugging away, though. He buys all his gear second hand. He just loves the game. He doesn't let anything stop him. But he may be skewered now.

Art: Let's hope not. What about the other guy?

Coach: Well, Sanders hurt himself hang gliding just last week. He did something to his shoulder. Talk about a contrast. He gets an MRI the next day 'cause his Dad can plunk down $875 like it was a penny. Carter owns that fancy restaurant, *Le Maître,* and half a dozen other businesses. It turns out that Sanders's family physician went to med school with the top specialist and Sanders has already had his operation. No chance he won't be starting next season. If you can prime the pump with a few bucks, the government will let the treatment flow. If you can't, you wait.

Art: Yeah, it stinks.

Coach: Don't get me wrong. I'm happy for Sanders, but he's had everything handed to him on a plate. You know, he gets the best of everything, the latest gear. He's not a bad guy, but spoiled and a bit full of himself, of course. He offered to give Ben his old equipment whenever something new comes on the market, but Ben insists on buying it. Still, Ben is better equipped than he could be otherwise, so Ben kind of benefits too from old man Carter's largesse. The thing is, if we don't do something, Sanders will be out there hot-dogging around catching the eye of the scouts while Ben will still be laid up, you know? That could be crucial. That might make a career difference, see?

Art: "Them that's got shall get, them that's not shall lose, so the Bible says, and it still is news."

Coach: That about sums it up. What's that saying from?

Art: The song "God Bless the Child."

Coach: Oh, yeah. Great song.

Art: You know, Coach, it's all relative. Kids I know in Africa see Ben's life as the impossible dream. They'd all give their right arm to be in his shoes.

Coach: Yeah, that puts it in perspective. Life ain't fair, and it's more unfair there than here. But damn it, Artie, this is Canada. At least at home we pride ourselves on being fair to our own.

Art: So why don't you and the team help Ben out?

Coach: We tried to fix it. The team was to have a big garage sale and raise the money for Ben's MRI. He was embarrassed as hell about it. He said he refused to be a charity case. So I told him we need him. This is as much for us as for him. He flat-out refused. Sanders had already offered to pay the whole shot, and Ben wouldn't take it from Sanders either, but it's different when it's the team doing it. Ben won't buy that. Ben has a lot of pride. Too much for his own good sometimes, but then again, that's why he's where he is in spite of his background. Only fierce independence would have kept him fighting to be in the game this long.

Art: This is really getting to you, isn't it, Coach?

Coach: Yes, and it's not just the kids, Art. There's seniors in this town hobbling around waiting for knee surgery. Damn it, Art, it's not Africa here. The government should give everybody the medical help they need. In a rich country like this, nobody should have to beg for the essentials.

DEBATE

Clarifying the Case and Identifying Relevant Facts

Doran says: Let's briefly review the case. Both Ben and Sanders are promising young talents, and both get injured and have to wait for a magnetic resonance imaging procedure, or MRI. Sanders's father is a wealthy businessman and pays for a private MRI for his son. Ben can't afford that. The team was planning a fundraiser to get him a private MRI too so he won't have to wait four to six months. But Ben will not accept the charity, since he finds charity degrading. Is that the basic scenario?

Warren says: Yes, Ben is fiercely proud, hard-working, poor, gets his equipment second hand, and works part-time. Sanders is a skilled player like Ben, although unlike Ben, Sanders gets everything given to him: the best equipment, private lessons, even a conditioning coach. Ben lacks these advantages, and he is outraged at being seen as a charity case.

Patrick says: And these boys are still in high school?

Warren says: Yes, but they are at the age where the scouts are starting to watch them. They are waiting to be picked to play in the Juniors in towns like Medicine Hat and Swift Current, the first big step toward the NHL.

Patrick says: So a concern here is that Ben may have to miss the next season, whereas Sanders won't, and this could hurt Ben's prospects for turning pro.

Warren says: Right.

Doran says: If Sanders gets his MRI more quickly, then presumably he will get his diagnosis more quickly, but does it also mean he will get treated for the problem sooner?

Warren says: Yes.

BACKGROUND

"The rapid growth of private MRI (magnetic resonance imaging) clinics, which permit people to purchase faster service and then use test results to 'jump the queue' back into the public system for treatment, is a troubling case. . . ."

Source: Roy J. Romanow, Commissioner, *Building on Values: The Future of Health Care in Canada—Final Report,* Commission on the Future of Health Care in Canada, November 2002, xxi, http://publications.gc.ca/pub?id=237274&sl=0.

Doran says: Why? Isn't there a backlog for physical therapy, surgery, rehab, and other procedures?

Warren says: Surgeons and physical therapists often have room to treat people. Our story takes place in the diagnostic part of the queue, where there is a bottleneck. Sanders gets in line for surgery first, in any case.

Doran says: Are private MRIs legal in Canada?

Warren says: It's iffy, but they are being done. Private clinics even advertise newer, superior scanners.

Doran says: How are MRIs delivered privately? Are they always done in private clinics?

Warren says: Usually. Some hospitals have rented out their machinery to private clinicians after hours, but I think that has been stopped.

Doran says: Do you know the cost of an MRI?

Warren says: As we speak, depending on how much competition they have from other clinics, they will price it from about $875 for a basic knee scan. This is one of the easy and profitable MRIs to do. The difficult ones may be left for the public system. They'd be a lot more expensive to purchase privately.

Patrick says: I suppose if they were not offered in Canada, patients could go down to the States, get an MRI, and then bring back the report to their physician in Canada?

Warren says: Yes.

Doran says: Why doesn't the government buy more of these machines if there is such a shortage? Are the costs that out of line?

Warren says: The costs are very high, around $3 million per MRI scanner to purchase, and hundreds of thousands per year to run and maintain.

Doran says: Ouch!

Warren says: There is also a shortage of technicians, and it takes time and money to train them and much more money to pay their salaries. So, adding more MRIs would require more staff to run them, and that adds greatly to their costs.

Patrick says: Is there evidence that shows that allowing private MRI shortens the wait times in the public system?

BACKGROUND

Chaoulli vs. Quebec (Attorney General), [2005] 1 S.C.R. 791 held that Quebec's ban on private health insurance violated both Quebec's Charter and the Canadian Charter of Rights and Freedoms. *McCreith v. Her Majesty the Queen* is another case concerning private insurance. In both cases, private MRI was sought because of delays in the Canadian public system. The Canadian Association of Radiologists (CAR) described the 22-month wait for MRI in Saskatchewan as "almost criminal" and warned that the province could face legal action from patients. "Denial of care is a violation of the *Canada Health Act*," said CAR chief executive Dr. Normand Laberge.

Source: Amy Jo Ehman, "Saskatchewan's 22-Month Wait for an MRI Is 'Almost Criminal' Says Radiologists' Association," *CMAJ* 170, no. 5 (2004): 776.

BACKGROUND

"There is clear evidence that Canada has under-invested in diagnostic technologies in comparison with other OECD countries and the result is long waiting times for essential diagnostic tests."

Source: Romanow, *Building on Values: The Future of Health Care in Canada—Final Report*, xxix.

BACKGROUND

"There is no evidence that these clinics will do better than public MRIs and CTs to improve wait times, safety, costs or quality. In fact, the evidence is that they are costlier and riskier. They cream the most profitable easiest tests and pull scarce personnel out of the public system. They create more problems as the public system struggles to provide the most expensive complex tests with less people and fewer resources."

Source: Ontario Health Coalition, *The Pulse,* September 2002, http://web.net/ohc/docs/09023pulse.htm.

Doran says: Yes, would things be worse in the public system without them?

Warren says: There are complaints from some groups that private MRI does not help the public system and, in fact, hurts it. On the other hand, people are waiting up to six months in the public system to get MRIs, so private clinics are offering their services to shorten wait times.

Patrick says: So, as things are, if someone tears a ligament or something, that person has to wait that long in the public system just to get the scan? Clearly, more diagnostic equipment and technicians are needed.

Warren says: Yes, but you can understand governments' reluctance to increase diagnostic procedures. More diagnostics can make for strains on other parts of the system. I have anecdotal evidence that people have needless exploratory operations now because of MRIs done in the States that show a possible problem that turns out to be benign. Before MRI, the apparent problem would never have been noticed. Add to that the lack of clarity about whether the private MRIs really reduce wait times in the public system, and you can see why the system managers avoid just pouring money into this one.[1]

Patrick says: Interesting, Warren. Well, if Ben does get an MRI, and if it turns out he needs surgery, I wonder how long it will take to receive the necessary operation. Do you know?

Warren says: I think it is pretty quick for the surgery. Weeks in Ben's case, I bet. It depends on the specialty needed, the demand for the needed procedure, availability of appropriate facilities in the area where it's being done, and other factors such as these—factors that commonly affect the responsiveness of a health care system.

Patrick says: Some might wonder whether there really is a problem in this case, though. If Ben really is talented and set on a career in the NHL,

---

[1] Private MRI clinics have been shown to do scans more often than hospitals, which raises a concern about unnecessary scans. See J. M. Mitchell and J. H. Sunshine, "Consequences of Physicians' Ownership of Health Care Facilities—Joint Ventures in Radiation Therapy," *New England Journal of Medicine* 327, no. 21 (1992): 1497–1501.

and an MRI costs (only!) $875, then it seems that it wouldn't be too hard to find a way to pay for it.

Warren says: Ben is from a large family. His parents can't help. He is strapped supporting his hockey habit with work after school—$875 is huge in those circumstances. His family is already deeply in debt and unable to take on more, given their meagre salaries.

Patrick says: I suppose that's right. For some, $875 is no big deal, but for others it's rent.

Doran says: The situation is particularly tough for Ben, since it has already cost him and his family a lot just to equip him and to pay the fees to get him on a team. Indeed, more and more Canadians are unable even to play organized hockey because they cannot afford it. Ben's family has made all those sacrifices to get him to this point, but this last obstacle is too great. Coming up with the extra $875 is simply beyond their means.

BACKGROUND

A Statistics Canada publication bears out the claim that there are declining rates of child participation in sports, and participation rates are higher for wealthier than for poorer Canadians.

Source: Warren Clark, "Kids' Sports," *Canadian Social Trends*, 3 June 2008, www.statcan.gc.ca/pub/11-008-x/2008001/article/10573-eng.pdf.

Warren says: Ben's coach says that the team would have a garage sale to cover the costs of a private MRI. However, Ben has been raised to be ruggedly independent, so he is totally unwilling to be a charity case.

Patrick says: So Ben's lack of resources puts him, yet again, in a difficult position that Sanders doesn't face. Ben either waits for the MRI, and thereby puts his hockey career in jeopardy, or he gets the private MRI, but only by accepting charity contrary to all he and his family hold dear.

Warren says: And pulling himself out of poverty by getting a shot at the Juniors and ultimately at the NHL makes the opportunity to be scouted for professional teams mean so much more to Ben than to Sanders.

Patrick says: Right. If Sanders doesn't make it in hockey, he likely has other lucrative career options. For Ben, it appears that pro hockey is his ticket out of poverty.

Warren says: Ben's grades aren't great because he puts it all into hockey, and working part-time doesn't leave him much time to study.

Doran says: Well, if I were Ben, I'd take the charity! Then, when and if I made it to the NHL, I'd repay the generosity in spades.

Patrick says: I'd probably do the same, Doran. So, is there really a difficult choice here for Ben?

Warren says: Only because Ben is so proud and independent is he on the team at all. It's a point of honour for him that he takes nothing he doesn't pay for. It has been hard enough on Ben that he sometimes buys Sanders's used equipment at a very good price. For Ben to go so far as to accept the team's charity would be a very difficult pill to swallow. It's that spirit of independence that has kept him on the team against the odds for a guy with no resources. He has fierce pride in supporting himself.

Patrick says: You seem to be saying that the decision for Ben becomes a choice between economic and social position on the one hand and self-respect on the other. Well, one thing we need to know to assess that claim is how much the wait for his MRI will affect Ben's chance of a career in hockey. I imagine it's not uncommon for young players to get injured and have to miss part or all of a season. Does this really seriously affect their chances?

Warren says: At this stage in his hockey development, Ben is likely to suffer huge disadvantages if he misses too much of the coming season. His skills may get rusty, his conditioning will no doubt suffer, he will miss the start of the season, and he will probably be viewed by the scouts as injury prone. As a result, he may not look very good to the scouts in the future if he is off for an extended period. There is a tide in the affairs of a young hockey player, which, taken at the flood, leads on to the NHL. The timing is crucial for Ben. His boat might be left high and dry at low tide after Sanders sails away. If, moreover, Ben does have to wait even the average time for an MRI, he may become more difficult to treat, and treatment may not be as successful. These would be disadvantages for any athlete, but in the fierce competition for the attention of the scouts and for a place in the top rung of the Juniors, this delay can be very significant.

MORAL ISSUES RAISED BY THE CASE

Patrick says: Okay, I think we've got the relevant background facts straight. The main moral issues raised by the case are pretty straightforward— they concern the permissibility of two-tier MRI in particular, and two-tier health care in general, given the apparent unfairness this involves.

Doran says: Perhaps we should limit ourselves to the more specific question, though. I would be content if we could clarify the simpler question of whether private MRI is morally acceptable in Canada. Clarifying our thoughts on this question would be very helpful since this is a matter of current concern in Canada. Also, if we reach some conclusions about this more limited question, it may serve as a template for thinking about the larger question of whether two-tier health care, in general, is morally appropriate in Canada.

Warren says: Yes, given the complexity of the problem, let's just stick to the more limited question of whether private MRI is morally permissible in Canada. A caveat, however, is in order. Whether or not two-tier medicine in Canada can be effectively delivered is largely an empirical question. As philosophers, we have no special insight into such matters. What we can do, however, is try to answer the following question: *Is two-tier MRI ever morally acceptable, even in principle, and if so, under what conditions?*

Patrick says: That sounds right. Well, why don't we begin as usual by stating our initial views on this issue.

Stating Our Positions

Doran says: The question of two-tier MRI in Canada brings to the fore a host of moral values: front and centre are questions of liberty, equality, fairness, compassion, self-respect, and so on. Those who favour liberty as a basic value may defend the permissibility of private MRI as a matter of principle; those who are motivated by compassion or care may also support private MRI if it means their loved ones will get needed care more quickly. On the other hand, fairness, equality, and the value of self-respect seem to speak in favour of a single system that distributes health care on medical grounds alone and does not give special advantages to those who happen to be affluent. I am torn by this difficult issue; however, I believe that two-tier MRI in Canada is morally permissible, but only if certain conditions are met. For me, the most important conditions are (1) two-tier MRI must not threaten the robust social safety net that should be available to all Canadians, and (2) where such a social safety net is lacking, two-tier MRI ought to be allowed only if it is the best means of providing this robust social safety net.

Warren says: First of all, let me say that I sympathize with those who seek private MRI, since it is a moral failing of the Canadian government not to support public MRI facilities adequately. As you say, this issue is extremely difficult. I agree with your first condition given Canada's current wealth, but that could change. From the **original position,** people would require different degrees of strength of the safety net depending on the society's wealth. Condition 2 is too simple, in my view. I wouldn't always require that MRI be the *best* means to provide a robust social safety net. To develop the details of my view on that, however, would take all day. It's enough to say that given its wealth, Canada should provide a robust social safety net, but it has failed to do so. Allowing private MRI, moreover, will not help provide such a safety net. My view depends on some empirical claims. For instance, I suspect private MRI will drain talent from the public system. Private MRI may cause other social harms as well outside the health care system. I think, therefore, that allowing private MRI is not morally permissible in Canada under current conditions.

THEORY

Some virtue theories speak only to matters of character and moral claims among individuals. They have nothing to say about the design of social institutions. Patrick's virtue theory is rather idiosyncratic, as it incorporates elements of "ideal observer" theories. The right act or policy is the one that a virtuous person with full information would see as right. This allows a broader application of his virtue theory.

Patrick says: Well, it seems unfair that those who happen to be wealthy have better access to such a basic good as medical care. However, I believe that private MRI would be morally permissible if certain conditions were met. If allowing private MRI benefits those in the public system, then I believe it is permissible. Private MRI may also be permissible, I think, even if it doesn't benefit others, provided that it doesn't harm those in the public system. A virtuous society would be a compassionate society, one that ensures that everyone has a reasonable stock of **primary social goods**—that is, goods that everyone (or almost everyone) needs to live well. So, as long as private MRI improves everyone's lot, or at least doesn't worsen things, then I believe it is permissible. This is just a rough statement of my current view, but I'll refine it as necessary as we proceed.

Doran says: It looks as if we all agree that two-tier MRI could be morally permissible under the right sorts of conditions, though we differ somewhat on the conditions that would need to be in place in order to make two-tier MRI morally acceptable. Now that we have the rough, initial statements of our views, how would you like to proceed?

Patrick says: Given the complexity of the problem, and given that each of us claims to support two-tier MRI in some circumstances but not in others, it may be best if we begin with some of the more straightforward and extreme views, such as that private MRI is always permissible, or that private MRI is never permissible.

Doran says: I agree. By understanding why these simpler arguments fail, we may also see why a more nuanced position with respect to two-tier MRI is best.

Warren says: Yes, once we consider these more extreme views, we can turn to our own positions, and see if there are any devils in the details.

A LIBERTARIAN ARGUMENT

Doran says: **Libertarians** would defend the existence of private MRI on the ground that it would be unjust for the government to prohibit it. The basic thought is that the government should not interfere with the liberty of its people unless it is necessary to prevent force or fraud. In the marketplace, people should be free to do what they want provided that it does not violate anyone else's rights.

Patrick says: That's right. According to libertarians, if I have justly acquired some wealth, then I have the right to spend my wealth in any manner that I choose, provided that doing so does not violate anyone else's rights. If, for instance, Sanders's father wants to purchase an MRI for his son, and if someone else wants to sell him one, then they should be free to make that exchange, provided that doing so violates no one else's rights.

Doran says: So putting these points together, the libertarian argument as it relates to the present case can be stated as follows:

(1) If a person freely consents to an action and the action does not violate the rights of others, then the government is not morally permitted to interfere with that action.

(2) If a person does not engage in force or fraud, then the person does not violate the rights of others.

(3) Sanders freely consents to getting a private MRI without engaging in any force or fraud.

(4) Therefore, the government is not morally permitted to interfere with Sanders's getting that private MRI.

Patrick says: That sounds like a libertarian argument, but the libertarian position, of course, goes well beyond just arguing for the permissibility of private MRI. Libertarians also argue that publicly provided health care is inherently unjust. This is because they contend that the taxation needed to fund a public health care system is inherently unjust.

THEORY

"[T]axation of earnings from labor is on a par with forced labor. . . . Taking the earnings of n hours of labor is like taking n hours from the person; it is like forcing the person to work n hours for another's purpose."

Source: Nozick, *Anarchy, State, and Utopia*, 169.

Forcing people to pay for a public system, they claim, violates people's rights.

Doran says: That's true, the radical position being considered here maintains that not only should people be free to purchase private health care, but also taxation to fund a public system violates taxpayers' rights.

Warren says: Why should anyone believe such claims? It seems strange to me that one would want to have things like MRI governed by the free market rather than regulated reasonably by government, since the market can leave people like Ben out in the cold through no fault of their own. Why should we think that the taxation needed to fund a public system is unjust, and why should we think that the market should determine who receives health care and under what conditions?

Patrick says: I share your concerns, Warren. The premises in this argument seem to depend on an unreasonably narrow conception of rights. In particular, they seem to depend on the idea that the only rights people have are **negative rights.** But why should we accept that? Many of us believe that persons have **positive rights** to basic goods like education, health care, shelter, etc.

The Wilt Chamberlain Example

Doran says: It may help to see some of the intuitive pull of the libertarian's premises by looking at a famous example presented by Robert Nozick.[2] It goes like this. Suppose we start with a system that is considered fair by the libertarian's opponents. In this initial distribution everyone has equal wealth (or wealth is distributed according to the **difference principle** or whatever principle you consider a fair distribution principle).

Wilt Chamberlain, an amazing basketball player, then signs a contract with a team that allows him to get 25 cents for every ticket sold. A million people cheerfully go to see Wilt play in a season—they happily drop 25 cents in a box with Wilt's name on it. At the end of the year, Wilt has a lot more money than others in the society—$250,000.

THEORY

Philosophical analyses of rights commonly distinguish **negative rights** from **positive rights.** The former are characterized as rights to non-interference, while the latter are described as rights to be provided with money, goods, services, etc. Thus, for example, my right not to be physically harmed may be understood as a negative right, as it imposes a duty on others not to do a variety of things. If I also have a right to be assisted by others when I am in need, then I would also have a positive right to aid. A right to health care is understood as a positive right, then, since its satisfaction requires the provision of various goods and services.

THEORY

The **difference principle** says that a just society should distribute income and wealth equally, unless inequality benefits everyone, especially those in the worst-off group. It is one of the principles of justice favoured by John Rawls. For more on Rawls's theory of justice, see Chapter 2.

---

[2] Nozick, *Anarchy, State, and Utopia*, 160–64.

But how can we say that he is not entitled to his money? In the initial distribution, by hypothesis, people were entitled to their wealth. They then gave some of their money to Wilt

BACKGROUND

Wilt Chamberlain was an amazing player in days gone by. He once scored 100 points in an NBA game, and still holds 72 NBA records.

freely and happily. Now, if the government taxes Wilt's income in order to give to people in need, or to fund health care or other social programs, then it is taking something that properly belongs to Wilt. The government is treating Wilt merely as a means to some other end. And that, says Nozick, is inherently unjust.

Patrick says: I think the example does have intuitive pull. The idea is that if people start out with what they are morally entitled to, and if they voluntarily make choices that result in a new economic distribution (with Wilt having more money than others), then that new economic distribution is also just. If the government then steps in to take away some of the money that Wilt was voluntarily given, then that intuitively seems unfair to Wilt, since it violates his right to money he fairly acquired.

Warren says: Okay, I see the intuitive pull of this example. And I suppose libertarians claim that this point about Wilt Chamberlain can be generalized so that it applies to cases like the one we're considering.

Doran says: That's right. Suppose Sanders's father has played by the rules of society, has worked hard, and has earned a large fortune. It seems unjust that someone should now step in and take away some of his justly acquired wealth. Moreover, if Sanders's father wants to use some of his wealth to buy an MRI for his son, and if some physician who has justly acquired an MRI machine wants to sell him an MRI scan, then it seems that it would be unjust for the government to prohibit that. A system that takes away one's justly acquired holdings, or that prevents one from using one's justly acquired holdings in ways that one wants, does seem unjust.

Patrick says: So the Wilt Chamberlain example helps to motivate premises (1) and (2) in the libertarian argument. In support of premise (2), it suggests that Wilt's acquisition of wealth violated no one's rights, since he acquired his money not through force or fraud, but through a voluntary exchange of money for services. And given that Wilt did not acquire his money in a way that violated the rights of others, then, in support of (1), the example suggests

THEORY

A **redistributive tax** aims at redistributing wealth, typically by taking money via taxation from those who are relatively wealthy with the purpose of benefiting those who are relatively less wealthy (say, through welfare payments, day care subsidies for the children of poor people, pensions for low-income seniors, etc.), or with the purpose of promoting various social goods (such as the arts, parks, public schools, and public health care). Other taxes are not redistributive—for instance, taxes that are used to punish criminals, prevent crime, and secure the nation's defence. Libertarians oppose redistributive taxation but do not oppose non-redistributive taxation.

TECHNIQUE

The Wilt Chamberlain example is meant to have intuitive appeal. Doran has weakened that appeal by providing an example that is meant to have intuitive appeal in the opposite direction. Libertarians can give examples that elicit intuitions that support their view, but supporters of redistributive taxation can give other examples that elicit perhaps stronger intuitions that support their view.

that it would be wrong for the government to interfere with this voluntary exchange of money for services by imposing a **redistributive taxation** scheme that forced Wilt to give up a certain percentage of the money he's been given.

Is Redistributive Taxation Inherently Unjust?

Warren says: Both of the libertarian's premises are problematic. Let's start by looking more closely at the first premise. Suppose, for now, that Wilt acquires his wealth in a way that does not violate anyone's rights, since he does not use force or fraud. Does it follow from this that it would be wrong for the government to interfere with the exchange of money for services by forcing Wilt to pay taxes on the money he collects in order to fund social programs? More generally, is redistributive taxation inherently unjust?

Patrick says: To answer this question, let's see if we can follow the same basic strategy as the libertarian, but present an example that elicits intuitions on the other side—intuitions that support the claim that redistributive taxation is *not* unjust. If we can do this, then we will have less reason to find the original Wilt Chamberlain example persuasive.

Doran says: Good, so let's tell a story that parallels the Chamberlain example but elicits different intuitions. We begin with some initial distribution of wealth that is agreed to be fair—say, everyone has an equal amount of wealth. Now, suppose that Mary Andrews is a hard-working young woman just recently graduated from college. She is looking forward to her new career as a preschool teacher. Tragically for Mary, and through no fault of her own, she discovers a lump on her breast. It turns out to be cancer. Mary needs an operation, and she needs chemotherapy and radiation treatment. Though she suffers terribly, Mary is courageous and strong, and she is determined to live and to beat her cancer. So, Mary takes all of her savings and pays for her operation, and her chemotherapy and radiation. During this time she is very weak and so she must take time off from work, but because of the excellent care of her physicians and nurses, and because of her sheer strength and determination, Mary begins to feel better and she eventually is able to return to work. Unfortunately, at one of her follow-up appointments, she learns that her cancer has returned. She needs more chemotherapy and radiation.

With the chemotherapy her odds are 50/50 that she will be cured, but without it she will likely die within the year. Mary is determined to do battle again, but the trouble is, Mary has exhausted her savings and has not had time to replenish them. She simply cannot afford her treatments. She begs her bank for a loan, but it refuses. She is a credit risk—if she dies, the bank won't get its money back. For the same reason, her physicians are unwilling to have her defer payment. They want payment up front. Mary is powerless. She needs the treatments but she cannot afford them. Eventually, Mary realizes that she will die. There is nothing that she can do.

Patrick says: So here we have an example in which health care is governed by the free market. Since some people, like Mary, can't afford needed care, they must go without. A charity might, of course, step in and help Mary pay for the care she needs. But if she can't afford care, and no charities offer to help, then libertarians would say that this situation is unfortunate, but Mary has no *right* to the assistance of others.

Doran says: Right. But suppose we put the case of Mary Andrews beside the Wilt Chamberlain example, and we realize that there could be a public system that taxed Wilt and others who could afford to pay taxes. This money could then be used to fund a public medical system that could help save the lives of those who, like Mary, are unlucky and who fall ill. Is it still so obvious that it would be wrong to tax Wilt? Or do you have the opposite reaction that it would be unjust not to tax Wilt, if that was what was necessary to save Mary?

Warren says: Well, it seems clear to me that it would be better to tax Wilt and save Mary than to not save Mary and let Wilt keep all of his fortune. When you consider not just Wilt, but also Mary, and others like her, the Chamberlain example loses much of its intuitive force.

Patrick says: I agree that the Chamberlain example no longer looks that compelling once you begin to consider people like Mary who happen

> ## THEORY
>
> A **utilitarian** would agree with redistributive taxation if and only if it is the best way to maximize happiness, and minimize suffering, for all concerned. Given the **diminishing marginal utility** of money, it is very likely that utility will be maximized by taxing the wealthy like Wilt in order to provide the necessities for those that are very poor, like Mary. The idea of the diminishing marginal utility of money is roughly the idea that an extra bit of income is unlikely to benefit a person above a certain level of wealth as much as someone below a certain level of wealth. For instance, consider whether an extra $50 is likely to provide a greater benefit to a millionaire or to a person struggling to pay her rent.

TECHNIQUE

Patrick here is anticipating an objection the libertarian is likely to raise. By considering objections, and effectively responding to them, one provides more rational support for one's view.

THEORY

Immanuel Kant, in *The Groundwork of the Metaphysics of Morals*, writes, "Man, and in general every rational being, exists as an end in himself, not merely as a means for arbitrary use by this or that will: he must in all his actions, whether they are directed to himself or to other rational beings, always be viewed at the same time as an end. . . ."

To treat people merely as a means is to treat them in a way to which they do not freely consent. It is to treat them like tools, not like persons. Kant believes it is wrong to treat a person merely as means, because it disrespects a person's rational nature. According to Kant, a person is not a thing to be used, but a rational being whose decision-making capabilities are to be respected. The libertarian's point is that redistributive taxation is wrong because it treats those who are taxed in ways that they do not freely consent to, and hence, as mere means.

to be unlucky. However, the libertarian might respond to us by saying that even if a system of taxation that funded health care had good consequences, it is still wrong because it treats some (namely, those who are taxed) merely as a means to an end.

Doran says: Good point. But I wonder whether (a) it is always wrong to treat people merely as a means, and (b) whether people who are taxed really are treated merely as a means.

Kant clearly claims that people should never be treated merely as a means, but one could disagree with Kant. If the interference is relatively minor, and if the benefit is relatively large, one might believe it is *not* wrong to treat someone merely as a means. If Wilt and others who are wealthy are taxed and end up slightly less wealthy but still comfortable, and if doing this saves people who otherwise would have died or have been impoverished, then I do not think it would be wrong to do this, even if that is treating some as a mere means. The alternative strikes me as much worse.

Patrick says: Agreed. I think it's just plain false that we may *never* use people merely as a means. A compassionate society would ensure that its citizens' basic needs are met whenever feasible. It would not allow the distribution of things like housing, education, and medical care to be entirely up for grabs in a free market. To allow this would amount, in many cases, to rewarding the fortunate for their good fortune—their good genes, home, education, and so forth—and punishing the unfortunate for their bad fortune. If it is necessary to tax people in order to ensure that everyone's basic needs are satisfied, then that's what a virtuous society should do, even if this involves treating some people merely as a means.

Warren says: On my view, it is acceptable to sometimes treat people merely as a means. Specifically, when it comes to redistributive taxation, people in the original position would be in favour of it, insofar as it is necessary to provide a strong social safety net. Not knowing their own preferences for risk in the real world, it would be reasonable for people in the original position to avoid extreme libertarian or **egalitarian** policies and to occupy the middle ground with moderate redistribution. That way the choosers of rules in the original position would avoid being at the opposite extreme from where their real interests lie. That hypothetical endorsement, however, does not change the fact that some wealthy people's goals and reasons for them will be ignored in the real world by some kinds of redistributive taxation. Therefore, if we implement such policies in the real world, then some wealthy people will be treated merely as a means, but this is nevertheless the right thing to do, since this policy would be endorsed in the original position.

Doran says: While I also agree that it is sometimes permissible to treat people merely as a means, especially when such interferences are relatively minor, and when such interferences are necessary to prevent grave harm, I think it is worth considering whether redistributive taxation really does treat people merely as a means.

It could be argued that there is a straightforward sense in which redistributive taxation does not treat people merely as a means. Suppose you wanted to make a little extra money so as to take your family on a vacation next spring break. You learn about a part-time job that you could do in your spare time. The pay is $40 per hour, but you also realize that after taxes the pay will work out to $30 per hour. You have to decide whether or not it is still worth it to take the job. You decide it is clearly worth it. You then do ten hours of work and get your first cheque for $400 gross but only $300 net. It would now be bizarre for you to complain that you have been treated merely as a means because the government took $100 from you without your consent. Since you knew of the taxes, and agreed to pay them, it is not true that you were treated merely as a means when you were taxed. Similarly, when Chamberlain agreed to his lucrative contract, presumably he would have known (or at least he should have known) that he would be taxed, so that his net pay would be more like 18 cents per ticket rather than 25 cents. Nevertheless, he agreed to the contract. It is somewhat disingenuous, therefore, to suggest that Wilt was treated merely as a means when his net pay is "only" $180,000.

Warren says: That's a strong argument. I wonder, moreover, if we can't just say to the wealthy that a social

THEORY

Warren's version of **contractarianism** differs from John Rawls's theory on this point. According to Rawls, all rational people in the original position would agree to principles of justice that worked to the benefit of the worst-off group in society. Assuming redistributive taxation benefits the worst-off group, all people in the original position would choose it. If everyone agrees to redistributive taxation, then it does not treat anyone merely as a means. Therefore, Rawls would argue that taxation for these purposes does not treat anyone merely as means, since all people would agree to these taxes if they were choosing fairly.

Source: Rawls, *A Theory of Justice*. 83, 278.

UP FOR DISCUSSION

Do you think that redistributive taxation uses people merely as a means? If so, does that make it wrong? Is it always wrong to treat people merely as a means?

safety net would benefit them too should they fall from high position. There but for fortune go you or I. It could also be said that it benefits the wealthy by making the society more stable. This arguably preserves the conditions of their autonomy and so respects them as persons. And if this is correct, then we seem to have another reason why redistributive taxation needn't merely use people.

Patrick says: Yes, these are good points. I think we have done enough to show that redistributive taxation may well be permissible. If it is permissible, as we've argued, then premise (1) in the libertarian argument is false, since it implies that redistributive taxation is wrong. Libertarians would no doubt have plenty to say in response to our objections, but let's move on to premise (2) in the libertarian argument. This premise states that if a person does not engage in force or fraud, then the person does not violate the rights of others. So, for instance, Sanders's dad doesn't violate anyone's rights when he uses his justly acquired wealth to buy an MRI for his son from someone who freely chooses to sell him this service. It seems that this is at the heart of the most central claim made by those who support two-tier MRI. Unlike pure libertarians, they may not oppose government-provided health care, but what they do oppose is interference with their freedom to purchase private care if they are not violating anyone else's rights.

BACKGROUND

"In a free and democratic society where you can spend money on gambling and alcohol and tobacco . . . the state has no business preventing you and me from spending our own money on health care."

Source: Dr. Brian Day, quoted in Clifford Krauss, "As Canada's Slow-Motion Public Health System Falters, Private Medical Care Is Surging," *New York Times*, 26 February 2006, http://www.nytimes.com/2006/02/26/international/americas/26canada.html.

Dr. Day was head of the Canadian Medical Association in 2007–08 and founded the Cambie Surgery Centre, a private health care facility in Vancouver.

Doran says: Right, most who support private medicine probably do not oppose a public system. What they oppose is preventing people from exercising their freedom to purchase health care if that is what they choose, and if doing so violates no one else's rights.

The Complicity Objection to the Second Premise

Warren says: Well, the libertarian asserts, in the second premise of the argument, that the only way to violate people's rights is by force or fraud. And so, the libertarian reasons that if purchasing private MRI does not use force or fraud, then it does not violate anyone else's rights. However, I do not think we should accept the libertarian premise that force or fraud is the only way to violate persons' rights. One may be complicit in a large-scale violation of rights without exercising force or fraud.

Patrick says: I agree with you, Warren, that force and fraud aren't the only ways to violate the rights of others. And I think I get your point about being complicit in large-scale rights violations. But can you say a bit more about this?

Warren says: Sure. Private MRI may be one of ten thousand small cuts that bring down a great protector of the public interest, thereby undermining a basic right to health care. While my getting a private MRI may not involve my using force or fraud against any particular individual, that private purchase may be something a government legitimately opposes to protect citizens' access to care. If, for example, private procedures will lead to a worsening of the public system—say, because scores of physicians and MRI technicians abandon the public system in favour of the more lucrative private sector—then the government would be justified in opposing these private medical procedures. It is the duty of a government to look after access to health care of all citizens, thereby bringing about a fair balance of the liberty of the individual with the needs of the many. If private MRI erodes this right to basic access or rights to other primary goods, then a politician allowing private MRI, and a person who uses such a service, may well be complicit in large-scale rights violations.

UP FOR DISCUSSION

Do you think people can violate rights even if they do not engage in any force or fraud?

Doran says: So you hold that people have a basic right to health care, and that this right may be violated not by any particular individual's having a private MRI, but by a system which allows private MRI when it causes serious detriments to some part of the whole socioeconomic system? But, just to clarify, you're not asserting that private MRI necessarily interferes with rights?

Warren says: No, it is, of course, an empirical question whether private MRI is a villain in this piece. As long as there is robust universal public access to care in a wealthy society like Canada's, and no serious harm done, private MRI may be permissible. If it interferes with provision of that access or other governmental duties, private MRI is not permissible. In the original position, we would set rules so as to avoid any system in which our health depended on our economic good fortune. Whether or not private MRI interferes with rights to access to care or other primary goods probably depends primarily on the taxation system and on what the government provides for its people using tax money.

The Compassion Objection to the Libertarian's Second Premise

Patrick says: I'm quite sympathetic with your conclusion, Warren, that a person's rights can be violated even in the absence of force or fraud. However, I would, of course, appeal to the virtues, rather than the original position, to explain why.

Warren says: What's the virtue-based explanation, Patrick?

Patrick says: Virtue requires that we have compassion for others. A virtuous society is, therefore, one in which the government has compassion for its citizens. This entails, I believe, that the government must ensure that individuals are able to satisfy their basic needs for such things as food, shelter, education, and health care. The provision of health care, and other basic goods, can obviously be undermined in ways that do not involve force or fraud. They can be undermined, for instance, by putting the distribution of basic goods entirely in the hands of a free market. In such cases, it seems quite clear that some will receive the care they need while others will have to go without, as illustrated in the Mary Andrews example we considered earlier.

BACKGROUND

It is generally accepted among philosophers that it makes no sense to say that someone ought to do something, if that person is unable to do the thing in question. That is what is summed up in the saying "ought implies can."

Doran says: Patrick, I am not sure that you can say that a virtuous society is one that must ensure that individuals are able to satisfy their basic needs for such things as food, shelter, education, and health care. For such a requirement violates the principle that "ought implies can." As stated, your view implies that the government has a duty to provide various things, like food, education, and health care, even when it is impossible for them to provide those things. And that, clearly, cannot be correct.

Patrick says: Right, Doran. When I said that governments have a duty to ensure that citizens' basic needs are met, I was assuming that governments have the ability to do this.

Doran says: Not that I disagree with your concern for those who cannot pay for MRI, Patrick, but wouldn't those proponents of private MRI say that the government should also have compassion for those people who could afford to pay for private MRI? Requiring everyone to wait in a queue for months to receive an MRI is hardly compassionate if there are other options available to them that could get them an MRI virtually immediately.

Patrick says: That's true, Doran, and that is why I would not argue that private MRI is necessarily wrong. It depends on what effect private MRI would have on the public system. If, for instance, private MRI actually benefited everyone concerned, both those who opt out of the public system and those who stay in it, then I agree that compassion, along with other virtues, provides support for private MRI. My point above, however, is just that rights can be violated even if there is no force or fraud. A caveat is needed here, though.

> **THEORY**
>
> Although some virtue theorists avoid rights talk, virtue theorists can (and some do) employ the notion of rights within their theories. They hold, however, that morality cannot be understood entirely in terms of rights, and that virtue terminology therefore plays an important explanatory role in morality.

We're evaluating the libertarian claim that the only way to violate rights is by force or fraud. I'm trying to show that this claim is mistaken using the terminology on the table: as for my own view, I'm not sure whether I want rights to be a part of it. The duty to ensure that everyone has adequate food, shelter, health care, and so on, it seems to me, is best grounded in virtues like compassion rather than a right to these things.

Doran says: On the main point under discussion, I agree with both of you. Private MRI can be objectionable on the ground that it violates rights, even if it does not involve force or fraud. If allowing private MRIs seriously harms the public health care system, then it violates people's right to health care.

Warren says: Well, it looks as if there is considerable agreement among us. But before we examine our views further, why don't we consider the view that is almost the mirror opposite of the libertarian position on private MRI? While libertarians (and others) insist on the right to private MRI so long as there is no force or fraud, some philosophers insist that all private health care, including private MRI, would be inherently unjust. Let's call this the *egalitarian* view, since it asserts that everyone should have the same access to the same type of health care regardless of ability to pay.

AN EGALITARIAN ARGUMENT

Patrick says: Many people in Canada maintain that two-tier MRI is unjustified in principle. This is because it violates the idea of respect for the equality of all Canadians. To award some better or faster medical care merely because they can afford it, and to deliver inferior medical care to others merely because they cannot afford it, is deeply offensive to many. Just as we would find a health care system deeply offensive were it to give better care to whites than non-whites, or to the university-educated than to those without university educations, we should also find a health care system that favours the wealthy over the poor to be deeply offensive.

Doran says: It does seem unfair to give someone like Sanders better health care than Ben just because Sanders's family can afford to pay and Ben's can't.

Patrick says: Right, it doesn't seem fair. Although I don't agree with the egalitarian argument, I sympathize with the motivation behind it. Imagine, Doran, that you hurt your knee while training for an upcoming marathon. Your doctor orders an MRI, and so you take your place at the back of the line. Given current wait times, you would likely have to wait several months for the procedure. Then, as you wait in line, you see a rich and famous celebrity—imagine a Canadian Paris Hilton—waltz right into a private clinic and get an MRI that very day. After that, she gets treatment ahead of you in the public system. This seems intuitively quite unfair.

Warren says: Right, but I would say we have to go beyond our intuitions here. What if the best way to get health care for everyone, including those in the public system, was by allowing some private MRIs? If that were the case, and no serious harms were done outside of health care, then I would say that people in the original position might choose private MRI. It would depend, I must emphasize, on how private MRI affected the big picture, not just health care.

Patrick says: I believe you're right, Warren. If two-tier medicine were the best way to ensure that all Canadians have reasonable health care, and this wouldn't harm us in other areas of our lives, then it seems the compassionate and responsible thing to do for all involved is to allow private MRI. I read in *Maclean's* magazine that as of 2006, 875,000 Canadians were on wait lists for medical care. Moreover, the article pointed out that waits are expected only to get worse as our population ages.[3] *If* we can best improve the system by allowing private MRI, so that everyone can wait less and receive better care, then it seems that we should permit private MRI. To opt for an egalitarian system that is best for no one would not be virtuous.

---

[3] Alexandra Shimo, "The Rise of Private Care in Canada: All the Health Services Money Can Buy," *Maclean's*, 25 April 2006, www.macleans.ca/article.jsp?content=20060501_125881_125881.

Doran says: I agree, though I would put the point as follows: I think it is terribly unfair that some get better health care just because they are richer than others. And, I think that for this reason there is a strong *prima facie* reason to oppose two-tier MRI. But, *if* it is the case that we can improve the situation of everyone by allowing for some private MRIs, and *if* there is no fairer way to provide these benefits, then I'd judge that the great moral good of harm reduction outweighs this unfairness.

Patrick says: I might build on my previous point by noting that there are other important goods, like education, where we permit those who can afford it to opt out of the public system and to pay for private, arguably better, education. This doesn't seem unfair, provided that the public education system is good and private education does not harm the public education system, or harm the public in other important ways.

Doran says: Right, if allowing private schools hurts kids in the public system, then that would be problematic, but if it does not harm anyone, or if it actually benefits all concerned, then it would be extremely difficult to sustain an objection that it is unfair merely on the ground that it is unequal. By analogy, it is very difficult to see how an objection to two-tier MRI could be sustained *if* it makes no one worse off, much less if it benefits all concerned.

Warren says: From my perspective, two-tier education would be permissible on the same condition as two-tier medicine. It might work, for example, if private educators are required to give scholarships and fellowships to some who show ability but cannot afford private education. It would depend on the effects on the whole society. If private education brought public education into serious disrepute as second-best education or created a power elite, then that might undo any good that private education might achieve. It would be unfair. We have to look, as always, at the wide effects on society, not just effects within education.

TECHNIQUE

An argument by analogy is being employed here to try to support the point that the unequal provision of some important good (like primary education or health care) is not necessarily wrong, especially if it does not harm anyone concerned. The strength of this argument depends crucially on (1) whether or not the reader agrees that private, unequal primary education is sometimes not wrong, and (2) whether or not the reader agrees that the provision of primary education is relevantly similar to the provision of health care.

UP FOR DISCUSSION

Do you think that two-tier health care should be opposed because it is unfair to distribute health care on the basis of the ability to pay?

The Self-Respect Argument

Patrick says: Perhaps opponents of two-tier health care can further support their position by noting that not only does two-tier health care violate the moral equality of all Canadians but also that it is damaging to the self-respect of those Canadians who cannot afford to access private health care.

Doran says: How might two-tier MRI damage some people's self-respect?

Patrick says: Well, as I take it, the thought is that if some get better health care than others merely because they can afford to pay, then those who get the worst health care will be made to feel that they are somehow morally less important—second-class citizens, in effect. Take Ben, for instance. He has already had to struggle so much more than Sanders, but now if Sanders also gets better or faster health care than Ben for a similar condition, then Ben might well feel that his society views him as morally less important than Sanders.

Doran says: This argument reminds me of something Martin Luther King, Jr. wrote when discussing the effects of segregation on blacks living in the American South.

> . . . [W]hen you suddenly feel your tongue twisted and your speech stammering as you seek to explain to your six-year-old daughter why she can't go to the public amusement park that has just been advertised on television, and see tears welling up in her eyes when she is told that *Funtown* is closed to colored children, and see the depressing clouds of inferiority begin to form in her little mental sky . . .[4]

> Although I certainly do not wish to compare the degree of harmfulness of racial segregation to the degree of harmfulness of two-tier MRI, I can still easily imagine Ben feeling that he is somehow inferior to Sanders because he is denied, through no fault of his own, the care that would serve him best while Sanders is not. This would be a bitter pill to have to swallow.

Warren says: The concern about self-respect is certainly important. It is something that people in the original position would want very badly to protect. In the original position, people would realize that without

---

[4] Martin Luther King, Jr., "Letter From Birmingham Jail," repr. in *The Right Thing to Do,* ed. James Rachels and Stuart Rachels, 4th ed. (New York: McGraw-Hill, 2007), 293.

self-respect, the enjoyment of other goods is severely limited. Self-respect is, therefore, a primary good. If it is threatened at all, we should be wary. The crucial question though is how great a threat to self-respect is posed by two-tier MRI.

Patrick says: That's right. If two-tier MRI made the public system *worse,* then I would say both that people in the public system were not being properly respected by their government, and that this could have a very damaging effect on their self-respect. But if private MRI benefited those in the public system, or at least did not make them worse off, then this would not obviously be damaging to anyone's self-respect. For it could be explained to those in the public system that two-tier was permitted only on the condition that it did not harm them.

Doran says: I agree with that. The crucial distinction here appears to be whether or not two-tier harms those in the public system. If it harms people in the public system, then it may undermine their self-respect too, and for that reason may be unjust. However, if it does not harm those in the public system, then it should not cause a loss of self-respect. In that case, the argument that two-tier is wrong because it harms self-respect fails.

Warren says: There is another objection to the simplistic self-respect argument. Some harms may be borne with pride for the sake of others. If, for instance, Ben thought that the difference between himself and Sanders was necessary to help those worse off than Ben, he might bear the unfairness with full self-respect. In Canada today, however, it must be admitted that no such sacrifice should be necessary.

UP FOR DISCUSSION

Do you think unequal access to health care is wrong if it is damaging to some people's self-respect? Does two-tier health care necessarily undermine self-respect? How should we determine whether a policy undermines self-respect?

Patrick says: Agreed.

Doran says: This seems like a good place to pause and take stock of the arguments for, and objections to, private MRI that we've considered thus far. We agreed that both the libertarian argument for private MRI and the egalitarian argument against private MRI fail. We rejected the libertarian argument (in part) because it implies that private MRI is justified even if it harms those in the public health care system. And we rejected the egalitarian argument because it implies that private MRI would be wrong even if it brought benefits to everyone in both the private and the public system.

Patrick says: That's right. We also just considered the objection that two-tier MRI is impermissible because it undermines the self-respect of those in the public system. But we agreed that there's little reason to fear that private MRI would have this effect, unless it *harmed* those in the public health care system in some other way beyond loss of self-respect. However, it might not do this. So although the libertarian argument in favour of private MRI is unsound, the egalitarian and self-respect arguments *against* private MRI also seem to be problematic.

Doran says: We all seem to agree, as well, that private MRI is permissible, provided that it benefits, or at least doesn't harm, those in the public system.

Warren says: That's true as long as we consider the system to be the entire socio-economic system, not just the health care system. There is some merit, moreover, to the self-respect argument. We should be very concerned not to adopt policies that harm self-respect, and so if we are to allow two-tier MRI, we may want to find ways to compensate those who cannot afford to access the private health care system. As this shows, we may find something we can use in the ideas of the egalitarians. Similarly we may get some help from the libertarians. I do need, however, to find a mean between these extreme positions.

Patrick says: Since we all agree that two-tier MRI is permissible, at least under the right sorts of conditions, why don't we now consider what those conditions are? For instance, in order to justify private MRI, is it enough to demonstrate that it harms no one? Or does private MRI have to benefit everyone in order to be justified? And what sorts of harms and benefits are relevant here?

TWO-TIER ARGUMENTS

Is Two-Tier MRI Permissible If It Does Not Harm the Public Health Care System?

Doran says: One view is that private MRI is justified provided it does not harm the public health care system. Do you agree, Patrick? Should the government allow private MRI so that people like Sanders can get treatment more quickly, provided that this does not make things worse medically for people like Ben who must wait for their care in the publicly funded system?

Patrick says: I would say that this is not enough to justify private MRI. This is because there could be serious non-health-related costs to such a system. For instance, if the rich are able to get faster care than the poor, then those who cannot afford private care could possibly suffer serious setbacks in other areas of life, such as in competing for jobs, succeeding in education, earning income, and so forth. Sanders, for instance, might gain significant advantages over Ben when it comes to competing for a place in the NHL, even if private MRI doesn't make Ben's public health care worse. This seems unfair.

Warren says: I agree. As noted earlier, a system that had these effects could be damaging to people's self-respect. Think of Ben. He cannot pursue his main opportunity in life as effectively as Sanders, because he cannot get care as fast. He cannot get care as fast as Sanders because he is less wealthy. On the face of it, this looks unfair.

Patrick says: Warren and I appear to agree that in order for private MRI to be permissible, we need to show not merely that it doesn't harm the public health care system, but that it doesn't harm the public provision of other important goods.

Warren says: Yes, that's right, Patrick. Wouldn't you also agree, Doran?

Doran says: I agree that it is not enough to justify two-tier MRI merely by showing that there are no adverse effects to the health care system. In particular, if for some reason two-tier seriously harmed people in some other area of life, then it may still be unjust.

Is Two-Tier MRI Permissible If It Benefits the Public Health Care System?

Doran says: Would your reaction be different if private MRI not only did not make the public health system worse but actually benefited it?

Warren says: Again, it depends on the degree of benefit and effects outside the health care system. A small benefit to the public health care system would not be enough to justify private MRIs if that allowed for large differences in advantages in other vital areas of life. Let's say Sanders had his private MRI virtually the same day it was requested, while Ben's wait time was reduced from 180 days to 165 days. This extent of improvement may not be worth it, given the costs to Ben in terms of opportunities and self-respect.

Again, an insufficient justification has been given to show that private MRI is fair.

Patrick says: I agree with you, Warren. As mentioned earlier, I think we need to evaluate private MRI from a more global perspective. By that I mean we need to evaluate the permissibility of private MRI by considering not just health-related benefits and costs, but by considering benefits and costs with respect to other primary goods. So, showing that private MRI would provide health-related benefits for those in the public system is not sufficient to show that private MRI is permissible. What also needs to be shown is that there are benefits, or at least not significant costs, with respect to other goods.

UP FOR DISCUSSION

Could there be anything wrong with private medicine if it benefited the public health care system?

Doran says: Again, I agree. If two-tier MRI benefits everyone medically, then that is a strong reason in support of it, but if it ends up having grave non-medical costs as well, then that could make two-tier unjust, all things considered.

Patrick says: Well, why don't we describe the conditions under which two-tier MRI might be justified? Warren, why don't we consider your view first?

Warren's Social Contract View on When Two-Tier MRI Is Justified

Warren says: I believe that people in the original position would be especially concerned to avoid a situation that was bad for them if they turned out to be in the worst-off group in the real world. Given this, it would be rational for them to choose a society that protected their basic liberties and opportunities and that provided everyone (if the society could afford it) with an excellent safety net (a basic income, quality education, quality health care, ample opportunities for self-improvement, and the social conditions needed for self-respect, for example). I believe most people in the original position would accept this rule: *We should bias our decisions about allowing differences so as to provide a robust advantage to the least advantaged.* Call this **the robust advantage principle.** People in the original position would rule out private MRI if it threatened this robust advantage for the least advantaged, an excellent safety net in *wealthy* societies like our own. If private MRI were harmless, it could be allowed without benefit to the disadvantaged; but it is not harmless, and offsetting benefits are needed according to the robust advantage principle. Without significant benefits to offset significant harms, private MRI would undermine the robust advantage that a wealthy society usually owes to the least advantaged.

Doran says: Why do you think private MRI would harm the disadvantaged in Canada?

Warren says: First of all, it would likely drain talent, from technicians to physicians, from the public health care system. This would hurt the worst-off group the most, for it has no choice but to use the public system.

It would also harm the disadvantaged with respect to access to other primary goods outside health care, such as equal opportunity and self-respect. The case of Ben and Sanders is to the point here. Sanders gets a shot at the NHL with its promises of fame and riches, while Ben misses his chance of a lifetime. He does not have the same opportunities for self-fulfillment as Sanders and may suffer from considerable loss of self-respect. He either becomes a charity case or does not get an MRI in time. Either way, he is left with the impression that his society views him as a less important person than Sanders.

Doran says: So is your view that private MRI necessarily harms the disadvantaged?

Warren says: No. Suppose the social safety net were exceptionally generous. Suppose that even the disadvantaged were guaranteed first-rate health care, really good education, meaningful opportunities and, in general, the means to self-respect. In this case, private MRI could be made available as long as it did not damage that social safety net. People like Ben would no longer be harmed even if there were differences brought about by private MRI.

Doran says: Why not? Couldn't he still miss his chance to be in the NHL?

Warren says: Perhaps, but he would still have multiple opportunities for

BACKGROUND

"Medicare rests on the principle that an individual's financial resources should not determine access to services. In the commission's view, governments have a responsibility to guarantee that the public system has sufficient resources to ensure appropriate access to advanced technology.

"Increased investment within the public system for new diagnostic technology can remove the temptation to 'game' the system by individuals and health care providers through the private purchase of diagnostic tests that could allow them to jump the queue."

Source: Romanow, *Building on Values: The Future of Health Care in Canada—Final Report*, 8.

self-fulfillment. He would not miss his one big chance in life and become an embittered, washed-up might-have-been. In the original position, people would allow differences in wealthy societies provided that they were guaranteed real opportunities for an excellent life even if they did not occupy the wealthier class.

Doran says: Absent this robust social safety net, could we still justify private MRI if it benefited the disadvantaged?

Warren says: That depends on how much it benefits the disadvantaged. If private MRI could be shown to be necessary to provide really significant benefits to the disadvantaged, then that might be sufficient to overcome its negative effects. Suppose that it generated enough tax revenue to eliminate most homelessness: we might accept it even if it provided differences in opportunities, as long as there was no better way to eliminate homelessness and we could maintain self-respect, indeed take pride, in eliminating it. Of course, for reasons I have mentioned, I think it is extremely unlikely that private MRI could be so justified in Canada.

Doran says: Patrick, what do you think? What's your view on when two-tier MRI can be justified?

Patrick's Virtue-Based View on When Two-Tier MRI Is Justified

Patrick says: I've suggested that private MRI is permissible, provided that allowing it would benefit those in the public system, or at least not make them worse off. I'll now try to refine and clarify this view. But a warning is in order: the position I sketch below is still rather tentative.

If sufficient resources are available, I believe our government has (and governments in general have) an obligation to ensure that citizens have a reasonable basic level of primary social goods. I'm thinking of primary goods roughly in the Rawlsian sense—goods that everyone (or nearly everyone) needs to live well. This includes such things as food, shelter, education, health care, social and economic opportunity, and income. If everyone has a reasonable basic level of primary goods, then the government should allow private MRI, provided that this does not make those in the public system worse off, all things (i.e., all primary goods) considered, than they would be in a purely public system.

Warren says: We really have to consider *all* primary goods, though.

Patrick says: Right, Warren, we must look at all primary goods, not just health care.

Doran says: What if the government is not meeting its obligation to provide its citizens with a reasonable basic level of primary social goods? Would private MRI then be wrong?

Patrick says: There are two different situations we should consider. First, suppose the government does not have the resources to provide everyone with a basic stock of primary social goods. Second, suppose the government has the resources, but is failing to meet its obligation to provide basic primary goods. In either case, I think private MRIs are permissible, but only if this *improves* the situation, all things (i.e., all primary goods) considered, of the general public.

Doran says: Why do you believe your position is justified?

Patrick says: Well, I think that my view on private MRI can be justified from different moral perspectives, but I'll stick to my preferred virtue theory. As I've mentioned before, a virtuous society would be a compassionate, caring, and responsible society. For this reason, a virtuous society would be one in which the government ensures, insofar as possible, that everyone has a reasonable minimal level of primary goods. Without a basic level of these goods, one cannot live a decent life. If we allowed these goods to be distributed entirely by a free market, it is clear that some would have lots, while many others would have little or none. To allow this—that is, to allow some to prosper while many others suffer—with respect to such basic goods would be rather cruel and callous, among other things.

Suppose that the government is not providing everyone with a reasonable level of primary social goods. There might be two reasons for this: the government does not have the resources to do this, or it does have the resources but is simply not delivering the goods. Then, as I mentioned, private MRI is morally permissible provided that this benefits everyone concerned. In the first case, the government could impose a tax on private MRIs and use the money collected to improve everyone's lot. In the second case, the private sector could set up private MRIs and provide subsidies for those who cannot afford the fee. This would seem to be the virtuous thing to, all things considered. Allowing private MRI in either case would respect the liberty of the wealthy, for those who are fortunate enough to pay for private MRIs could get them. And the system would also show compassion for the less wealthy, since they would see their situation improved.

Now, if the government has ensured that everyone has a reasonable basic level of primary goods, then it seems it would be rather mean-spirited and unfair to prohibit private MRI, if this doesn't worsen the situation of others. A virtuous society would, of course, be concerned with the interests of both the rich and the poor. If a person has an interest in getting an MRI done quickly, and this person has the good fortune of being able to pay to have one done privately, and allowing private MRI wouldn't hurt others, then on what grounds could one reasonably object? I don't like the idea of the wealthy getting MRIs faster than others simply because they have more money. So there is a sense of unfairness here. But, again, it also seems unfair and mean-spirited to make the wealthy wait in line simply because that's what others must do. That's taking egalitarian ideals too far.

Warren says: This raises an interesting question of how far is too far. Suppose there is such a high tax on private MRI that the practice is able to continue, but only just. The taxes are used to minimize wait times for public MRI. Of course, the private entrepreneurs would say this is unfair, but what would a virtuous society do?

Patrick's reply: As I said, I think a virtuous society would be one that looks out for the basic interests of both the rich and the poor. By allowing private MRI, we can let the wealthy avoid waiting for an MRI. And by taxing private MRI, we can improve the lot of those in the public system by helping to reduce their wait times. Of course, some will still complain, but this system looks pretty fair to me, since it balances a concern for all affected.

Doran says: Let's bring this back to Ben and Sanders. Suppose they live in a society that provides its citizens with a reasonably decent social safety net. Patrick, I take it that your view is that Sanders should be allowed to purchase a private MRI, provided it does not worsen Ben's condition, all things considered (i.e., all primary goods considered). Further, if they are living in a society that fails to provide a decent minimum, then Sanders should still be allowed to get a private MRI only if this can be used to benefit those who are less fortunate, like Ben (say, by shortening wait times in the public system or by taxing these services and using the proceeds to benefit the worst off).

Patrick says: Yes, that's the basic idea.

Doran says: One question I have for you, Patrick (though it is a question that I might well ask of Warren's view, too) is how you think the idea of a "reasonable basic level of primary social goods" should be understood. Specifically, is this something that should be indexed to the general level of wealth of the society, or is it something that is like a floor that does not move over time? For example, does this reasonable minimum mean that everyone should be ensured merely that their basic survival needs are met, that they have basic health care and education, and that is more or less it; or is it something that is more flexible, so that in an affluent society it would not just be that basic survival needs are met, but also that everyone has access to quality education and health care, comfortable lodgings, opportunities for advancement and leisure, access to technological gains from indoor plumbing to high-speed Internet access, and so on?

Patrick says: Good question, Doran. I've been thinking of the reasonable minimum not as fixed, but rather as fluid. What counts as a reasonable minimal or basic level of primary goods is relative to how much wealth there is in society. In lean times, the reasonable minimum may not be much—perhaps just enough to survive. In times of abundance, however, the reasonable minimal level will be more than that. The wealth should be shared so that inequalities between the rich and the poor do not become so great that the rich have an unreasonably large advantage over the poor when it comes to things like education, income, opportunities, and so forth.

Warren says: Well, that helps to clarify a concern I had. I was wondering why you suggested that a "compassionate and caring" society would ensure only a "reasonable *minimal level* of primary social goods." That sounds rather stingy to me. I would think that a compassionate and caring society would be a lot more generous than providing a decent minimum. I would think that if it had the resources, a compassionate and caring society would want its citizens to have a very generous social safety net—the kind of social safety net that was the envy of the world. But I see now that that is what you're suggesting.

Patrick says: That's right, Warren, I'm proposing that the government has an obligation to ensure that its citizens have a reasonable basic level of primary goods. But as I just noted in response to Doran's question, what counts as a reasonable basic level is relative to how much wealth there is in the society. In good times, where there is an abundance of resources, the reasonable basic minimum will be quite generous.

Notice, moreover, that in order to ensure that others are not made worse off (all things considered) by allowing private MRI, the government would have to ensure that the general public has a rather generous basic level of primary goods. This is because others will in fact be made worse off (all things considered) if the gap between the "haves" and the "have-nots" becomes too great.

Warren says: It seems, Patrick, that you and I agree that when deciding on MRI policy we need to take a global view, avoiding the ills of flat egalitarianism on the one hand, and avoiding the problems attendant on wide class distinctions on the other. Between these extremes we seek a system that leaves incentives to improve MRI technology and training without its becoming a tool of the elite to enhance its position. That may be a tall order when we have trouble just seeing how it affects wait times, but it has to be seen as part of an overall health care policy which in turn is a cornerstone of social policy. We differ primarily on why we should do this.

UP FOR DISCUSSION

When, if ever, do you think two-tier MRI is morally permissible?

Patrick says: Right, and I think this helps to strengthen our view. We are arguing for a view that can be supported by your contract theory and my virtue theory.

COMMENTS ON CANADA'S CURRENT PUBLIC HEALTH CARE SYSTEM

Doran says: There is a large amount of agreement in your two views, though you've approached the question from very different perspectives. But the practical implications are not entirely clear. So I think we should wrap up our discussion by returning to the question we began with: Is private MRI permissible in Canada? More specifically, is two-tier MRI permissible in Canada today, given our current health care system, and given the current distribution of primary goods in general?

Warren says: In Canada, we have a wealthy society. We would need good reasons to believe that it is likely that the overall effect of private MRI on society would further a robust advantage to the least advantaged. This would require a wide-ranging investigation of private MRI's socio-economic effects. If a convincing argument can be made for private MRI in these terms, which I doubt, the electorate should decide its merits, but private MRI should not have been allowed before it was put to that test.

Patrick says: Like Warren, I don't think we can give a simple "yes" or "no" answer to this question, since the answer depends on empirical issues that are a matter of some controversy. A conditional answer will therefore have to do for now. Given the amount of wealth in our country, I think that the public health care system is not at all up to par. The government is not providing a reasonable basic minimum, given the available resources. So my view implies that private MRI is permissible, only if allowing it will help to improve the public system and, of course, not impose significant costs in terms of other basic goods. *If* this can be demonstrated, then I think that private MRI is permissible in Canada.

UP FOR DISCUSSION

After considering the various arguments for and against, do you think two-tier MRI should be allowed in Canada? Why or why not?

FROM THE POLITICAL TO THE INDIVIDUAL

Doran says: If we assume, for the sake of argument, that the use of private MRI is unjustified at present in Canada, then the following interesting question arises: *Do you think Sanders's dad is doing something morally wrong by using the private system to get his son an MRI?* Our earlier discussion of the complicity objection to libertarianism suggests that you guys would object to a person's taking advantage of such a situation. But some may think that this seems rather harsh. One may put the point in the language of virtue theory: Wouldn't a compassionate, responsible father utilize the system of private MRI to benefit his son, even if he wished that the general provision of medicine were more just? What do you think? Here the question is being shifted from the political to the personal. Before we wondered about the just or virtuous society, but now we are asking about the virtuous parent and the actions it is permissible for him to take in a situation of injustice.

Warren says: Given the system we have in Canada today, I do not think people do wrong when they seek private MRI for serious medical reasons. It is the politicians who do wrong when they put people in the position of having to seek private MRI. I mentioned as we were stating our positions that I had sympathy for people seeking private MRI in Canada given the excessive wait times for necessary diagnostics. My sympathy is even greater for a parent seeking MRI for a son or daughter. I doubt that I am alone in this. By my **sympathy metarule,** any strict rule against complicity that required us to ignore such sympathies would be rejected or modified in the original position.

THEORY

Recall that Warren uses a **sympathy metarule** as part of the conditions under which people in the original position choose rules. This says, "The people in the original position must choose rules that people with ordinary human sympathies could follow." Sympathy is construed broadly. See Chapter 3 for more details.

Doran says: So people with wealth can just enjoy their privilege without compunction, according to rules chosen in the original position?

Warren says: No, it's not that simple. People in the original position would accept rules governing social policy that indict the inadequate system we now have in Canada where private MRI is concerned. Politicians would still have a strong moral duty to tie private MRI to the public good if they allowed it at all. All citizens, including Sanders's dad, have, moreover, a duty to hold politicians to account for the injustice to people like Ben and to demand an adequate public diagnostic system as part of a fair social system generally. In my view, the wealthy are not required to join the poor in their misery, but they are not permitted to ignore that misery.

Doran says: Well and good, but what social contract rules are we talking about here that underlie these duties, in your view?

Warren says: Well, generally speaking, our current MRI policies contravene the robust advantage principle of which I spoke earlier: *We should bias our decisions about allowing differences so as to provide a robust advantage to the least advantaged.* Sanders's dad, however, is not one who is directly allowing the differences. Politicians are. The duty of Sanders's dad, as a man of wealth and thus of some political influence or potential influence, is to shake up the politicians to get them to abide by the robust advantage principle. It's the duty of the whole electorate, really, to demand a fair system of health care from our elected representatives.

Patrick says: Though I don't agree with the theory supporting Warren's view, I largely agree with his view on this issue. If Sanders's father happens to have the resources to pay for an MRI for his son, then it is quite understandable that he would take advantage of his good fortune. In fact, it would seem rather callous and irresponsible if Sanders's father made his son suffer and wait for an MRI when he has the means to get him one right away. But those who have the good fortune of being wealthy enough to afford private care should use whatever influence and resources they have to help ensure adequate care for those in the public system. It would be selfish and insensitive of the wealthy to simply ignore the suffering others must endure due to a lack of adequate public health care. As Warren noted, the moral failing here lies not with Sanders or his father, but with governments in Canada. They are simply not meeting their obligations to ensure that residents of this country have reasonable health care. I believe there's an additional moral failing on the part of those who own and operate private MRI clinics. They might show more compassion toward those in the public system by using some of their profits to help improve the public system. One way to do this, for instance, would be to offer free or heavily subsidized MRI for the poor.

CLOSING ARGUMENTS

Warren says: I believe it is very likely that two-tier MRI is not justified in Canada today. This is because such unequal access to medical diagnostics ignores the robust advantage principle: *We should bias our decisions about allowing differences so as to provide a robust advantage to the least advantaged.* I have argued that a decision in favor of two-tier MRI appears to ignore this required bias.

The robust advantage principle does not require us to always favour the least advantaged as an excessively egalitarian society might do. We are not required, for instance, to make everyone else radically worse off just to bring about a small advantage to those on the bottom. We should avoid that egalitarian extreme.

By the same token we should avoid the libertarian extreme. While the robust advantage principle does not require us to always put the disadvantaged first, it does not let us ignore them, either. In wealthy societies, at least, we can afford to make sure that everyone has both necessities and opportunities.

The robust advantage principle could, nonetheless, justify inequalities in access to medical care under a variety of circumstances. Here are some examples: (1) a robust social safety net is in place, and the effects of having two-tier do not worsen the condition of the worst-off members of society; or (2) a robust social safety net is in place, and introducing two-tier worsens the condition of the worst-off members of society but not to the point where they slip through the net, and two-tier greatly improves the condition of the vast majority; or (3) a robust social safety net is not in place, and two-tier is a good way to help bring about these robust advantages for the worst off; or (4) a robust social safety net is not in place, and two-tier is the only way to save the society from disastrous consequences.

The situations in the first two examples are not like ours in Canada today, since our government has not provided a sufficiently generous social safety net. And I believe we are not in the third or fourth situations either, since I see no credible evidence that allowing for two-tier MRI is a good way to enhance the advantages of the worst-off group, or is necessary to ward off disaster.

Patrick says: I agree with most of your conclusions, Warren. However, I am less certain about whether a system of two-tier MRI (or two-tier health care, generally) is justified in Canada today. Specifically, it *might* be the case that carefully regulated two-tier MRI could work to increase the primary goods available to all Canadians. Carefully regulated two-tier MRI *could perhaps* improve the lot of poorer Canadians by shortening queues in the public health care system, increasing the amount of dollars available for each patient in the public system, and benefiting the social system in other ways by taxing private clinics. As you noted, this is largely an empirical question, and I am not sure where the facts lie.

Doran says: Well, for much of this debate I have been content to listen and to ask questions. However, earlier I argued along with both of you that the libertarian reasons in support of a right to private health care are not compelling, and that the egalitarian arguments against private health care are not necessarily decisive, and can be defeated, at least in principle.

I also think I agree with your views on when two-tier MRI can be justified. For example, it can be justified if a robust social safety net is in place, provided that it does not harm that social safety net; and it can be justified if a robust social safety net is not in place, provided that it improves the condition (broadly construed) of the worst off. In addition to the contractarian and virtue-based arguments developed by you two, I find the arguments by analogy with private primary education to be helpful on this point. I think that, on reflection, most of us would think there was something wrong with a policy that allowed for private education to the detriment of the public education system. And I think most of us would be willing to support a policy allowing private primary education, provided that the public education system was of high quality and that people in it were not made worse off by the existence of a private tier.

Like Patrick, I remain very uncertain about the benefits and costs of two-tier MRI (and two-tier health care generally). It may well be the case that carefully regulated two-tier could actually work to the significant benefit of the least advantaged by shortening queues, making more public money available per patient, generating greater revenues by taxing the private system, etc. I just don't know.

Finally, I am not yet persuaded about the permissibility of parents' taking advantage of private health care for their children, if it turns out that this private system itself is unjust. In general, I think it is wrong to support unjust institutions, even if such institutions benefit oneself or one's loved ones. And I am quite reluctant to give up that principle. Of course, I think it is understandable if a parent avails herself of the best care possible for her child, even if that care morally ought not to have been available in the first place. I wonder, though, if such behaviour

UP FOR DISCUSSION

If two-tier MRI should not be permitted, do you think it is wrong for parents to use it to benefit their children? Why or why not?

is in fact morally permissible, or if it is merely **excusable.** This is a particularly tough question, since it raises one of the most difficult problems in moral philosophy—how to reconcile (1) the belief that we ought to respect the moral equality of all persons, and so reject institutions that violate this principle with (2) the belief that a morally decent person is properly partial toward his or her loved ones.

SUMMARY

Here is a summary of the main questions, concepts, and arguments covered in this chapter.

- Magnetic resonance imaging (MRI) is a technique for scanning for muscle and joint injuries. Both the scans and the machines that scan are referred to as MRIs.
- A two-tier system of health care is a system in which one tier, or level, is publicly funded and one tier is privately funded. The idea is that those who can afford the additional private care can access a higher level of care.
- The main question explored is whether private MRI is morally acceptable in Canada. This is part of the larger question of whether two-tier health care is justified in Canada. Subordinate questions include the following: Is two-tier MRI permissible if it does not harm the public health care system? Is two-tier MRI permissible if it benefits the public health care system? Is it permissible for a patient to use private MRI in Canada, even if private MRI in Canada is unjust?
- Although the debate is largely restricted to specific questions, it takes place against the backdrop of the national debate in Canada over the permissibility of a two-tier system of medical care. Some tentative ideas are ventured in this regard. Conclusions in the debate are conditional, depending on the empirical question of the effects of two-tier access to MRI on the public health care system.
- Libertarian arguments against redistributive taxation and in favour of a right to private health care are considered and found to be ultimately unpersuasive.
- Egalitarian arguments against private MRI are then considered, and are also found to be ultimately unpersuasive.
- Warren, Patrick, and Doran argue that two-tier MRI can be justified under certain circumstances. Given certain empirical assumptions, Warren doubts that those circumstances apply in Canada today. Patrick and Doran are somewhat more cautious about the empirical assumptions.
- Under the assumption that two-tier MRI is unjust in Canada, Patrick and Warren agree that it would, nonetheless, be permissible for a patient to use private MRI. Doran is not yet convinced.

Review Questions

1. Why do libertarians oppose redistributive taxation?
2. What is the Wilt Chamberlain example, and what is its point?
3. Why is this argument rejected?
4. Why is the argument that people should have a right to use their justly earned wealth to freely purchase private MRI rejected?
5. What two arguments do egalitarians give to oppose two-tier MRI?
6. How do Warren, Patrick, and Doran respond to these two arguments?
7. When do Warren, Patrick, and Doran think two-tier MRI is justified?
8. What arguments do Warren, Patrick, and Doran give for this view?
9. Why does Warren think two-tier MRI in Canada is probably unjust?
10. Why do Warren and Patrick think it is permissible for a patient to use private MRI in Canada, even if private MRI in Canada is unjust? Why is Doran unconvinced?

WWW.MCGRAWHILL.CA/OLC/SMOLKIN

MICROALLOCATION OF SCARCE RESOURCES

INTRODUCTION

In this chapter we will be discussing disaster scenarios in which all medical professionals in the area are required to drop all non-emergency care and come in to the hospital to help. The case used in this chapter to motivate discussion concerns an emergency room in a small town overwhelmed by many injured incoming patients from a vehicle accident. There are insufficient resources to treat everyone immediately. The more serious patients cannot be transferred to other hospitals because they will not survive the journey. The number of critically ill patients exceeds resources to treat them. A **triage** nurse faces extraordinarily difficult ethical decisions about whom, among equally urgent patients, to direct first to the lone physician on duty. Such rare cases test existing triage principles and stimulate discussion on the appropriate treatment priorities in emergency situations.

Some health care professionals may find our interest in such cases puzzling because these cases seem too rare to bother with. In fact, though, they are just what is needed to put great stress on the principles we use every day, stress that will test our commitment to and understanding of those principles. It can be argued, moreover, that a discussion of

DEFINITION

Triage: from the French *trier*, "to sort." It is defined as "the process of determining the order in which a large number of injured or ill patients will receive medical treatment, with priority usually given to those patients with the most severe ailments or the greatest chance of survival . . ." (*Canadian Oxford Dictionary*).

disaster scenarios is of great practical importance. Emergencies that stretch resources to this degree are rare in our society, but they are, tragically, not rare in many other societies. Further, it is virtually certain that such emergencies will, at some time, occur in Canada. Witness the often-voiced concern about the rapid spread of epidemics like bird or swine flu, the possible dire predictions of terrorist attacks, earthquakes, environmental disasters, and so forth. We need to have a clear understanding of the rules we should follow to handle such crises.[1] Clarity about how to handle admission of equally urgent patients fairly in these crises may also guide us in other more common situations where patients must be triaged in emergency and non-emergency situations.[2]

Warren will use his social contract method to arrive at a set of principles to prioritize patients in emergency situations. Doran and Patrick will challenge Warren's argument and will work with him to begin to develop a set of fair rules. In the end, Doran argues that triage nurses should follow principles that are largely limited to certain medical considerations. Warren and Patrick go further and argue that a greater number of non-medical considerations should sometimes influence who should receive care first.

LEARNING OBJECTIVES

After completing this chapter, you should be able to:

- Define *microallocation* and distinguish it from other types of allocation in health care
- Explain the CTAS guidelines, and discuss why these guidelines are too simple to deal adequately with all triage scenarios
- State Warren's, Doran's, and Patrick's views on whether Alice acted permissibly in caring for her Aunt Lena ahead of Terence
- Discuss the role impartiality should play in the treatment of patients, and how impartiality is limited by the sympathy metarule on Warren's view
- Explain and discuss the rules "worst first," "first come, first served," and "hopeless second"

---

[1] See, for instance, National Advisory Committee on SARS and Public Health, *Learning from SARS: Renewal of Public Health in Canada* (2003), http://www.phac-aspc.gc.ca/publicat/sars-sras/naylor/. See also Canadian Institutes of Health Research, *Report on the Pandemic Preparedness Research Initiative: Report on Activities & Outcomes* (June 2006–June 2008), http://www.cihr-irsc.gc.ca/e/32573.html.

[2] See, for instance, "Senior's death triggers calls for ER changes," *CBCNews.ca,* 26 April 2006, http://www.cbc.ca/bc/story/bc_er-nanaimo20060426.html. See also Thomas A. Mappes and Jane S. Zembaty, *Biomedical Ethics,* 6th ed. (New York: McGraw-Hill, 2005), chap. 9, "Social Justice and Health-Care Policy."

- Distinguish between excuse, mitigation, and justification, and explain how the sympathy metarule helps identify whether a particular act is excused, mitigated, or justified
- Describe Patrick's and Doran's objections to the sympathy metarule
- Understand why minimize YPLL evolved into substantial benefit under the force of objections
- State some of the challenges for substantial benefit
- Explain the fair turn and innocents first rules
- Discuss whether a person's moral responsibility should ever affect triage decisions
- Describe some relevant third-party interests that may affect the proper order of care in an emergency situation

DRAMA

Please note: This case is based on various true stories, although names, places, and some uncontroversial elements of the case have been changed to preserve anonymity and confidentiality. Discussions of this and similar cases with health care professionals have also informed this fictional case. The drama merely raises issues. The philosophical arguments are to be found in the debate following the drama.

CHARACTERS

Alice: *a triage nurse for twenty years*
Gurpreet: *a nurse training with Alice to serve as a triage nurse*

The scene is a small town in southern Ontario.

Alice: Now, Mr. Bains we called a level 1, and sent him in right away. Why was that?

Gurpreet: Well, to tell you the truth, I was a bit surprised at that. He did not seem like a likely candidate for an **MI.** He kept saying it was probably just heartburn, but he wanted to check.

Alice: That's the thing, you just can't tell. You know you might see somebody who is fit like Bains and dismissive of his pain, but it's tricky. If they have unexplained chest pain, send them in.

Gurpreet: My goodness! Was that woman with the broken wrist ever ticked when Bains went in ahead of her. Oh, my! Alice, I thought she would . . .

DEFINITION

Level 1 is a category triage nurses use for patients who need a physician's care immediately.

DEFINITION

MI stands for myocardial infarction, a heart attack.

Alice: Get used to it, Gurpreet. People are always angry. They always think they should go first. Parents with kids get outraged sometimes when you treat somebody ahead of their kid. You just have to do your best. You're always triaging in your head. There's this constant assessment and reassessment of your patients. People come in, sit down, get worse, get better. You have to be watching everybody all the time.

Gurpreet: What happens when you have a couple of people at the same level at the same time? I mean, suppose you have someone like Bains, and then someone like that young woman with the type 2 diabetes . . . you know the one?

Alice: Yeah, I think I see where you're going with this.

Gurpreet: So she came in first because of numbness in her foot but doesn't have chest pains at first, then in comes Bains and she starts having the pains. Now you've got the two of them both at level 1. Today we have Dr. Anderson and Dr. Horst both in, but suppose one of them was out of town? I would take that young woman first.

Alice: Yes, Ashley—she's the woman with diabetes. She would probably be more urgent than Bains in that case, so sure, you do have to make decisions about who goes first even within levels. And in some kinds of cases you can take a couple of people at once. Dr. Anderson is a good multi-tasker. Dr. Horst is not, though. Anyway, sometimes you just have to choose. It's not often that you can't call in extra help or get a nurse to hold the fort until Dr. Anderson or Dr. Horst can get to it. But when you do get these tough choices, it can be really hairy. I mean, suppose Bains came in kind of grey with left-side weakness. It might be tough to say whether he was more urgent than Ashley. What would you do then?

Gurpreet: Well, I guess to be fair, I'd just take them in the order they came.

Alice: Of course, if it's like you say, Ashley was there first, but for something else, and they both get into real trouble at the same time, then it isn't so clear what's fair. I'll tell you though, the people who work here are really good people. They might look at it and say, "Well, here's Ashley with nothing, living in the shelter, never had a break. And there's Bains, the wealthy dentist, all the advantages." You know, I think we tend to give the people who are the most vulnerable the edge when it comes to a tie. You might have noticed that indigent people get royal treatment here.

Gurpreet: It seems like a kind of reverse discrimination.

Alice: Yeah, maybe.

Gurpreet: But what if you thought Ashley was unable to recover because of her other conditions, but you thought you might be able to save Bains?

Alice: Well, sometimes a patient really has no hope of recovery, but we can't know that. I guess if it seemed really obvious that one person was a candidate for comforts only but the other could have a long life, then the one who had a real chance should go in first. But look, I've been on the job twenty years, and I've never had a decision like that.

Gurpreet: I need to ask about these what-ifs because, you know, you never had a day like last Thursday in your whole career before, either. You had to make tough choices like you'd never made before. I don't know what I'll face in my career. I need to be ready, Alice. I'm not trying to be pushy. I'm just scared that I won't know how to think about some of the things I might see.

Alice: Point taken, Gurpreet. Last Thursday was a regular Armageddon.

Gurpreet: I don't really know how you made those decisions; I was so busy putting pressure on a wound with Horst barking orders and everything going crazy all around us.

Alice: Well, you kind of go on instinct when it's that bad, or it's like you're just doing what you know from experience. I sort of feel like I'm programmed by my earlier imaginings about what I would do if I was in that kind of a fix.

Gurpreet: Is it too soon to talk about it, Al?

Alice: No, Gurpreet, I've got some distance now. But it's still fresh in my mind. Maybe now is the right time even if there is no good time to talk about it.

Gurpreet: It must be so hard, when you know everybody in town, to make choices like that. I was talking to the mayor yesterday. He said it all started when Terence walked right out on the highway without even looking. He was really very inebriated, the mayor said.

Alice: Terence always was drunk.

Gurpreet: The van full of people heading for the conference swerved to avoid Terence, but hit him and then lost control. They hit Harvey's truck head-on.

Alice: Yeah, that about fits with what I heard. Les saw most of it happen and told me.

Gurpreet: Where was Dr. Anderson?

Alice: Dr. Anderson was already at the Northern Health Conference in Mayville. By the time she got back here, it was all over but the crying.

Gurpreet: By the time they called me in to Emerg it was already chaotic.

Alice: It didn't take long to get that way. They brought Terence in first. He was unconscious with a serious head wound. Right behind him was Aunt Lena. You could have knocked me over with a feather. She was in awful shape. They were both level 1.

Gurpreet: You're really close to Lena, aren't you?

Alice: God, yes. I was emulating Lena when I got into nursing in the first place. She's been my hero.

Gurpreet: Well, she's been a hero to this whole town from what I gather.

Alice: Yes, there's not much good work here that she hasn't had a hand in. Anyway, I saw Lena and did not even think. I took her straight in to see Dr. Horst. Lena told me to let her wait and take care of Terence. I didn't listen. Dr. Horst was sewing up this carpenter who had mangled his hand. He just handed off the carpenter to Jesse to keep the bleeding under control and started right to work on Lena.

Gurpreet: What happened to Terence?

Alice: We had him in the next room, and told Dr. Horst about him. Dr. Horst just said okay and worked furiously on Lena while I went back to call everybody in and tell a level 3 in the waiting room that it was going to be a long time. I could hardly talk.

Gurpreet: Is Lena going to make it?

Alice: Maybe. She's got a lot of internal injuries. Harvey was sitting right beside her in the truck, and he died on impact, they think. She's so tough. God, I hope she'll make it.

Gurpreet: I guess you didn't even have a chance to catch your breath before the others came in.

Alice: You got that right. Those people from the van were not hurt as bad, but we all had somebody to work on. That's when you came in and I put you to work on that young guy who looked like he might bleed out. It was him or that really old man who was unconscious, so I chose the young guy. The old fellow had probably already had a good shot at life at his age. They both pulled through in the end.

Gurpreet: Was Terence still alive then?

Alice: I'm not sure. Jesse was with him. She just said by the time Dr. Horst had Lena stabilized, it was too late for poor old Terence, and I didn't have the heart to ask any more about it.

Gurpreet: Are you okay, Alice?

Alice: Yeah, I feel bad about it, but I think I did the right thing.

Gurpreet: Nobody could have done better, Alice.

DEBATE
Clarifying the Case and Identifying Relevant Facts

Patrick says: Well, I think it's pretty clear what happened in this case.

Doran says: Yes, but it's a little hard to remember who is who. Aside from the nurses Gurpreet and Alice, there are a great many patients and health care workers to keep track of.

Warren says: Maybe a quick review would help. The action takes place in a rural setting where one often finds a scarcity of resources that one would not find in a larger centre. There's Bains, a wealthy dentist and a patient in emergency. He gets in ahead of other patients because chest pain makes him a level 1. Dr. Angela Anderson, an emergency physician, was away during the big accident, leaving all the cases to Dr. Hans Horst, the other emergency physician in this small town. Ashley, a patient in the emergency department with type 2 diabetes, was used as an example by Gurpreet to try to contrast with Bains.

Patrick says: Oh yes, that's not something that actually happens in the case. Rather, Gurpreet is just juxtaposing two patients in her imagination. She wanted to consider two level 1 patients competing for resources.

Warren says: That's right. Then there is Terence, an inveterate drunk, who caused a terrible traffic accident which made him a patient in the emergency department. He gets treated after Alice's Aunt Lena, and he ends up dying. Remember that Alice put Aunt Lena, a pillar of the community, ahead of Terence.

Doran says: There was another important decision Alice made, too, but the patients did not have names.

Warren says: Yes, a young patient is treated ahead of an elderly man. In addition, there are sundry other characters who do not figure prominently in the story: Harvey, one of the drivers, who died on impact in the accident; Jesse, an emergency department nurse; the carpenter whose wound treatment is put on hold while more urgent patients are treated; and the mayor and Les, who witnessed the accident. Some of the unnamed patients were in the van that swerved to avoid Terence and hit Harvey's truck head-on.

BACKGROUND

"The Canadian Triage and Acuity Scale (CTAS) was introduced during the late 1990s. . . . The CTAS is now being implemented as a national triage standard for Canada's emergency health care system. Prior to its formulation, hundreds of rural and urban Canadian emergency departments (EDs) had developed home-grown triage systems to sort patients by urgency. There was, and still is, huge variation in rural ED triage across the country." The CTAS guidelines were drawn up as a consensus document by the CTAS National Working Group of nurse and physician specialists in emergency department triage and have been validated by a number of publications. The CTAS directs triage nurses and doctors to place patients in emergency departments on a five-point scale, where patients at level 1 require immediate treatment, patients at level 2 are slightly less urgent, etc.

CTAS

Acuity	Triage level	Physician assessment	Nurse assessment
Critical	1	Stat	Stat
Emergent	2	<15 min	<15 min
Urgent	3	<30 min	<30 min
Semi-urgent	4	<1 h	<1 h
Non-urgent	5	<2 h	<2 h

Note: Stat is the abbreviation of the Latin statim, "immediately."

The CTAS has been criticized for requiring unrealistic response times, especially for emergency departments in rural communities, where hospital resources (including personnel) are in short supply. An alternative system, practised in some rural settings, is known as the Sundre Scale (as it was developed in the small town of Sundre, Alberta). The Sundre Scale differs from the CTAS in that its response times are much less demanding.

Sundre Scale

Acuity	Triage level	Physician assessment
Critical	5	Stat
Emergent	4	<1 h
Urgent	3	1–3 h
Semi-urgent	2	3–12 h
Non-urgent	1	>12 h

Source: Quotation and other information taken/adapted from James M. Thompson and Graham Dodd, "Ruralizing the Canadian Triage and Acuity Scale," Canadian Journal of Emergency Medicine 2, no. 4 (2000): 267.

MORAL ISSUES RAISED BY THE CASE

Patrick says: The essential problem concerns the treatment of patients in emergency situations, and who should be given priority. The guidelines nurses have just tell them to take patients in order of medical urgency, but in cases like this one, where the hospital's emergency department is overwhelmed, questions about these guidelines are bound to arise.

Doran says: Sure, we want to know whether other factors besides urgency are morally relevant. We need to know how to make decisions when cases are equally urgent, and yet the patients cannot all be cared for at once. This is the general issue we should investigate.

Patrick says: Yes. The specific question we could debate is *whether Alice acted permissibly in our drama.* For example, Alice took other considerations, like age and merit, into account, when deciding on who should be treated ahead of whom. In answering this question, we will no doubt consider the more general issue: *What rules ought to be followed when deciding on the order of care in emergency situations where needed resources are scarce?* But let's begin with Alice. Were her decisions justified?

Stating Our Positions

Warren says: I believe we will be able to justify Alice's decisions by appeal to principles people would accept in the original position.

Doran says: Although I feel great sympathy for Alice, I believe she made decisions that were not hers to make as a triage nurse. For instance, I am quite uneasy about her decision to take Lena ahead of Terence.

Triage nurses should base their treatment decisions impartially on *clinical* factors, and not on personal affection, judgments of guilt or innocence, and so forth.

Patrick says: I'm also a little uncomfortable with Alice's decision to put Lena ahead of Terence. But given her special relationship with Lena, I don't think we can morally blame her for doing this. Indeed, I think that from my virtue ethics perspective, her actions can be shown to be morally permissible. More generally, I believe that acting virtuously requires that we allow *non-clinical* considerations to play a role in prioritizing patients.

DEFINITION AND BACKGROUND

Clinical factors are considerations that may affect the proper order of care, arising from an assessment of the medical needs of the particular patients; *non-clinical* factors are those that do not arise from an assessment of the medical needs of the particular patients. An example of a non-clinical factor might be the guilt or innocence of the patients waiting for treatment. Nurses, at least, are sometimes suspicious of rules that allow the use of such non-clinical factors.

MICROALLOCATION RULES: CLINICAL CONSIDERATIONS

Warren's Argument for Fair Microallocation Rules: Worst First, First Come, and Hopeless Second

Warren says: I think that if we consider what we would accept in the original position we can generate a set of high-level rules governing microallocation.

Before I get to specific rules governing microallocation, though, it seems to me that a reasonable general rule to choose in our own interest as seen from the original position is the rule of **impartiality:** health care professionals should usually be impartial in helping patients.

I say "usually" because the rules chosen in the original position must be consistent with human sympathy. For this reason, we would also accept a rule about making rules I call **sympathy,** the **metarule** that the rules be chosen and interpreted so they can be

BACKGROUND

"While macroallocation of resources concerns public health policies, microallocation is concerned with selecting which individuals are to receive scarce or insufficient health care resources."

Some use the term *mesoallocation* to refer to allocation at the level of institutions, and *macroallocation* to refer to allocation at the level of governments deciding among health care and other areas needing support. We are looking at the issue of microallocation under conditions of scarcity. The principles we consider and defend in this chapter are not necessarily appropriate to mesoallocation or macroallocation.

Source: Quotation taken from P. A. C Fortes and E. L. C. P. Zoboli, "A Study on the Ethics of Microallocation of Scarce Resources in Health Care," *Journal of Medical Ethics* 28 (2002): 266–69.

followed by people with ordinary human sympathies. That is why our first rule, impartiality, must be limited. Indeed, the sympathy metarule imposes a limit on all of our rules.

DEFINITION

Impartiality is used here in the ordinary sense, meaning "freedom from bias, favouritism or prejudice."

DEFINITION

A **metarule** is a rule that governs the production, use, and interpretation of other, lower-level rules. Warren explains the sympathy metarule in Chapter 3.

Doran says: So, you suggest that the justified rules for deciding how to distribute scarce health care resources must be rules that are generally applied impartially, yet consistent with human sympathies. I already have some questions about these claims, but before they are asked, why don't you explain what specific microallocation rules you think would be chosen in the original position?

Warren says: We all have a strong interest in reasonable access to care, so we wouldn't want to be bumped by less needy people who have help from insiders. Of course, some of us will need care more urgently than others. That is why we would accept the rule **worst first:** treat the worst cases in the emergency department first.

Patrick says: That sounds right, but it may depend on what you mean by "worst." Do you mean, for instance, those who will die without immediate treatment, those who are suffering the most, those with the most to lose if they die, or something else?

BACKGROUND

As noted on page 296, the CTAS guidelines are a set of rules about how to make medical judgments following, in effect, the worst first rule. CTAS does not deal with ties, exceptions, and some other things that occupy us in this debate. We want to understand the more general picture, including the exceptions to worst first in a fair system.

Warren says: By "worst" I mean those who are most urgently in need of treatment in the medical judgment of the triage nurse. In Canada our CTAS guidelines define five levels of urgency. Within different levels of triage, the worst first rule would still require the triage nurse to make distinctions. For example, at level 1 a patient who is liable to die if not seen immediately would be placed ahead of a patient at level 2, who could wait for more than 15 minutes. At level 3 where both patients could wait for 30 minutes, the one who was likely to be in more pain than the other might be admitted first. Medical judgment will be influenced by both pain and loss of function that the patients may suffer. Permanent loss of function is more serious, of course, than temporary loss.

Patrick says: Okay, that somewhat helps to clarify the worst first rule. What other rules ought to be adopted?

Warren says: Once we have taken the worst first, we might think that it would be fair to apply the **first come** rule within a given triage level: first come, first served.

Doran says: That idea seems reasonable to me. Respect for persons requires that we take patients who are equally badly off on a first come, first served basis. On its face, at least, there'd be something disrespectful in passing me over and taking you, if I have been waiting longer and we are in equal need of care.

However, a possible exception to the worst first and first come rules might be a case where the patient who arrived first can only survive for a very short period of time, while those behind that person are in urgent need of medical care from which they could substantially benefit.

THEORY

The Kantian takes respect for persons as the very foundation of ethics, not something to be justified by appeal to the rules chosen in the original position.

BACKGROUND

Traditional triage practices on the battlefield and in other emergencies in the field sort patients into a number of categories, depending on considerations of urgency. They also sort patients into the categories of those that can be saved and those that cannot be saved. Those that cannot be saved may be given comfort measures, but priority in terms of life-prolonging measures is given to those that can be saved.

Warren says: Yes, respect for persons would be in all our interests, as seen from the original position. As to the patient who cannot be saved for long, consider, in support, the following claim: If two patients arrive in a terribly overcrowded emergency department, patient A first and patient B second, and both are level 1, the triage nurse should turn aside A, whom the nurse judges to be hopeless in the long term, in favour of B, who might have a chance for a long life if treated.

Now we see we should add the first of perhaps many exceptions to worst first and first come—**hopeless second:** do not treat hopeless cases ahead of those where there is hope.

UP FOR DISCUSSION

Should first come play a role in treatment decisions? Why should those who were lucky enough to get to the hospital first be treated ahead of those who are equally badly off but who took longer to get to the hospital?

Patrick says: By "hopeless in the long term," do you mean something along the lines that the patient won't survive even with treatment?

Warren says: Well, at least the patient won't survive for a significant period of time. We are talking about hours, not days. Someone who can be kept alive with heroic medical efforts for only a few hours is clearly in this category with respect to another patient who can have some months of good-quality life if treated immediately. Hopeless patients are patients for whom comforts only are medically indicated.

Doran says: I am not sure if hopeless cases should be defined so narrowly. But we can explore this issue with greater precision later.

Patrick says: Right. Are there any more rules that you think we would choose from the original position, Warren?

Warren says: Maybe, but let's see what we've got so far: consistent with human sympathy, health care workers should impartially follow the rules of (1) worst first, plus (2) first come. This is the basic set of rules; however, there are exceptions. The first exception is what I've called (3) hopeless second: do not treat hopeless cases ahead of those where there is hope.

Patrick says: This looks like a good start. Before we start discussing further exceptions to the basic principles, why don't we see whether there's agreement on the sympathy metarule, which is supposed to govern the interpretation and application of the principles. Doran, do you have any objections to the sympathy metarule?

Doran's Objection to the Sympathy Metarule

THEORY

Impartiality is often thought to be basic to fairness. Think of what we require, for instance, from a judge in the court system. Fairness is the fundamental moral idea in John Rawls's contractarian theory.

TECHNIQUE

Demanding an illustration of a principle is a technique designed to elicit the strengths and weaknesses of that principle.

Doran says: I think I agree with the general microallocation principles, but I'm not sure about the sympathy metarule. Isn't it a bit odd for a contractarian like you, Warren, who makes fairness central to morality, to want to restrict impartiality?

Warren says: Actually, as seen from the original position, it is in our interest to have public servants generally operate impartially. It is, however, also strongly in our interest to promote human sympathy and the bonds of family and friendship. These bonds would be destroyed if we tried to be utterly impartial.

Patrick says: I agree that we can't ignore such bonds, given the importance of such virtues as love, friendship, loyalty, and so on.

Doran says: Can you give me some examples of when sympathy might play a proper role in triage decisions?

Warren says: To give you an accurate picture, I will have to give you four kinds of cases. The sympathy metarule might allow for a **mitigation,** an **excuse,** a **justification,** or none of the above. The first three come in increasing order of rarity, with justified actions contrary to normal triage being very rare indeed.

Patrick says: Let's start with mitigation. When is sympathy acceptable as a mitigating factor?

Warren says: If a nurse or a physician gets a close friend somewhat faster treatment in the emergency department than would otherwise be given, then we might well have a case of a wrong action that would be less blameworthy because of the strong bonds of sympathy that motivate it. In the original position we would recognize the powerful pull of sympathy and not want to rake the nurse or physician over the coals for this. The action would be impermissible, but not the darker sort of offence that, say, quicker service in exchange for a monetary reward would be. Even if a very serious punishment is contemplated in some cases of favouritism, the mitigating factor of strong bonds of sympathy may lessen the punishment in this case.

Patrick says: I think I agree with you so far, Warren. The virtuous person would of course be loyal and have a special kind of concern for close friends. This makes it difficult to place much blame on the nurse or physician in the situation you describe. But virtue also requires fairness, so as you say, Warren, her action may still be wrong, since it was unfair to others.

Doran says: I'm not so sure I like the direction you guys are going, but carry on. I'd like to see what counts as an excuse.

Warren says: Excuses are much rarer since they require that the pull of sympathy be overwhelming. Consider a case in which a triage nurse is very sympathetic to the poor and the downtrodden. A homeless person who evokes great pathos in the emergency department is given a place in the queue that should, by triage rules, have gone to a wealthy businessman who is also waiting and slightly more urgent. In this case the nurse did the wrong thing, but her action is morally excusable because he or she was temporarily overwhelmed by sympathy and incapable of exercising normal judgment.

Patrick says: That would be a very rare case indeed. But I'm not entirely sure why you see this as a case in which sympathy excuses, rather than merely mitigates. Does it have to do with the fact that the nurse was so *overwhelmed* by sympathy that it impaired her reasoning capacities?

Warren says: Yes, the triage nurse would find it emotionally impossible to be impartial in this circumstance. One would not expect this from professionals generally. Most cases that appear to be like this could be subsumed under cases of mere mitigation, because the pity for the homeless patient would not be strong enough to be overwhelming. Nonetheless, if it overwhelmed the nurse's reasoning capacities, it would be excusing.

Doran says: Perhaps some people are too kind-hearted to be triage nurses. What I don't expect to see, however, is a genuine case of justification.

Warren says: The kind of cases I have in mind rely on the people in the original position recognizing that there are some bonds so strong that it would be foolish to make rules that ignore them. That would result in the rules being ignored. Suppose a triage nurse sees her own small child brought in from a serious incident at the daycare nearby. Several other children are brought in at the same time with similar injuries and urgency. The nurse would be duty bound to let someone else take over. Suppose that can't be done in this circumstance. If the nurse got prompt treatment for her own child simply because it was her own, rather than taking the children at random as she would otherwise have done, could that nurse be said to have done something morally wrong? I think in the original position we would recognize the futility of asking for superhuman impartiality. The nurse's action would be justified.

Patrick says: I'm inclined to agree with you, Warren. The virtuous nurse would of course strive to be fair and impartial, but not to the point that she would treat her seriously injured child as just one among many children in need. Since it is *her* child in need, it seems that a special sort of concern and treatment is warranted.

Still, I am trying to get clearer about the limits of the sympathy metarule in your view. Maybe it would help to see a case in which there is no mitigation, excuse, or justification, but sympathy is still present.

Warren says: Well, suppose a nurse has strong sympathies for people of his own race and favours them in ways that bend the triage admissions policies. That would be wrong. Sympathies for one's race are sympathies one can and ought to limit severely, unlike the parent's sympathy for the child. In the original position we would want to avoid the evils we might suffer from racism and would require that the effective sympathies be those that are, like the mother's for the child, part of being human and strongly in our interest. In the original position we would know we are likely to benefit from strong family bonds, while strong racial affiliations lead to strife that is not in our interest.

Patrick says: Right, but we need to tread carefully here. **Nepotism** as well as racism can undermine our interests.

Warren says: Yes, to prevent nepotism, those in the original position would insist on rules that require public servants to **recuse** themselves when in a conflict of interest. In some cases, however, that can't be done. Rules that require parents to ignore the ties that bind them to their children would be honoured more in the breach than the observance. It is in our interest to preserve respect for the rules by not making them inhumanly strict. The sympathy metarule moderates the rules so that where strict adherence is not in our interest as seen from the original position, there is a mitigation, excuse, or justification available depending on the degree and kind of sympathy. Where it is greatly in our interest to promote a particular kind of sympathy, like the bond between parent and child, we must allow exceptions in rare cases where no alternative is available. Too many exceptions would undermine the rules, as would no exceptions. It is a delicate balance.

THEORY

Warren tries to avoid ethical relativism by appealing to human sympathies that are independent of culture, like the bond between parent and child. It is, however, an empirical question what human sympathies exist and what their relative strengths might be. Often, we are forced to make reasonable guesses about empirical matters while we wait for social science to enlighten us about the facts.

Patrick says: That's for sure!

Doran says: Warren, you described one case where the sympathy metarule allows for partiality—the case where one takes one's own child first, instead of taking equally badly off patients in random order. This is a vanishingly rare case. Are there other circumstances, perhaps slightly less rare, where sympathy would justify partiality? For instance, what if you had two patients, equally in need of urgent care, where the patient second in line was the triage nurse's parent, or sibling, or best friend? Would the triage nurse be justified in acting on her sympathies?

Warren says: I think the cases you are imagining may be as rare as my original case of justified partiality. Having said that, I would think that a triage nurse, if and only if he is unable to step aside and delegate responsibilities to others, may permissibly put his mother or sibling ahead of someone else, provided that they were both equally in need of immediate care. In the original position, it will be recognized that people with ordinary human sympathies may not be able to overcome the bonds of immediate family; however, with respect to friends, I think such a decision would be viewed as unjustified, though there are mitigating factors.

Doran says: And so sympathy alone would not have justified Alice in putting her mentor Lena ahead of Terence? Sympathy, in her case, would only work to mitigate or excuse the wrong?

Warren says: Yes. Sympathy will mitigate or excuse, not justify, Alice's actions.

Patrick says: But you don't think Alice acted wrongly, do you? Don't you think it was morally permissible for Alice to put Lena ahead of Terence?

Warren says: Yes. I will argue later that other considerations, in addition to sympathy, will render her decision permissible.

Patrick says: I see. I think we're in agreement about this case thus far.

UP FOR DISCUSSION

Do you think a triage nurse could ever be justified in putting his own child ahead of other similarly urgent cases?

TECHNIQUE

Warren is "biting the bullet" here. The initially counterintuitive idea that someone concerned about fairness would abandon strict impartiality is accepted but explained.

Doran says: I understand your reasons, and accept overwhelming sympathy as a mitigating factor, but I would not say that a triage nurse acts permissibly if she puts her own child at the head of the queue. Such an act, while highly understandable, is also unprofessional. Just as a judge or a professor ought not to play favourites when evaluating a family member's case or work, and just as an attorney ought to try as hard as she can for her client even if she is repulsed by him, I don't think health care workers should allow their medical decisions to be influenced by family ties.

Warren says: Strict impartiality is, nonetheless, not a reasonable choice from the original position. Humanized impartiality is. We must make exceptions to rules that allow for human sympathies; otherwise we will have rules that will not be followed. This does not mean that we simply follow our sympathies in ordering patients for care. It does, however, allow for these rare exceptions to straightforward application of the CTAS guidelines. Remember that justified exceptions to the guidelines will be very rare indeed.

Patrick's Objection to the Sympathy Metarule

Patrick says: I share your concern about allowing sympathy to influence the decisions of medical (and other) professionals, Doran. And I certainly wouldn't accept a general rule that says it's always okay to give one's family and friends special consideration. But, as Warren has been arguing, we cannot ignore the various worthwhile bonds we form with family, friends, and others. In some very special cases, partiality is called for. Nevertheless, although I've expressed general agreement with the role you accord to sympathy, Warren, I also want to raise a question or two about the sympathy metarule and examples of its application.

Warren says: Go ahead.

Patrick says: What motivates the sympathy metarule is that you want to choose rules in the original position that are consistent with human sympathy. But if that's so, you not only need rules that are consistent with the sympathy of those distributing medical resources, but you need rules that those of us in the queue for medical services could follow. Do you think that people in general would agree to triage nurses sometimes bumping family members ahead of them?

Warren says: As Alice notes in our drama concerning the CTAS guidelines, people may be upset at the application of fair rules. That does not make the rules unfair. The impartiality rule requires that the triage nurse should be as impartial as is humanly possible. That, I think, is a rule we could accept in the original position. It gives us the best we can get within human limits. I am assuming that those in the queue, with occasional exceptions among the ones being bypassed, would generally feel much the same sympathy as the triage nurse in these extraordinary cases. There is a difference of degree that you overlook. From the original position we would not accept a system in which only insiders and those they favour would be adequately treated. Impartiality has to be strong, just not absolute.

BACKGROUND

There are a variety of practice standards beyond the CTAS guidelines that affect health care providers. For example, each province in Canada has its own practice standards for nurses, and the Canadian Nurses Association publishes a nationally accepted *Code of Ethics* for nurses.

Patrick says: Okay. From my virtue ethics perspective, I would agree that sympathy ought to play a role in allocation decisions. But there's a role for other virtues, too—for example, compassion, benevolence, charity, empathy, loyalty, and so on. So I would like to know why you single out sympathy as a relevant consideration. Or perhaps you construe sympathy more broadly than I do?

Warren says: Yes, I seem to be construing sympathy much more widely than you are. Other positive emotions contribute to it. The key idea is that people in the original position are going to see it as in their interest to have rules applied impartially. However, they will also realize that people have various deep personal attachments that cannot always be set aside in the name of impartiality. They will thus agree to rare exceptions to the impartial application of rules—otherwise, the moral rules would be overly demanding and unlikely to be followed.

THEORY

A widely accepted dictum in philosophy is that ought implies can. That is, it is absurd to say that something ought to be done when it cannot be done. Warren's claim is not, however, that people cannot ever be impartial in these triage cases involving close family members; rather, it is that, under special conditions, they need not be impartial, even if they could be.

Patrick says: I see. There's one last point of clarification before we move on. You are not merely claiming that we shouldn't require impartiality because people are incapable of it, are you? You are saying that in some special and rare cases, impartiality would be morally inappropriate—that is, partiality is morally called for in those situations. Is that right?

Warren says: Right.

Doran says: The basic set of rules you have defended so far, Warren, is still not adequate for handling the full range of cases health care workers are confronted with. So why don't we consider some other cases and see whether the rules proposed are able to handle them?

Objection to the Sufficiency of Hopeless Second

Doran says: Earlier you proposed the rule we've called hopeless second: do not treat hopeless cases ahead of those where there is hope. This seems a little too simple.

TECHNIQUE

Here a hypothetical case is used to suggest the need for either an additional microallocation principle or a modification of the hopeless second principle.

Patrick says: Yes, Warren, what would you say about this case? Suppose we have a not-quite-hopeless patient who arrives at the emergency department in need of immediate medical attention. If this patient receives treatment, he will survive a few months, or perhaps a year or so at best, so he does not qualify as a hopeless case. A few minutes later, another patient arrives who also needs immediate care. Let's suppose that if treated, this patient can be expected to live another fifty-plus years. Now suppose the emergency department does not have enough resources to treat both of them. It seems to me that, in this case, the patient who will live longer should get priority. But the basic set of rules does not seem to permit this.

Minimize YPLL (Minimize Years of Potential Life Lost)

Warren says: I agree that the patient who arrives second should be given priority, so we need to move beyond hopeless second. Let's have a look at a rule explicitly in use in health care. Some physicians would appeal to **minimize YPLL,** the rule that we should bias decisions in favour of minimizing years of potential life lost. It would be in our self-interest in the original position to accept a rule like this. It is a rule that lets us suffer small losses but avoid large ones.

Patrick says: I am not at all sure that minimize YPLL would allow us to avoid only small losses. For instance, suppose a 55-year-old is admitted to the emergency department with heart trouble. A few minutes later, a 45-year-old comes into emergency complaining of the same thing. Minimize YPLL seems to imply that we should bump the 45-year-old ahead of the 55-year-old, if the physicians can treat only one of them. The 55-year-old may well have lots to lose in this case. So it seems that bumping the 45-year-old ahead of the 55-year-old would be wrong.

Warren says: I agree; that would be wrong.

Doran says: Yes. I agree with your intuitions, Patrick, that we should treat the person who is expected to live another fifty years ahead of the person who is expected to live only another six to twelve months, especially if the one person has already led a long life while the other has not. The minimize YPLL principle is able to accommodate this intuition;

BACKGROUND

Minimize YPLL is primarily not a microallocation principle as we use it here. Usually it is a principle adopted in epidemiology and the insurance industry. It is used as a way of measuring the impact of a disease or other negative health determinant. As such it operates at the mesoallocation (institutional) or macroallocation (governmental) level.

As a microallocation principle (operating at the level of individuals), minimize YPLL is somewhat like hopeless second, which tries to minimize potential life lost by passing over patients with little to gain from treatment. However, minimize YPLL goes further than hopeless second in what it would permit.

TECHNIQUE

Notice, again, a counterexample is used to demonstrate that a particular principle is false.

THEORY AND DISCUSSION

One might wonder why we should trust our intuitions about what is right or wrong in these sorts of cases. The answer, in part, is that we are seeking **reflective equilibrium;** that is, we are seeking moral principles that cohere with the moral judgments about cases that we are most confident about. We therefore need to test our proposed moral principles against various cases. See Chapter 1 for a discussion of reflective equilibrium.

however, it turns out that this principle is too simple, for it implies something that is surely false—that, in cases where only one patient can be treated, we should bump the 45-year-old ahead of the 55-year-old. Given that minimize YPLL is vulnerable to counterexamples, it is clear that we need a different principle to deal with these cases and others like them.

Substantial Benefit

Doran says: Perhaps the principle we are looking for is something like the following: If a patient stands to benefit substantially from being treated first, while the patient ahead of him in the queue will not benefit substantially from being treated, then the patient who will benefit substantially should be treated first. Let's call this principle **substantial benefit.** Notice that this principle would support our judgments that it would be permissible to treat someone who is expected to gain fifty years of good life ahead of someone who is expected to gain only six to twelve months of good life. And notice that this principle would support our judgment that it would not be permissible to bump the 45-year-old ahead of the 55-year-old, since the 55-year-old would certainly gain a substantial benefit from treatment.

Warren says: That sounds better than minimize YPLL, for it applies only when there is a large difference between patients. From behind a veil of ignorance, we would accept the substantial benefit principle since it would be more likely to serve our interests whatever triage category we might fall into. Where it serves our interests, our interests are strong. Where it neglects them, our interests are slight. Where the gap in interests is not great, we would have to appeal to other rules. Of course, what is a large difference will be context-relative and depend on difficult judgment calls.

Patrick says: Substantial benefit looks like a move in the right direction. In order to test this principle, though, we need to spell out the notion of a substantial benefit.

Doran says: This is a difficult task. Perhaps substantial benefit should be looked at as a matter of quantity and quality. A year of high quality could be a substantial benefit, but a year or more of poor quality would not be a substantial benefit.

Patrick says: What would this principle imply about a case like this? Suppose a person who can walk has a higher quality of life than someone in a wheelchair. If that's true (and I'm not saying it is), is it permissible to bump that person ahead of the one in the wheelchair? Surely that would be wrong.

Doran says: Of course that would be wrong. On the one hand, I want to say the benefit has to be health related. But, on the other hand, we need to prevent the able bodied being put ahead of those who are wheelchair bound. The best way to do that is to just deny that those in wheelchairs have lower-quality lives. Certainly, the wheelchair bound can substantially benefit from life-prolonging measures!

Warren says: From the perspective of the original position we don't want to say that someone who is permanently wheelchair bound would automatically be bumped. There's bound to be some vagueness about substantial benefit, but it helps to look at some cases using such a principle.

Patrick says: Good. So it seems that substantial benefit is an improvement over minimize YPLL. It allows us to explain why it would be permissible to give priority to the patient who will live fifty years over the not-quite-hopeless patient who will live one year of poor quality. We can also explain why it would *not* be permissible to give priority to the 45-year-old over the 55-year-old. Both would receive a substantial benefit from treatment. But other difficulties remain.

Fair Turn

Warren says: I agree. Suppose we have a 77-year-old man admitted to the emergency department with a critical heart condition, and shortly after he arrives, a 5-year-old child comes in with a similar problem. In the original position we would accept a rule that says that if the emergency physicians can treat only one of the patients, then the child should be bumped ahead of the elder. The child would suffer a large loss if left to die. The elder would suffer a relatively small one in terms of years of potential life left to live. These last years of the elder would, nonetheless, be a substantial benefit to him.

Patrick says: That's exactly the kind of case I had in mind! It reminds me that Alice put a young man in treatment before a much older man because the elder one had already had "a good shot at life." Both could get a substantial benefit from treatment, so we need another principle to justify putting the younger patient first.

BACKGROUND

Some philosophers call this the "fair innings argument." See, e.g., Michael M. Rivlin, "Why the Fair Innings Argument Is Not Persuasive," *BMC Medical Ethics* 1, no. 1 (2000), http://www.biomedcentral.com/1472-6939/1/1.

TECHNIQUE

Notice how Warren avoids a counterexample by clarifying how the principle is to be understood.

Warren says: From the original position, I think we would accept a rule that favours those who haven't had a fair turn at life over those who have. So what I'm proposing is the **fair turn** rule: Patient B can go ahead of patient A (who arrived first) if A has had a fair turn at life and B has not. This rule explains why it is permissible to bump the 5-year-old ahead of the 77-year-old, even when the 77-year-old, if treated, will have a life worth living.

Doran says: The principle is too loose, I think, as it would allow a 1-year-old to bump a 40-year-old. I don't think that would be right, however. The 40-year-old may be in the midst of her life projects—family, career, etc.—and she may have small children dependent on her for care, and so forth. Her "turn at life" is not done, so she should not be passed in the queue by someone else who is no worse off than she is. Likewise, I suppose, if a small child was ahead of the 40-year-old, the small child should not be passed over in the queue either.

Warren says: The fair turn rule would allow the 1-year-old to bump the 40-year-old only if we agree that forty years is a fair turn. But if we think of fair turn as *average life expectancy,* then the principle can avoid your counterexample.

Patrick says: The fair turn principle will still meet with difficulties, even if we base the idea of fair turn on average life expectancy. The average life expectancy of a male in Canada is about 77, while the life expectancy of a female is about 82.[3] Now, suppose patient A is an 80-year-old male, and patient B is a 75-year-old male. Fair turn, if understood in terms of life expectancy, seems to imply that B should be given priority over A. But that doesn't seem right, does it?

Doran says: Good point. This is tricky stuff! But perhaps it is not unreasonable to maintain that, other things being equal, the 75-year-old should be able to bump the 80-year-old, since the younger man has not had the benefit of an average life expectancy, whereas the older man has. That's not unreasonable, is it?

Patrick says: I'm not sure what to say about this case. The age difference between A and B is pretty small, and B is just two years shy of having had a fair turn. So I'm not sure we'd be justified bumping

---

[3] Statistics Canada, *The Daily,* 20 December 2006, http://www.statcan.ca/Daily/English/061220/d061220b.htm. (Data collected in 2004.)

B ahead of *A* on the ground that *B* has not yet had a fair turn at life. I think we'd have to appeal to other considerations to justify doing this.

Warren says: Right. When life spans are close, the triage nurse could ignore differences or look at other factors like the general health of the candidates. There are many other influences on fairness that the nurse would not know about, of course. What if the 75-year-old had many unfair social advantages over the 80-year-old? Exceptions to fair turn should be based on purely medical evidence. Health status determines who gets resources. Normally, triage nurses cannot be expected to take account of social advantages one patient may have had over another because they do not know about them.

Patrick says: But even then we are met with hard cases. Here's another one. Suppose patient *A* is 73 and has enjoyed 13 years of retired life. Patient *B* is 60, and is now looking forward to his retirement. They both stand to benefit substantially from treatment, and neither has had a fair turn at life, if life expectancy is 77 years. Yet I'm inclined to say that it would be okay to bump *B* ahead of *A*, because *A* is much closer to having had a fair turn at life than *B*. What do you guys think?

Doran says: We could say that where *B* has not come close to having had a fair turn, and *A* has obviously had nearly a fair turn, then *B* goes ahead of *A*. Or we could bite the bullet and say that *B* should not go ahead of *A*, since neither has had a fair share of life, and since *A* has been waiting for treatment longer than *B*. Neither position strikes me as irrational.

Warren says: There is going to be some arbitrariness here. Patient *A* may have been virtuous and *B* vicious, for instance. There are all sorts of unknowns. The quality of life measure is, for practical purposes, very difficult to make precise. And it may be the case that rules that are general enough to be of use to triage nurses will also be rules that contain some vagueness or arbitrariness. The problem with shrugging this off here is that the decisions of triage nurses may be a matter of life and death.

BACKGROUND

In 1961, a committee at the University of Washington, which came to be known in the press as the "God Committee," was formed to determine who would get access to a new life-saving treatment, dialysis. The committee used social circumstances of candidates rather than clinical assessment of need or potential medical benefit. This caused a storm of controversy and helped to give rise to the field of health care ethics.

Source: Gregory E. Pence, *Classic Cases in Medical Ethics*, 2nd ed. (New York: McGraw-Hill, 1995), 297–313.

UP FOR
DISCUSSION

Do you think it would be permissible to bump a 60-year-old ahead of a 73-year-old in the case Patrick raises?

Patrick says: Right. When patients are close in their needs, I think the nurse will perhaps have to consider various *non-clinical factors*—factors like whether the patient has dependents, whether the patient is responsible for his or her condition, the patient's contribution to society, and so on.

Warren says: These justifications of exceptions could go either way. We might admit one patient because of the patient's large family or, instead, admit the other because he is orphaned and has suffered enough from loss of family to merit special treatment.

Doran says: I don't think that non-clinical considerations, like those just mentioned, ought to play a role in a triage nurse's decisions about whom to treat.

Patrick says: I'm inclined to think they should play a role, at least sometimes. But I'm not entirely comfortable with this position. So why don't we explore the question whether we should adopt principles that would give a role to these other kinds of factors?

MICROALLOCATION RULES: NON-CLINICAL CONSIDERATIONS
Moral Responsibility

Doran says: Okay. Let's first consider this: Should moral responsibility play a role in prioritizing health care? Consider this case. Suppose that Alice knew that Terence, the drunk, caused the accident. He was brought in before Lena, one of the victims of the accident. Both are level 1 and are in serious need of immediate medical care, but only one patient can be treated, while the other must wait. What do you guys think—would it be permissible to give priority to Lena because she is an innocent victim and put Terence second because he caused the accident?

Warren says: Normally, the nurse would not know who was who among the accident victims, and the police and ambulance attendants would not say anything. There might, however, be a rare case where the nurse knows or is told. Alice is in that situation because she knows many people in her small town, including some of the incoming patients. Such cases put our principles to the test. Generally, we would expect non-judgmental, impartial triage according to the impartiality rule: health care professionals should usually be impartial when

UP FOR DISCUSSION

There are, of course, other cases of moral (and non-moral) responsibility that can give rise to questions of proper allocation of health care. For instance, should a person's culpable failure to take adequate care of himself be a consideration when deciding priority of care?

helping patients. That's natural in the original position. We don't want nurses acting as judges and juries. We don't want them distracted by judgments of guilt or innocence or value of persons. It would not be in our interest in the original position to allow access to care to be so clouded with nurses' individual judgments about things outside their training, if such judgments could be avoided, for this could leave any of us out in the cold.

Doran says: So you think the patients' moral guilt or innocence should be completely left out of the triage nurse's decision?

Warren says: No, triage nurses are human, not superhumanly capable of staying within their area of expertise. Suppose Alice knows Terence is responsible. In such a case, Alice might find it nearly impossible to treat the drunk and let his victim die. In some extreme cases, then, we might make exceptions to worst first and first come on the basis of known guilt plus sympathy. Normally, however, we would expect triage nurses to use only clinical factors to make a decision.

Patrick says: It's not just that it's nearly impossible to treat the drunk ahead of his victims, Warren. It's that it would be *morally wrong* to do this, in the kind of case described. I believe the drunk's victims warrant greater compassion and sympathy, and so they ought to be given preferential treatment.

Warren says: In rare cases where it is nearly impossible to ignore our sympathies, the rules would be undermined if we required strict impartiality. That is why, in the original position, exceptions to impartiality would be required. Consequently, it is morally wrong to treat the guilty first in some rare cases where there is no doubt who is the perpetrator and who is the victim.

Doran says: I have a slightly different take on this. In general, I accept the moral principle that if one of two people should have to suffer more, it should be the person who is at fault for the injury, and not the innocent victim. So, I think it is only fair that Lena be placed ahead of Terence if they both cannot be treated immediately. However, we are talking about the factors a triage nurse should be considering. And I guess I lean toward the view that we want our health care professionals making treatment decisions

UP FOR DISCUSSION

If two people well known to the triage nurse come into an emergency room, one after the other, suffering from chest pain, and the first patient is someone who has led a life of donut-eating sloth, and the second is someone who has taken excellent care of himself, would it be wrong, other things being equal, to treat the second patient ahead of the first?

UP FOR
DISCUSSION

When, if ever, would a triage nurse be justified in putting one patient ahead of another, on the ground that one of the patients was at moral fault for an accident?

based on health care considerations, period. As a triage nurse, then, I think Alice ought not to ask herself who was at fault for the accident, but should instead follow the rule that a patient is a patient. Again, the best support I have for this may be an analogy with other professions. An attorney charged with defending someone he knows is guilty would not be justified in failing to vigorously defend his client, but should follow the standards of his profession. I think the same is true of triage nurses—they ought to stick to clinical considerations.

Innocents First

Warren says: It seems that Patrick and I accept a principle that we can call **innocents first:** Patient A, who is innocent and who cannot wait for care, ought to be given priority over patient B, who is known to be at fault for the injury and who also cannot wait, other things being equal. The rule of innocents first is one reason I think Alice was justified in treating Lena ahead of Terence in the revised case in which Alice knows for sure that Terence is at fault.

Patrick says: Well, I accept it in the same spirit that I accept any principle. That is, it may hold as a general rule of thumb, but like all principles, there are bound to be exceptions.

Doran says: What about this sort of case? Suppose a prison vehicle was crushed in an avalanche, and both the driver and a convicted felon, about whose moral fault we have ample evidence, were seriously injured and in need of emergency medical care. Unlike the case of Terence and Lena, neither person did anything to bring about the injury. I don't think considerations of a person's guilt or innocence, virtue or vice, should affect triage decisions. Do you?

Warren says: I am not so sure I agree with you, Doran. Suppose, for example, that in the case you imagined, the prisoner that is injured is an infamous child molester and murderer, while the other person who is injured is the police officer assigned to guard him. If both were level 1, would the nurse be required to ignore her abhorrence for the molester and take him first because he came in just ahead of the police officer with whom she strongly sympathizes? I think that's asking too much.

Patrick says: I agree. As we've noted, medical professionals will often lack the information needed to make accurate judgments about patients and their guilt or innocence, virtue and vice, etc. But where they do have this information, I think preferential treatment based on these and other non-clinical factors is sometimes morally justified.

Doran says: I don't know. I understand the nurse's temptation to treat the police officer ahead of the criminal, but I am not sure that it is justified. As I said before, we should be reluctant to give nurses the authority to queue people up for care according to their perceived moral worth.

Warren says: In reality, the practice is "don't ask, don't tell." Ambulance drivers would not tell nurses about a patient's guilt, innocence, or any other non-medical characteristics. Nurses would not ask. In a case like that of the molester, though, the sympathy metarule allows the nurse to attend to the police officer first. These are extreme cases that rarely come up but which demonstrate the limits on our principles.

Third-Party Interests

Patrick says: Thus far we have been focusing on exceptions to worst first and first come that concern harms and benefits to particular patients. But there seems to be another category of exceptions to these and perhaps other rules that involve harms and benefits to **third parties.**

Warren says: Yes, I was thinking the same thing. Indeed, there seems to be an incredibly complex range of cases that may provide exceptions to the combination of the worst first and first come rules as well as to other principles we have begun to contemplate. To see what I have in mind, consider the following three cases:

1. *Childless person vs. parent of young child:* Patient A, a childless person, arrives in the emergency department with chest pain. Patient B, a single parent of a young child, arrives in emergency shortly thereafter with chest pain, too. Both are level 1 and are in serious need of immediate medical care, but only one patient can be treated while the other must wait. (We will call this the dependents case.)

2. *Drunk vs. doctor:* Patient A, the town drunk, arrives in the emergency department with chest pain. Patient B, the

UP FOR DISCUSSION

Should the moral responsibility of patients for their own or others' suffering ever influence a triage nurse's decision about whom to treat first when two patients are at the same level of medical urgency? Does your answer change if the patient is not morally responsible for his own or others' injuries but is a felon who was convicted of a crime?

UP FOR DISCUSSION

Worst first clearly takes priority over first come. What about the principles like fair turn or innocents first? Should innocents first come into play before fair turn, for example?

neighbouring town's only doctor, arrives in emergency shortly thereafter, also with chest pain. Both are level 1 and are in serious need of immediate medical care, but only one patient can be treated while the other must wait. (We will call this the public good case.) (Note: This case puts more emphasis on the public good than the case of Lena and Terence, which is focused on gratitude and perhaps the moral fault of Terence for Lena's injuries.)

3. *Person with highly infectious disease vs. person without infectious disease:* Patient A arrives in the emergency department with symptoms of a highly infectious disease and needs immediate care. Treatment of this person will put health care workers at significant risk of contracting the disease. Patient B arrives in emergency shortly thereafter with chest pain. Both are level 1 and are in serious need of immediate medical care, but only one patient can be treated while the other must wait. Should A be treated first, or should A be quarantined while B is treated? (We will call this the innocent threat case.)

In each of these cases, the principles of worst first and first come support treatment of patient A, but common sense suggests that in at least some of these cases it would be permissible to treat patient B first because of the rights or interests of third parties. If this is correct, then we would need to identify some principled reason that explains and organizes our judgments in these third-party cases.

Patrick says: These are interesting and tricky cases, Warren. The challenge, of course, is to explain which third-party interests matter and *why*.

Public Interest

Warren says: I would say that we can account for some of these cases by appealing to a rule we could call **public interest:** *Where the public interest is great enough, a patient may be given priority over those who came earlier.* This rule leaves open the possibility that not just prevention of great harm but promotion of enormous public benefit might also motivate us to treat a patient ahead of others. What counts as a sufficient public interest depends on balancing the needs of the patient who is passed over against extreme benefits or harms to the community.

Patrick says: Aren't you flirting dangerously with utilitarianism?

Warren says: Not necessarily; the position seems to be more like **extremitarianism.**

We are not saying that the greatest good needs to be promoted—rather, just that when much greater harm to others will result if B is not treated ahead of A or much greater benefit to others will result, then B may be bumped ahead of A.

DEFINITION

There is no recognized ethical term **extremitarianism.** This is a word Warren made up playing on **utilitarianism.** For the extremitarian, the harms or benefits have to be extreme before they can justify exceptions to worst first and first come.

Patrick says: Okay, but what about the dependents case, then? I'm torn here. I want to say that the virtues suggest we should bump B ahead of A and, in general, give priority to patients with young children. But I'm worried about unfairly discriminating against patients who can't have children or simply choose to remain childless.

Doran says: I am inclined to say that B should *not* be put ahead of A in the dependents case, because it would not respect A as a person, and because no general public good will be served by doing so. I worry that allowing the patient with young children to go ahead of those without children would unfairly discriminate against the childless.

Patrick says: Right. There's a tricky balance here. The virtuous person would seek to balance fairness against compassion for the parent and child. I think we'd need to know more details to say what considerations are most salient in these cases. There are lots of difficult issues to sort out here. For instance: How much greater benefit is enough to count as sufficient to override the principles of worst first and first come? And does it really make a moral difference that, in the public good and innocent threat cases, the interests being protected are those of individuals in society at large, whereas in the dependents case, the interests being protected are primarily those of the patient's immediate family?

UP FOR DISCUSSION

Should considerations of public interest, or the fact that one patient has dependents and the other hasn't, ever affect triage decisions?

Warren says: At least one factor in answering these questions is the application of the public interest rule. Is the public interest in protecting the community's children great enough to justify a preference for patients with dependents?

Patrick says: It seems a bit odd to make protection of children subject to public interest. Surely there is more to favouring the interests of kids

UP FOR DISCUSSION

Consider this rule: *Give special protection to the vulnerable.* Would such a rule help justify putting parents ahead of the childless to help protect children? What theoretical considerations would have us adopt such a rule? Consider objections and replies.

than just the wisdom of public policies. I would think that if a preference for patients with dependents is justified, it is justified out of direct concern for the patient and his or her dependents.

Warren says: I agree. Public interest is only one factor in the decision to bump the parent ahead. The other rules we are discussing may also come into play as well as rules we have not put out for consideration here.

It is worth reiterating, though, that whether we are speaking of the public good or just the interest of an individual third party, only in rare, extreme cases should triage nurses take the public interest into account. Patient B should be bumped ahead of patient A when there is an extreme and obvious difference in guilt and innocence or when, to take another instance, it is obvious that treating B over A would serve a great public good or prevent a great public harm. Extremitarianism rides again.

Medical Interests

Doran says: I am going to part company with you again. In the dependents case, I doubt that common sense would suggest that it is okay to bump the childless person in favour of the parent of a young child. It seems to me that triage nurses should not consider things like whether or not a patient has dependents when deciding whom to treat first. The nurse should focus on who needs care most, who was waiting for care longest, whether the patient would substantially benefit from care, and so on. But non-medical considerations, such as whether one person is a parent, or an only child, should not figure into treatment decisions. In part, this is because nurses are almost never going to be in a position to know who has dependents and who hasn't. But it goes deeper than this, for I just don't think that such factors should be relevant to treatment decisions. Parents and non-parents are equally deserving of care. To pass over a person with no kids to save a parent seems to discriminate against those who are childless.

Warren says: Yes, it is only in rare cases that nurses are in a position to know about the dependents, but in those rare cases that knowledge could be morally relevant because of the way the sympathy metarule restricts impartiality and because of other rules that may come into play. To say it is never relevant is to make too strong a claim.

Doran says: My views on the cases of public good and innocent threat are similar to yours. I agree that the only doctor in town may be treated ahead of the layperson, and the person without the highly infectious disease may be treated ahead of the one whose infectious condition makes him a great threat to the medical staff. But my reasons are different from yours. It is not quite public benefit that justifies this exception to ordinary triage considerations, rather it is something like **medical benefit** that justifies these decisions. This principle can be stated as *Where the medical interest is great enough, a patient may be given priority over those who came earlier.* For it seems what links public good and innocent threat is that if the person second in line is not treated, a great *medical* harm will happen. For instance, a great medical harm will befall the community if the doctor dies, or if the medical staff is incapacitated by some new plague. Triage nurses, as medical professionals, have a legitimate interest in promoting medical well-being, and so in these highly unusual cases they may treat second first so as to prevent medical disaster.

Patrick says: Well, I'm not sure that we can justify the preferential treatment in these cases just by appeal to either the public interest or the medical benefit principle. Each principle seems to capture *part* of what justifies special consideration, but each leaves something out as well. The public interest and the medical benefit justify putting the doctor ahead of the drunk, for instance, but I believe it's also supported by considerations about what kinds of life each is living. The doctor is apparently leading an admirable and worthwhile life, while the same can't be said for the drunk. I know this is a potentially dangerous path to head down, but in the extreme cases we're considering, I think these sorts of considerations are unavoidable.

Doran says: As you know, I disagree that nurses should take into consideration the virtue of their patients when making triage decisions.

Warren says: In most cases I think that is right, but there are the extreme cases where I would want to reserve room for exceptions. I also think that the attempt to narrow consideration to medical interests, while a good idea generally, will not work in all cases.

UP FOR DISCUSSION

Can you think of an example of the public interest requiring that patient B go ahead of patient A while medical interest does not require bumping A?

UP FOR DISCUSSION

Although Warren and Patrick argue that triage nurses can be justified in allocating resources in ways that are not impartial in some exceptional cases, the issues of what triage rules nurses should be taught, or what rules should be codified as part of official triage guidelines, are separate matters. They are not examined here but rather left for readers to consider.

COLLECTING OUR THOUGHTS

UP FOR DISCUSSION

Do we need principles to guide triage nurses in cases where the public interest requires treating B ahead of A, but the fair turn principle requires treating A ahead of B? Think of a hypothetical case where these principles could conflict. How would a utilitarian prioritize these principles? What about a Kantian, and a social contractarian? How would you decide which principle ought to take priority in this case?

UP FOR DISCUSSION

Apply the principles defended by Warren, Doran, and Patrick to Alice's decision to treat Lena ahead of Terence. Given these principles, did Alice act permissibly?

Patrick says: There is so much more to be said on this and the other complex issues surrounding third parties. We have hardly broached the subtle distinctions between the problems presented by different third-party interests. I think that a complete account is beyond what we can accomplish now, so let's stop and collect our thoughts.

Doran says: Yes, let's stop here. Although there are disagreements, there is a fair amount of consensus among us, despite our coming from different planets with respect to theory.

Patrick says: I suppose that indicates that we are probably on to something useful with Warren's set of principles. Not surprisingly, we are rather tentative about some of our conclusions, and there is some disagreement over the extent to which non-clinical factors should play a role in prioritizing patients.

Warren says: True, we are far from confident in the really hard cases, and some disagreements persist. I am encouraged, however, that our rules manage to address these difficult issues with any success at all. Perhaps we have here the beginnings of a position on matters that seemed barely accessible to reason.

Doran says: At the very least, we have raised some challenging issues for others to think through and debate.

SUMMARY

Here is a summary of the main questions, concepts, and arguments covered in this chapter:

- This chapter focuses on questions of microallocation of scarce health care resources, that is, selecting which individuals are to receive scarce health care resources.
- The main questions explored are the following: Who should be given priority in the treatment of patients in emergency situations when CTAS (Canadian Triage and Acuity Scale) guidelines do not settle the issue? Are other factors besides clinical urgency morally relevant? How are we to make decisions when cases are equally urgent yet patients cannot all be cared for at once? In particular, was it right for Alice to treat Lena ahead of Terence in our drama?
- The rules we arrive at should generally be applied impartially, although we need to recognize that health care workers are only human. Warren employs the sympathy metarule: that normal sympathies need to be taken into account when choosing rules in the original position.
- According to Warren, whether sympathies justify, excuse, or merely mitigate blame will depend on the kind of case. Doran thinks sympathies may mitigate blame, but that the sympathy metarule won't justify violating the impartial application of fair rules.
- Patrick, Doran, and Warren agree on the rule that the worst-off patient should be treated first. In cases where several people are similarly badly off, patients should normally be treated on a first come, first served basis. (These are the worst first and first come rules.) However, there are some exceptions to these rules.
- The hopeless second rule was intended to provide one of these exceptions. It was replaced by a more inclusive rule, substantial benefit: if two patients both need immediate care but the second patient (B) to arrive in the emergency department can benefit substantially from care while the first patient (A) cannot benefit substantially, then B may be treated first.
- Articulating the idea of substantial benefit is very complicated. It involves considerations such as whether A stands to gain only a little in quality of life from the treatment whereas B stands to gain much more; exceptions will depend on whether A has had a fair turn at life but B has not. Quality of life and fair turn are key notions, although they are difficult to specify in the abstract. Sometimes it may be permissible to take a person who has not had a fair turn at life over someone who has led a full life; the difference in the expected quality of life of the two patients must be large, however. Further, these judgments may be very hard to apply in concrete cases, and so the discretion of health care workers must be relied upon.
- Lastly, we discussed a category of exception to the worst first and first come principles that is based on non-clinical matters. Here Warren and Patrick accepted two rules, innocents first and public interest. These rules state that worst first and first come may be overridden in cases of extreme and obvious moral responsibility for an injury (like Terence's case), or extreme moral vice (like the child molester case), or in cases of great public interest like the public good case (about the town's only doctor).
- Doran, on the other hand, argued for fewer exceptions to the rules of worst first, first come, and substantial benefit. He argued that these principles should not be overridden in cases of moral fault, vice, or public good, or where one patient had young children but the other did not. However, he accepted that triage nurses would be justified in violating these rules in rare cases, where doing so was necessary to promote great medical interests.

Review Questions

1. What are the impartiality, worst first, first come, and hopeless second rules?
2. State an objection to each rule. Can the rule be revised to meet the objection?
3. What is the sympathy metarule?
4. Distinguish justifications from excuses and mitigations. How are these distinctions significant in the application of the sympathy metarule, according to Warren?
5. What are the minimize YPLL, substantial benefits, and fair turn rules?
6. Why do Doran, Patrick, and Warren reject minimize YPLL in favour of substantial benefit? What problems do they see with the substantial benefit rule?
7. What is the innocents first rule? Why do Warren and Patrick accept this rule, and why does Doran reject it?
8. What is the public interest rule? With what would Doran replace it and why?
9. Why does support of the public interest not require utilitarian moral theory (accepting happiness maximization as what is morally required)?
10. Explain the disagreement that remains among Patrick, Doran, and Warren at the end of the debate.

WWW.MCGRAWHILL.CA/OLC/SMOLKIN

ALTERNATIVE MEDICATIONS AND PROFESSIONAL RELATIONSHIPS

INTRODUCTION

In recent years, increasing numbers of Canadians have been turning to **complementary** and **alternative medicine** to treat everything from the common cold to cancer. By *complementary and alternative medicine,* we mean the kinds of drugs, therapies, practices, and so on, that are not used in conventional Western medicine. Examples of this include acupuncture, homeopathy, naturopathy, and herbal therapy. When these drugs and therapies are used together with conventional treatments, they are commonly referred to as complementary medicine. When used in place of conventional drugs and practices, they are called alternative medicine.

The basic question explored in this chapter is whether it is morally permissible for physicians to administer alternative medicine to patients who request it. At first glance, there may seem to be nothing morally wrong with this, since competent patients have a right to request whatever course of treatment they think is best. But the issue is complicated by the fact that many alternative therapies are untested and therefore potentially harmful. Moreover, patients who opt for alternative medicine may be forgoing conventional forms of therapy that have been proven to be life-saving or at least life-extending.

These considerations (and others) make the provision of alternative medicine by physicians a morally complicated matter.

Our drama begins with Ms. Nolle learning that she has a cancerous tumour. Although there is no cure, the standard treatment which involves chemotherapy and radiation is expected to prolong her life. Nolle, however, adamantly refuses the standard treatment. As she is leaving the hospital, her nurse mentions to her the existence of an alternative herbal treatment that appears to have worked for her friend. Nolle is excited about the prospects of this herbal treatment, and she finds a physician, Dr. Anderweg, who is willing to administer the herbal injections to her. Anderweg does not agree that Nolle's choice is the best for this kind of tumour; however, he respects her decision, and is willing to administer the injections.

Although this drama raises many interesting ethical issues, our focus is on whether Anderweg behaves permissibly in administering the herbal injections to Nolle. The more general question that we explore is whether physicians, in general, are morally permitted to administer alternative treatments at their patients' request. Warren uses social contract theory to argue that Anderweg acts permissibly in Nolle's case, and that physicians, in general, should be given very ample discretion to administer alternative therapies to their patients. Doran and Patrick take issue with many of Warren's claims.

In addition to exploring an important ethical issue, one of the primary purposes of this debate is to illustrate how a philosophical position can evolve and improve by responding to criticism. While reading this chapter, you should therefore pay particular attention to Warren's *ample discretion principle*, which specifies what Warren regards as acceptable limits on the kinds of treatments physicians can provide to their patients. You should also note Patrick's and Doran's use of counterexamples in an effort to reveal flaws in Warren's principle. These examples force Warren to revise the ample discretion principle several times over the course of the debate. In the end, Warren arrives at a principle that he thinks is justified and that demonstrates that Anderweg acts permissibly in Nolle's case. Doran accepts the final statement of the principle but doubts that it applies to Nolle's case. Patrick goes further and argues that Warren's principle, even when fully revised, is false.

LEARNING OBJECTIVES

After completing this chapter, you should be able to:

- Explain Warren's, Doran's, and Patrick's views on whether it was permissible for Dr. Anderweg to administer the herbal remedy H to Nolle, and whether it is permissible, in general, for physicians to administer alternative treatments to their patients who request them
- Define Warren's best interest principle

- Describe Warren's final statement of the ample discretion principle
- Understand why Warren thinks the ample discretion principle would be chosen in the original position
- Distinguish the various versions of the ample discretion principle, and explain how it evolves under pressure from the venom, psychic surgery, and prayer counterexamples
- Describe Doran's view on why it was not permissible for Anderweg to administer H to Nolle
- Explain Patrick's reasons for thinking that it was not permissible for Anderweg to administer H to Nolle, and why he thinks, in general, that it is not permissible for physicians to administer alternative treatments to their patients

DRAMA

Please note: This case is based on various true stories, although names, places, and some uncontroversial elements of the case have been changed to preserve anonymity and confidentiality. Discussions of this and similar cases with health care professionals have also informed this fictional case. Ms. Nolle is presented as a rough-spoken person. This is deliberate: we want to emphasize the distinction between being competent and being educated or cultured. Patients should not be thought to be incompetent merely because of the way they present themselves. The drama merely raises issues. The philosophical arguments are to be found in the debate following the drama.

CHARACTERS

Ms. Nolle: *a patient with a cancerous tumour, serous papillary carcinoma of the endometrium, stage 3*

Dr. Trad: *Ms. Nolle's attending physician*

Ms. Einverstand: *a nurse caring for Ms. Nolle*

Dr. Anderweg: *a physician who treats Ms. Nolle at home*

Mr. Swan: *a quality control administrator at the hospital where Dr. Trad and Dr. Anderweg admit*

Scene 1

The scene is a hospital ward. Dr. Trad briskly approaches the bed where Ms. Nolle is recovering from having a tumour removed.

Nolle: You look like grim death, Doctor. What's the bad news?

Trad: (*Taken aback*) Well, in fact, the news is not all that good. I'm afraid you have a serous papillary carcinoma of the endometrium, stage 3, which is . . .

Nolle: (*Interrupting*) Tell me what I've got—in words I'll understand.

Trad: (*Continuing coolly*) . . . which is a rather rare cancerous tumour. (*Trad softens his voice*) The prognosis, that is, your outlook is for up to 24 months of life if you accept **chemotherapy** and **radiotherapy** but only about 6 months if you don't take treatment. (*Nolle holds up her hand*) Let me explain these treatments.

Nolle: Nope. Those are two treatments I know all too well. Hank had that stuff done to him before he died. I swore to God they'd never do that to me.

Trad: I am familiar with your husband's case. Yours is different, believe me. If I were in your shoes, knowing what I know, there is no question in my mind that I would take these treatments. Nothing else works.

Nolle: You're not saying it'll cure me.

Trad: No, no, but it will give you some relatively healthy time. Every bit of time is precious.

Nolle: You've got that right. That's why I sure won't spend the last of my time like Hank did. If you haven't got a cure for me, I'm just not interested.

Trad: Don't be hasty. This is an enormously important decision.

Nolle: And I'm the one making it. There's no way I'm getting **chemo,** not over my dead body. (*Laughing heartily at Trad's uncomfortable expression*) I know you don't think I'm taking death serious, but laughter is still the best medicine.

Trad: You don't have to decide right this minute. Please think carefully about this. I'd like you to talk to . . .

Nolle: Getting resigned to dying would kill me. Ha! You should have seen your face when I said that, Doc.

Trad: Very well. We'll talk again when you're more accustomed to your diagnosis.

Nolle: When hell freezes we will. Look, if you got no cure, forget it. I've made my own decisions all my life. I know enough to know chemo is no good for me. I'm not about to give up and just try to die slowly. Don't waste your time.

Scene 2

In the same ward, Nurse Einverstand is helping Ms. Nolle get ready to leave the hospital after Nolle's refusal of radiotherapy and chemotherapy for her tumour.

Nolle: Thank you, dear. You're an angel. I don't have much stuff to take home, 'cause I never did intend to stay here long.

Einverstand: Well, I'm so glad you're well enough to go home.

Nolle: Hell, I'm not well at all. Not one bit. I'm just not going to sit around here getting chemo and radio till I drop. There's other stuff to try. I don't know where to find it, but I'll sure as hell look. I'm going to find a cure or die trying. (*Laughs heartily*)

Einverstand: Oh yeah, there are alternative therapies. My girlfriend used one and is doing great two years beyond her expected time.

Nolle: No kidding! What's she taking?

Einverstand: Oh, it's this new herbal thing that she gets injected. I don't know much about it except that it's not a medically accepted treatment.

Nolle: I knew it. Natural cures, that's the stuff.

Einverstand: Oh—well, I shouldn't get your hopes up . . .

Nolle: Why the hell not? Hope is all I've got. Now you tell me where I can find out about getting some of this herbal stuff.

Einverstand: I'll call my friend and call you with the information.

Nolle: Cross your heart and swear to God?

Einverstand: (*Laughing*) Yes, of course. (*Crosses her heart*)

Scene 3

Six months have passed. Einverstand waits in a meeting room. Anderweg enters. Anderweg has been administering injections of a herbal remedy to Ms. Nolle at home. Her condition has worsened, there has been much growth in the tumour, and she has been readmitted to hospital. She wishes to continue the herbal treatment in the hospital.

Einverstand: Dr. Anderweg?

Anderweg: Call me Ken. Nice to meet you. Hilda Nolle told me you're an angel.

Einverstand: She's such a neat old girl. What a shame it didn't work for her.

Anderweg: Well, there was only a snowball's chance.

Einverstand: What? You've been giving Ms. Nolle the injections. Don't you believe in this therapy?

Anderweg: I believe a patient has a right to choose, but I told Hilda that if I had a **radiosensitive tumour,** I would not be trying something untested on it instead of radiotherapy. But you know Hilda. It was alternative therapy or nothing.

Einverstand: It seemed to work on Marjorie.

Anderweg: "Seemed" is the operative word here. Maybe your friend just got lucky and had a remission. Maybe the herb only works for certain cancers. It was worth a try. When medicine has no cure, I don't mind patients trying anything if they've got little or nothing to lose. Hilda joked with me that her cure might not be 100% effective, but resignation is 100% fatal.

Einverstand: Actually, the treatment gave her something and still does. She told me when she came in that she probably would have died months ago without your treatment. She wants you to keep injecting her. She says it's her only hope.

Anderweg: Hope is a gift. She got six good months at home, too. She might have done no better with chemo and radiotherapy.

Trad: (*Entering the room, grim-faced*) She might have had that with nothing. She might have had two years with proper treatment. I'm surprised you aren't dancing around her bed with a rattle and feathers.

Einverstand: Dr. Trad!

Trad: (*Turning to Einverstand*) Nurse, if you ever again persuade one of my patients to give up medically approved treatment for . . .

Einverstand: (*Interrupting*) Don't take that tone with me. I didn't persuade Hilda of anything. I doubt anyone ever has. She is very strong willed. She asked me for information and I gave it to her.

Trad: Sure. *Information!*

Anderweg: This won't get us anywhere. Don't you believe in honouring patient autonomy and a patient's right to choose her own therapy, when we have no cure?

Trad: Therapy! Since when have double-blind controlled studies been done on this stuff?

Einverstand: The patient thinks it's working and she wants to continue treatment.

Trad: If you two get up to your quackery in here, I'll have you up before the appropriate disciplinary bodies so fast your heads will spin. (*Trad storms out*)

Scene 4

In an administrator's office. Einverstand and Anderweg sit across from Mr. Swan, a hospital administrator dealing with quality control.

Swan: I have taken your request and the patient's request to our legal counsellors and I have spoken with Dr. Trad.

Anderweg: Did you get the recommendation of the Ethics Committee?

Swan: Oh yes, and I have given it careful consideration, as have our legal counsellors, but we cannot agree with it.

Einverstand: So it's "No"?

Swan: To allow this treatment would make the hospital particularly vulnerable. Dr. Trad has warned us that the injections could perhaps worsen the patient's condition by spreading the cancer.

Anderweg: Given that she will never take chemo or radiotherapy, she has nothing to lose with this alternative.

Swan: I'll let you and Dr. Trad argue the merits of that, but I can tell you that this hospital has a great deal to lose.

Einverstand: Surely you are being overcautious. If all we can give her is **palliation** . . . (*The phone rings*)

Swan: (*Picking up the phone*) Excuse me. Hello. I can't talk now . . . Ah. I see. (*Putting down the phone with exaggerated care*) Ms. Nolle is dead.

Einverstand: Oh, that's awful news. It's too bad the herbal therapy didn't work for her . . . Well, we did try to respect her wishes.

Swan: This hospital takes patient autonomy seriously. Still, I will be guided by legal advice.

Anderweg: Tell me, what is the Ethics Committee for?

Swan: Now, Dr. Anderweg, you know as well as I do that it is subcommittee of the Quality Committee, which is a subcommittee of the Board and, as such, has a purely advisory function. We accept most of the advice of the Ethics Committee, but in this case it took patient autonomy a little too far.

Einverstand: You'll be hearing from my association. We nurses have a very different view of the matter.

Anderweg: So, I hope, does the College of Physicians and Surgeons. We'll do what we can to bring this institution into this century.

DEBATE
Clarifying the Case and Identifying Relevant Facts

Patrick says: Let's begin by making sure that we're clear on the relevant facts of the case. Many are spelled out, but key pieces of information are missing.

TECHNIQUE

It is always important to try to establish the relevant facts before beginning the debate. Factors such as whether Nolle was informed, whether the alternative medication, H, had been scientifically tested, the likely effects of conventional treatments, and others, all make a difference to the moral evaluation of Anderweg's, and others', behaviour.

Warren says: Well, just to summarize, Ms. Nolle was a strong-willed elderly woman whose husband had died an unpleasant and lingering death while getting the standard treatment. She refused to even consider that treatment for her cancerous tumour. Nurse Einverstand mentioned to her an alternative therapy, H—herbal injections that a friend of Einverstand had used with apparent success. Nolle chose H over standard therapy, even though she was told that her case was different from her husband's. Ms. Nolle wanted to try treatments that were intended to be cures, not merely ways of delaying death. Dr. Anderweg agreed to give her these injections, although he said that he himself would have taken the standard treatment. Ms. Nolle died after six months of treatment.

Doran says: Dr. Trad mentioned that there was a risk that the injections of H could cause the cancer to spread. Did Anderweg advise Nolle of this risk, and any others?

Warren says: There was a small chance that injections could dislodge cells from the tumour that would spread the cancer to other sites. Since Nolle's chances were slim in any case, this was not a significant risk, in Anderweg's opinion. There was also a danger of bleeding or infection from the injections. These were more serious risks, but Anderweg was confident that he could control them or deal with them if they arose. He did not discuss these risks with Ms. Nolle.

Doran says: So Anderweg didn't discuss these risks with Nolle. Hmmm.

Patrick says: Warren, I was wondering about the following. Given Anderweg's skepticism about H, why didn't he just refer Nolle to a naturopath—someone who specialized in the sort of medicine Nolle requested?

Warren says: Even if Anderweg could have found a naturopath, I suspect that he was worried about having someone without his training giving the injections because of the chance of bleeding and infection. Still, there might well be some very skilled naturopaths in the area. Anderweg was also concerned about the cost to Nolle, thousands of dollars, if a naturopath took the case. The *Canada Health Act* would cover the treatment if Anderweg gave it, but not a naturopath.

Patrick says: That's an interesting point about the funding, Warren. Do you know why our health care system would pick up the bill for the herbal treatment only if it were administered by a medical doctor? Is this a matter of general policy with respect to alternative therapies? If so, do you happen to know the rationale behind the policy?

Warren says: The *Canada Health Act* is written so as to favour MDs over alternative practitioners. In the Act, "insured health services" means "hospital services, physician services and surgical-dental services." The rationale has been that there is evidence for the effectiveness of physicians' and surgeons' practices while there is not for alternative practices. This is currently a matter of much debate as revisions to the Act are contemplated.[1]

UP FOR DISCUSSION

Should our public health insurance cover unconventional and alternative health care services?

Doran says: Was Nolle offered any counselling to help her think through her decisions about treatment? It seems that this would have been a good idea.

THEORY

Kantian respect for persons is typically taken to require informed consent in order to treat a person always as an **end,** and never merely as a **means.**

Defenders of an **ethic of care** would also encourage extensive counselling and open discussion by the entire medical team with a patient, so as to reach the solution that best responds to the patient's needs.

Warren says: I don't think anyone considered counselling. The tumour was progressing rapidly. Nolle was anxious to get started. Also, she was the type to dismiss counselling. She wasn't likely to listen to anybody's advice but her own.

Doran says: What was Anderweg's opinion about the likely effect of traditional therapy if Nolle received it?

Warren says: Anderweg thought Nolle had no chance in any case, and the standard treatment could only delay death. He knew he could not guarantee Nolle that she would not have nasty side effects from standard treatment. He thought H would be innocuous as far as side effects were concerned.

Doran says: Thanks for providing these details, Warren. I think have a better handle now on the relevant background facts. Patrick, do you have any other questions for Warren?

Patrick says: Yes. I was wondering whether there is any research at all on H that suggests that it could actually help Nolle's physical condition, aside from a possible placebo effect. Was H undergoing clinical testing?

---

[1] *Canada Health Act* (R.S.C. 1985, c. C-6), Definitions.

BACKGROUND

"The prevalence of complementary and alternative medicine (CAM) use has been estimated to be as high as 65% in some populations. However, there has been little objective research into the possible risks or benefits of unmanaged CAM therapies."

Source: Tyler C. Smith, Besa Smith, and Margaret A. K. Ryan, "Prospective Investigation of Complementary and Alternative Medicine Use and Subsequent Hospitalizations," *BMC Complementary and Alternative Medicine* 8, no. 19 (2008). (Available at http://www.biomedcentral.com/1472-6882/8/19.)

According to the Mayo Clinic: "Alternative cancer treatments won't play any role in curing your cancer, but they may help you cope with signs and symptoms caused by cancer and cancer treatments. Common signs and symptoms such as anxiety, fatigue, nausea and vomiting, pain, difficulty sleeping, and stress may be lessened by alternative treatments."

The clinic recommends that patients "[u]se alternative cancer treatments as a supplement to treatments you receive from your doctor—not as a substitute for medical care. While alternative cancer treatments, such as acupuncture, may reduce nausea or pain, they generally aren't powerful enough to replace medications from your doctor. Work closely with your doctor to determine the right balance between traditional medicines and alternative cancer treatments."

Source: http://www.mayoclinic.com/health/cancer-treatment/CM00002.

Warren says: There was some **anecdotal** evidence suggesting that H may be effective in treating cancer, but H had not been scientifically tested.

Patrick says: Okay. If there are no more questions for now, I think we can move on.

MORAL ISSUES RAISED BY THE CASE

Patrick says: One interesting question raised by the drama is whether competent patients have a right to choose their course of treatment. I suppose most of us would agree that they do. A related and more difficult question is what it takes for a patient to qualify as competent. But this is a question we explore in Chapter 5, so we can set it aside here.

Doran says: We have an MD, in this case, giving unproven herbal medicine, and we have a nurse recommending an alternative treatment that she knows little about to a patient that she scarcely knows. There is a gigantic range of alternative medicine being marketed. Some of it may have merit; most of it is pure charlatanism. Given this, we could consider debating whether it was reckless for Einverstand to suggest H to Nolle and unprofessional for Anderweg to administer it. This raises important moral questions about the professional responsibilities of health care workers.

Warren says: The case also raises the more general question of whether it is morally permissible for doctors in general to administer unproven alternative therapies.

Patrick says: Yes, that seems to be the main general question raised by the case. And given the increasing demand for alternative medicine, discussing that issue would be very timely.

Doran says: Right. But let's begin with the more specific question of *whether it was morally permissible for Anderweg to administer H, given that Nolle requested it.*

Patrick says: Sure. We can use this as a springboard to the more general question Warren noted: *Is it morally permissible for doctors, in general, to administer alternative therapies if their patients request them?*

Warren says: Sounds good to me. Let's get going.

Stating Our Positions

Warren says: I believe that it was permissible for Anderweg to administer H. It was in Nolle's best interest.

Doran says: I would say Anderweg's actions were probably not morally permissible. Nolle needed to receive more information about her treatment options, and she needed to receive counselling to ensure that she was making the best choice for her. I also think that it may have been better for Anderweg to refer Nolle to a competent naturopath if one was available.

Patrick says: As an MD, Anderweg should, in general, stick to treating patients with drugs that have undergone, or are currently undergoing, rigorous clinical testing, or at least have been proven effective over the course of time and have been generally accepted by medical professionals. Because H does not fall into these categories, I believe it was irresponsible and reckless of Anderweg, as an MD, to give it to Nolle. If Nolle really wanted H, Anderweg should have referred her to a naturopath or some other specialist in alternative medicine.

Doran says: So it looks as if Patrick and I are inclined to think that Anderweg should not have given Nolle the alternative treatment, whereas you see nothing wrong with his doing this, Warren.

Warren says: That's right. I think Anderweg could've administered almost any therapy that Nolle chose.

UP FOR DISCUSSION

The Canadian Nurses Association *Code of Ethics* (2008) contains the following rule. "Nurses respect the informed decision-making of capable persons, including choice of lifestyles or treatment not conducive to good health." Does this rule determine whether Nurse Einverstand should help Ms. Nolle use alternative medications? Do you think Einverstand acted inappropriately when she mentioned unproven therapies to Nolle? What role should nurses play in recommending therapies?

Source: Canadian Nurses Association, *Code of Ethics for Registered Nurses* (Ottawa: CNA, 2008), 12. (Available at http://www.cna-aiic.ca/CNA/practice/ethics/code/default_e.aspx.)

BACKGROUND

In some jurisdictions, nurse practitioners, in addition to doctors, may prescribe and administer therapies. It is likely that the same ethical issues arise for those practitioners.

Patrick says: Really? That seems like an excessively permissive position. But I suppose much depends on what you mean by "almost," so perhaps you could clarify. Is there *any* therapy it would be wrong for Anderweg to administer to Nolle, assuming that she requested it? What if she was ill informed and chose badly?

THE BEST INTEREST PRINCIPLE

TECHNIQUE

Warren is starting with an idea with which he is not completely satisfied, but by inviting questions and objections he will be able to test it until he can reject or strengthen the idea. We can often clarify our ideas by putting them under stress in this way.

THEORY

One reason for taking the patient's best interest to heart is the general duty of beneficence recognized by intuitionists like W. D. Ross. Ross would have to argue, however, that in this particular circumstance, beneficence outweighed other countervailing duties.

Warren says: Of course few of us are as well informed as the experts in health care we consult, so bad choices might happen on a regular basis. Let me propose the following principle: *If a treatment is in a patient's best interest, and the patient requests it, then that treatment is permissible.* This principle is too simple, but let's use it as our starting point and refine it as problems emerge.

Patrick says: Warren, the notion of a patient's **best interest** is central to your principle. Are you thinking of *best interest* just in terms of a patient's physical condition, or do you have something more general in mind, something like the patient's overall condition, where this includes mental well-being?

Warren says: I mean to take *best interest* very generally so as to include the use of medically useless treatments that have a useful placebo effect on the patient; so her psychological, physical, and any other kind of well-being can be promoted. The idea is that a treatment is in a patient's best interest if the net benefit to the patient, judged in terms of her overall well-being, is higher than with any other treatment.

Doran says: So, since you think it was permissible for Anderweg to administer H to Nolle, I assume that you think H was in Nolle's best interest, even though the standard therapy could offer her up to 24 months of life instead of just 6?

Warren says: Yes, she seems to have had 6 months of good life in lieu of 24 months of misery.

Doran says: Why do you assume Nolle would have had 24 months of misery if she received the standard care?

Warren says: My assumption is based on what she and others said in the case.

Doran says: Trad says that the prognosis is for up to 24 months of life, if Nolle accepts the chemotherapy and radiation. Also, he says that

Nolle's case is different from her husband's case. So I don't think you can assume that she would have experienced 24 months of misery if she went with the standard treatment.

Warren says: Nolle would probably have been miserable with a treatment that she viewed as horrifying, even if her course was different from her husband's. It is not the physical effects of chemo and radio-therapy that would necessarily have undermined her well-being, but her resignation and hopelessness. She clearly preferred a life, even a short one, with hope, over the longer, less appealing life offered by Trad. As Anderweg said, hope is a gift. He also said that for Nolle it was alternative therapy or nothing. So the standard therapy was not a live option for her.

Doran says: Well, I can agree with you, Warren, that *if* Nolle had six quality months on the alternative therapy, that this could be better than a longer life of poor quality. What I question, however, is your claim that she would have been miserable if she had taken the standard treatment. We just don't know that. Perhaps if Nolle received counselling and support, she would have had a longer, better life with the standard care. We just don't know. So I have doubts about your claim that the alternative therapy was in her best interest.

Warren says: Doran, you are right to raise doubts. It is possible that, over time, she might have been better off with the standard therapy because she had come to accept it as her best option, but from what I know about the case that was very unlikely. The evidence suggests that the alternative treatment alone gave her hope during six months of life and that was better than resignation, which she said was "100% fatal."

Patrick says: But what were the various alternatives? We seem to be assuming that Nolle had just three options: the standard treatment consisting of chemotherapy and radiotherapy, the herbal treatment, or nothing. But perhaps there were experimental cancer treatments that would offer her more hope, and more months of life, than H. Warren, do you know whether Anderweg looked for any experimental cancer drugs or treatments that he could have offered to Nolle?

UP FOR DISCUSSION

Do you think that H was in Nolle's best interest? Suppose you do not. If Nolle would not take the conventional therapies, and given that there were no experimental treatments, was H in her best interest then?

Warren says: He looked for other treatments, but for that particular kind of cancer there were no experimental drugs that he thought would help.

Patrick says: Okay. I acknowledge Nolle's right to choose the course of treatment she thinks is best. So, although I think she acted foolishly, I recognize her right to refuse the standard course of treatment and seek an alternative therapy. What troubles me about this case is that a *medical doctor* provided an untested and unproven alternative therapy. Even if we grant your claim that H was in Nolle's best interest, I'm not at all convinced that it was permissible for Anderweg to give it to Nolle.

Warren says: Why?

Patrick says: You based your position on the best interest principle: *If a treatment is in a patient's best interest, and the patient requests it, then that treatment is permissible.* But I believe this principle is false, and I have a **counterexample** that I believe proves this.

Doran says: What's the counterexample, Patrick?

Patrick's Venom Counterexample to the Best Interest Principle

Patrick says: Suppose that Nolle had been raised among a group of religious extremists who believed in the miraculous healing power of minute doses of snake venom. And suppose that instead of H, Nolle asked Anderweg to give her injections of venom. I'm assuming that the injections of venom would be small enough that they would pose no greater risk of harm than H. I'm also assuming that the injections of venom would give her hope, just as H did. So I'm imagining a case that mirrors the actual case in all relevant respects, except that it involves venom therapy instead of herbal therapy. My intuitions are that it would be morally wrong for Anderweg to comply with Nolle's request for snake venom. If I'm right, then your principle is mistaken, Warren. Can you provide us with a strong argument in support of your view—one that would show that my intuitions about the snake venom case are incorrect?

Doran says: I think this is a convincing counterexample, Patrick. I share your intuition that it would be wrong for Anderweg to comply with such a request.

Warren says: Interesting example, Patrick; however, I am willing to bite the bullet on this one. I maintain that Anderweg's treatment of Nolle with herbal injections, or with any other treatment that is in her best interest and that

---

TECHNIQUE

Recall that a **counterexample** is an example that purports to counter a general claim, principle, analysis, argument, etc. Patrick's aim is to show that Warren's best interest principle is false. His counterexample is intended to show that some treatments might be impermissible even when patients request them and they are in those patients' best interest.

TECHNIQUE

When confronted with a counterexample, one can attempt to show that the example does not in fact counter the claim, principle, etc., in question. That is what Warren tries to do. Warren will accept the strange view that even venom injections, under extremely restricted circumstances, could be permissible. He will then try to convince Doran and Patrick that it is strange but true.

she requests (possibly even venom), is morally permissible. I'll argue for this by way of what I will call the **ample discretion principle**—a rule that would be chosen in the original position.

THE AMPLE DISCRETION PRINCIPLE

Warren says: It would be in the interest of the rule choosers in the original position to accept this principle: *Physicians may exercise ample discretion to decide whether or not to use any treatment that the patient chooses, provided that it is in the patient's best interest.* Like computer graphics, medicine is an art based on sciences. To limit physicians to scientifically proven treatments would be to rule out possible help from physicians that might be critically important to the choosers of rules once they are patients in the real world. If you don't know what shape you might be in, you need the right to **autonomy** to protect your interest if you get into a tough situation, for example, a situation where normal medicine cannot help you.

> **THEORY**
>
> Here is an example of Warren's use of his **social contract** ethical theory. To understand this you need to remember what the original position is and how it is used in contractarian ethics. You can see this at length in the statement of Warren's theory in Chapter 3.

Autonomy in the medical context, however, is a poor thing if some of the very people who are best equipped to help you exercise autonomy, namely physicians, are prevented from helping. I think it is clear that, in the original position, we would reject any rule that forces us and forces our doctors in the real world to stick to what is scientifically confirmed.

> **DEFINITION**
>
> Warren's argument for the ample discretion principle employs the concept of autonomy. **Autonomy** is often understood as self-determination, making one's own uncoerced choices.

Limiting discretion would, moreover, limit medical research and discovery. That is clearly contrary to the interests of patients who reject or have run out of standard options. In the original position we would protect our interest by providing for the ample discretion of physicians. It's hard to say exactly how much is *ample,* but Anderweg was within reasonable limits.

Doran says: So, in short, your argument is that whatever rules parties choose in the original position are justified, and that they would choose a rule that gave physicians ample discretion in hopeless cases, provided that the therapy is in the best interest of the patient. Is that right? Nolle's case was hopeless anyway, so anything goes when Anderweg prescribes.

Warren says: That's not exactly it. You are right that I treat rules as justified if they would be accepted in the original position. As to the second point, however, we come to ample discretion through autonomy. First we need to establish that a strong right to autonomy would be chosen in the original position. Ample discretion is then needed to allow people to exercise autonomy. The case, moreover, does not have to be hopeless, although that is the clearest kind of case. The choice of the rule or principle of ample discretion is dependent on the patient's strong interest in autonomy when the patient is choosing a treatment. It is Nolle's strong right to choose that would wither if willing physicians like Anderweg were prevented from honouring her choice.

Patrick says: I agree, Warren, that physicians ought to have the liberty to try out new drugs and therapies. But this should be done in the right sort of setting. This is what clinical trials are for. If H were part of a clinical trial, and the risks were clearly laid out for Nolle, then I would have no objection to Anderweg complying with her request for H. But that is not the case in this situation. Your ample discretion principle gives physicians too much liberty. For that reason, I think the principle would not be chosen in the original position.

Doran's Indeterminacy Objection to Warren's Principle

Doran says: I agree. It's not clear to me why people in the original position would choose the ample discretion principle rather than some other competing principle. Perhaps people in the original position will choose a rule that instructs physicians to do what is in their best interest, and protects patients from taking reckless decisions; or perhaps they will choose a rule that instructs physicians to do whatever the patient chooses, or a rule that instructs physicians to do whatever the patient chooses provided it is not too harmful. Your contract argument does not conclusively prove that a principle of ample discretion is justified.

Warren says: Actually, I think that "conclusively prove" is too strong a phrase. One can be persuasive short of a conclusive proof. In fact, I don't think that any ethical theory is capable of providing us with moral certainties or absolutes that would come from a conclusive proof. It is enough if we can give good reasons for why people in the original position would choose more or less discretion for physicians, without knowing for sure what they would choose.

Doran says: Fair enough, but my problem remains. I just do not see what reasons people in the original position would have for selecting your preferred rule, ample discretion, over some other seemingly plausible rule—for example, *Do what is in the patients' best interests, while protecting patients from their ill-informed choices.* So I am not convinced that your way of thinking about the case gives us a strong reason to accept the ample discretion principle and to say that Anderweg did what was permissible.

Patrick says: I'm with Doran on this one, Warren. Can you say more about why you believe the ample discretion principle would be chosen over competing principles?

Warren says: Okay, let's see how ample discretion can be defended against competing principles. You suggested an alternative principle a moment ago, Doran, namely, *Do what is in the patients' best interests, while protecting patients from their ill-informed choices.* This is a highly **paternalistic** principle, one that gives too much power to the physician, so I do not think it could be considered in their interest by the choosers of rules. That principle would let Dr. Trad tell Nolle what to do. The other principles you suggest are just not sufficiently restricted to protect patients' interests. Protection of our interests is what we consider in the original position.

> ### DEFINITION
>
> **Paternalism** is the interference with a person's liberty for that person's own good. For an excellent introduction to the concept of paternalism, see http://plato.stanford.edu/entries/paternalism/.
>
> Utilitarians have no objection to paternalism when it maximizes happiness. Kantians, on the other hand, would reject paternalism for rational adults, since it violates their autonomy. Warren seems to be siding with Kantians on this point.

Doran says: But using your contract argument, wouldn't patients want to protect themselves from their poor choices? I might request some inefficacious therapy over a proven treatment because I am desperate for a miracle cure, or because I am simply afraid of some aspect of the standard treatment. Surely, doctors should not be given the discretion to act on these choices. In Nolle's case, the concern is that she is motivated by misunderstanding and desperation.

Patrick says: Right. And parties in the original position may want to protect themselves from not just their own bad judgment, but also from the poor choices of their doctors. Perhaps Anderweg is just weak-willed, for instance, or lacks the courage to stand up to Nolle, and so gives in to her too easily.

> ### TECHNIQUE
>
> Doran and Patrick are chipping away at the plausibility of the ample discretion principle to undercut one of the premises of Warren's argument that Anderweg acts permissibly. If one of Warren's premises is not true, his argument is unsound. His conclusion about Anderweg might follow logically from the ample discretion principle (and so the argument would be logically valid), but following from a falsehood is no recommendation for his conclusion about Anderweg's action.

UP FOR DISCUSSION

Do you think that people in the original position would accept the principle of ample discretion, or would they choose a more paternalistic principle—say, one that ensured that doctors gave only the medically recommended treatments?

Warren says: I take your points. I agree that parties in the original position will want to make sure that physicians are not given the discretion to act on their own or their ill-informed patients' whims. But the provision that the physician should act in the best interest of the patient rules out a weak-willed physician just giving in. That's clearly wrong by the principle.

Doran says: But what if the patient is incapable of making rational choices, for instance? Can the doctor just go ahead and do whatever he thinks is in the patient's best interest even if it is a very weird treatment? Suppose Anderweg thinks Nolle is **incompetent** to choose?

Warren says: There is an important difference between the rules that would be chosen affecting **competent** and incompetent patients. Incompetent patients require protection that is much more paternalistic, and the discretion of the physician would be much less. Since incompetent patients cannot protect themselves or decide to take big risks that might help them achieve their goals, very conservative care is warranted.

Rules set in the original position would honour only adventurous choices made with the **valid consent** of competent persons.[2] Anderweg would, of course, still be required to pursue the best interest of an incompetent Ms. Nolle, but within stricter limits. He could not do anything experimental or too strange at his own discretion, like using H. If Nolle is deemed incompetent, then Anderweg should just play it safe. If we are going to support autonomy with ample discretion, then it must be for competent patients or their surrogate decision-makers to validly consent to treatment.

BACKGROUND

Competence comes in degrees. Someone could be more or less competent to perform some task. Beyond that, we may be more willing to deem someone competent as the risks one runs by exercising autonomy become smaller.

THE AMPLE DISCRETION PRINCIPLE REVISED: VALID CONSENT OF COMPETENT PATIENTS ONLY

Doran says: Okay, Warren, so it seems you would like to replace the initial statement of the ample discretion rule with the following: *Physicians*

---

[2] To say that a patient consents is just to say that *the patient willingly accepts the treatment*. Since Nolle demands H, *a fortiori*, she willingly accepts H. But, of course, to say that a person consents to treatment does not guarantee that this consent is valid.

may exercise ample discretion to decide whether or not to use any treatment to which a competent patient gives valid consent, provided that it is in the patient's best interest.

Warren says: Yes, that's right.

Patrick says: Warren, I have a couple of questions about the revised principle. First, what exactly do you mean by *competent*?

My second question is this: Now that you have restricted the application of the ample discretion rule to competent patients, I'm not sure why you need the further clause that the chosen treatment is in the patient's best interest. Why not just say this: *Physicians may exercise ample discretion to decide whether or not to use any treatment to which a competent patient gives valid consent.* This principle would seem to be more consistent with the goal of protecting autonomy.

UP FOR DISCUSSION

Do you think physicians should be free to give *competent* patients unconventional treatments if they are in the patients' best interests and the patients validly consent to them?

Ample Discretion, Patient Competence, and Valid Consent

Warren says: Let me take your first question first. Patient competence is an exceedingly complicated issue that we cannot fully address here.[3] But perhaps we can agree on the following. Competence involves a capacity to make choices based on comprehension of relevant information and the consequences of one's choices. A person can be competent in one area, but not other areas. For instance, a person can be competent to make health care decisions, but not competent to make important decisions about financial matters because of a phobia about money. To be competent to make health care choices, it seems one must be capable of understanding one's condition, treatment options, the probable consequences of each treatment, and their respective risks and benefits. One must then be able to make a decision based on this information. When I speak of patients being competent or incompetent, I am speaking of their having or lacking this ability.[4] Before he agrees to Nolle's request for H, then, Anderweg must ensure that Nolle is competent in this sense.

Patrick says: I agree with most of your remarks about competence. But how do we tell whether Nolle is competent?

---

[3] We focus more explicitly on the issue of competence in Chapter 5.

[4] An excellent discussion of competence and of informed consent can be found in chapter 3 of Beauchamp and Childress, *Principles of Biomedical Ethics*, 5th ed.

BACKGROUND

The matter of assessing competence is not without controversy, although a commonly used process seeks to determine whether the patient "(a) can comprehend and retain relevant information, (b) believes the information, and (c) can weigh the information in the balance and arrive at a choice."

Source: Paul Biegler and Cameron Stewart, "Assessing Competence to Refuse Medical Treatment," *Medical Journal of Australia* 174, no. 10 (2001): 522–25. Quoted in Alexander Kuehl, ed., *Prehospital Systems and Medical Oversight,* 3rd ed. (National Association of EMS Physicians, 2002), 508.

Warren says: In legal and medical contexts, persons are generally assumed to be competent unless there is good reason for doubting this. So the question is whether we have a good reason for doubting Nolle's competence. She is requesting a non-standard course of treatment over a more conventional treatment that has been clinically tested. But that, by itself, does not show that she's incompetent.

Patrick says: I agree that the mere fact that she requests an unconventional treatment is not sufficient to show that she's incompetent. But we have good reason to question Nolle's competence, given her complete refusal to seriously consider the course of treatment that the medical community in general thinks is best. Her experience with her husband, who did not do well with the standard course of treatment, prevented her from being able to think rationally about her own situation. She wouldn't even allow Trad to explain the relevant differences between her own condition and her husband's. This leads me to question whether she is competent to make decisions about her course of treatment.

TECHNIQUE

Here, Patrick and Doran are not disagreeing with the revised ample discretion principle; instead, they are questioning whether this principle applies to Nolle's situation.

Doran says: I am not sure that the problem is that Nolle is incompetent. I don't think she lacks the capacity to make her health care decisions; my concern is that she does not give valid consent.[5] In this case, in order to give valid consent, Nolle needs a better understanding of her treatment options and the likely effects of her choices. She then needs to deliberate about them in a way that is consistent with both her goals and the facts at hand. My concern is that because Nolle will not even consider all of her treatment options, she does not really understand the likely effects of the conventional therapies and alternative therapies as they relate to her circumstances. Because she lacks the relevant information, her consent to H is not valid.

Warren says: She knows enough about the risks to know how to pursue her goal of living in hope of a cure. Nolle prefers a short life of hope to a longer life of resignation. She knowingly chooses to take a chance on non-standard treatment that gives her hope instead of resignation. So her consent to be treated with H is valid. She is

---

[5] We focus more explicitly on the issue of valid consent in Chapter 5.

not ignoring evidence relevant to her goal of maximizing hope. She is ignoring evidence relevant to the medical view about her chances, but she does not want the evidence for the medical view in case it undermines hope. "Where ignorance is bliss, 'tis folly to be wise." It would be different if Trad had offered her a cure or a means that supported hope. Since hope makes her life worthwhile to her, Nolle would be a fool to abandon hope and accept resignation by becoming informed about the improbability of her long-term survival.

Doran says: It is not that I necessarily disagree with her final decision, Warren, but she should have seriously considered her options. Anderweg should have made sure she was properly informed. Perhaps with more discussion with Anderweg, and perhaps even with Trad, Nolle could have come to see that there were advantages offered by the standard therapy; or perhaps they could have found a way to encourage Nolle to choose *both* the standard therapy and H.

Patrick says: I wonder whether it is responsible for a physician to encourage hope in competent patients when the situation is known to be hopeless (or nearly hopeless). If Nolle truly was competent, Anderweg should have been honest with her; he should have made it clear to Nolle, while being as sympathetic as possible, of course, that the odds of survival were heavily stacked against her, and that taking H would likely do nothing to change that.

In any case, as Doran notes, if Nolle had seriously considered her options, she would have seen that it didn't have to be a choice between H and the standard therapy, between hope and resignation.

Warren says: Nolle did consider her options seriously and with sufficient information. Her options were to live in resignation or to live in hope. Nothing Anderweg could have told her could have made any difference to her goal of living in hope unless it was to make it more difficult to achieve that goal. For her, accepting standard treatment would be an admission of defeat, engaging death with delaying tactics. One cannot give up and maintain hope at the same time, and the standard treatment was, for her, giving up. That is why Anderweg withheld the details concerning standard treatment and arguments for standard treatment that she did not want or need to hear. He respected her choice of hope. Physicians often leave out the gory details that we do not need to hear when knowing them cannot help us.

Ample Discretion and Patient Autonomy

Patrick says: What do you have to say in response to my second question, Warren? Now that you have limited the application of the ample discretion principle to the valid consent of competent patients, why do you need the best interest clause? Why not just say this? *"Physicians may exercise ample discretion to decide whether or not to use any treatment to which a competent patient gives valid consent."*

Doran says: Right. Warren, you argued that parties in the original position would choose the ample discretion principle in order to protect their autonomy. But wouldn't the version of the principle Patrick just suggested give patients greater autonomy than your principle, when it comes to health care decisions?

Warren says: In the original position we would want to have autonomy with safety precautions built in. Unlimited autonomy is not in our interest, although a very strong right to autonomy is. Finding the balance is difficult, but we would accept certain limits on our autonomy, like being required to wear seat belts, for example, which would prevent us from sacrificing our lives or well-being because of a moment of temporary carelessness or because we had insufficiently understood the information about the possible outcomes. Similarly, we want autonomy with some safety precautions in our medical decision-making. We need physicians to be good advisers and guides to our medical decisions.

The restriction on physicians is a safety precaution to prevent a competent patient being granted a request that could be harmful because, for instance, that patient does not fully understand a complicated set of medical facts the doctor has explained. It allows the patient much choice and the physician a great deal of latitude in fulfilling patient choices. It would allow all sorts of alternative medications to be used by physicians. Patients, however, sometimes need physicians to talk them out of bad decisions, not just accept them because they are the patients' choice. When the patient has very little to lose by treatment, the treatments may be quite strange, but the physician is still restricted to pursuing the best interest of the patient.

Patrick says: Okay, but now I don't see autonomy as having any real significance, on your view. The ample discretion principle says that doctors can provide any treatment a competent patient validly consents to, provided that the treatment is in the patient's best interest. But how is this any different from just saying that MDs can administer any treatment provided that it is in the patient's best interest? Adding the bit about what a competent patient requests doesn't seem to add anything of significance to the principle. Ultimately, it is the physician, not the patient, who determines the course of treatment.

Warren says: The piece about the valid consent of competent patients does add much. A patient can request and get many things that a physician would not think to provide if the physician was guided only by his or her own knowledge and the patient's best interest. A physician might, for example, realize that a traditional cure that a patient requests, previously unknown to the physician, would be a powerful placebo for that particular patient. An innumerable variety of treatments is added.

BACKGROUND

A controversial alternative treatment for MS (multiple sclerosis) is marijuana, sometimes demanded by patients as a natural alternative treatment. This illustrates the kind of case Patrick considers generally:

"Some scientists feel that more research may show cannabinoids useful in treating MS. Marijuana may protect nerves from the kind of damage that occurs during the disease. They also suggest that animal study results, knowledge of CB1 receptors in the brain and users' reports of decreased symptoms after using marijuana support this possibility. However, others advise caution in using marijuana to treat MS, given the modest therapeutic effects cannabinoids have demonstrated so far and the potential of long-term adverse side effects."

Source: http://www.riversideonline.com/health_reference/Articles/GA00014.cfm.

Patrick says: I'm not sure, Warren. To illustrate my point, consider the following example. Suppose that patient A is ill and requests treatment x. Suppose also that A's doctor thinks that x would help A, but, all things considered, treatment y is in A's best interest. So A wants x, and x is beneficial, but A's doctor is not permitted to administer x, according to your principle, because another treatment, y, is in A's best interest. It seems, then, that your principle does not give patient autonomy much teeth, since it doesn't allow competent patients to determine their course of treatment, unless what they want is also what their doctor thinks is in their best interest.

Warren says: Treatments are rarely so well evidenced that all physicians agree on what is best. The patient can get a second opinion. The patient can, furthermore, refuse treatment. The physician may, in such a situation, offer a second-best treatment which has now become the one in the patient's best interest because the patient adamantly refuses what would have been best. In that way, the patient may get x rather than y.

I say *may*, rather than *will*. The physician may refuse to offer certain treatments if they pose enough risk of harm or the physician thinks the patient does not really understand the choice, for instance. There may be allocation issues as well. Suppose an 80-year-old demands a triple bypass which would be indicated if the patient were younger. The physician may think it is too likely to kill the 80-year-old and should be given instead to a 40-year-old. Autonomy gives us the right to refuse, and the right to choose, some treatments without the interference of narrow ideas about physicians' roles. It does not let us have anything on the shelf to which we take a fancy.[6]

Patrick says: Okay, I think I now have a better handle on your principle and how it preserves patient autonomy. Patient A can in fact get x, which is the treatment she wants, by refusing to take y, which is the treatment her doctor thinks is genuinely best. But then I don't see how the best interest clause helps to protect patients from their bad choices. When a patient refuses to take the three best treatments, for instance, the fourth then becomes the treatment that is in the patient's best interest. That is a very unusual way of thinking about which therapy is in a patient's best interest.

Warren says: It is not unusual in practice. In a rare case in which a patient will accept only a really poor treatment, the physician should refuse to give it; patients will usually come to a reasonable decision with education. In some cases, like Ms. Nolle's, the treatment serves other interests of the patient than medical ones, and the physician should be allowed to help the patient to pursue such powerful interests as hope. But let's move on—I can see that Doran is eager to ask a question.

THE AMPLE DISCRETION PRINCIPLE REVISED (AGAIN): HARM AVOIDANCE

Doran says: Let's return to the proposed principle: *Physicians may exercise ample discretion to decide whether or not to use any treatment to which a competent patient gives valid consent, provided that it is in the patient's best interest.* We disagree about whether Nolle was sufficiently informed to give valid consent, and so we disagree about whether this principle would justify Anderweg's behaviour. But beyond this disagreement, I think the principle itself is flawed. Even if a competent patient validly consents to a certain treatment that is in her best interest, it may be wrong

---

[6] Warren's example of the 80-year-old who demands a triple bypass raises questions of fair allocation of scarce medical resources in emergency situations, an issue we discuss at length in Chapter 9.

for the doctor to administer the therapy. One reason it might be wrong is that the chosen treatment would harm **third parties.** For instance, the principle, as it now stands, seems to allow patients to receive, and MDs to provide, unfair distributions of medical resources.

Warren says: If you call Nolle's consent invalid, you will have few valid consents. I have more sympathy with your second point about third parties, though. Can you give an example to illustrate your point, Doran?

Doran says: Sure. If I need a kidney, it might be rational for me to request that my doctor provide me with the next matching kidney that becomes available. But there might be someone else who is entitled to the kidney, perhaps because he has been waiting longer, and his condition is worse. I don't see anything in your principle that would prohibit my doctor from allowing me to receive the kidney. To avoid such counterexamples we can revise the principle as follows: *Physicians may exercise ample discretion to decide whether or not to use any treatment to which a competent patient validly consents, provided that it is in the patient's best interest, and that it is consistent with the equal opportunity of all who are seeking medical resources.*

Warren says: I was assuming physicians would not exercise discretion in ways that would harm people other than the patient, but you are right that we need to make some explicit condition in the ample discretion principle.

Patrick says: That principle may not go far enough, since we want to ensure against other harms besides violations of equal opportunity. We want to guard against certain harms to third parties in general. Part of my concern about Anderweg administering H to Nolle is that this could harm the reputation of doctors in general, and undermine public confidence in the medical profession, if it became public knowledge. That may also be part of Dr. Trad's worry about Dr. Anderweg prescribing H.

> **TECHNIQUE**
>
> It is typical for principles to become more complex as qualifications are added to reply to objections. If too many qualifications are added, philosophers start to speak of death by a thousand qualifications.

Warren says: Yes, but the danger of damage to the reputation of the profession in Nolle's case would come mainly through public misunderstanding of the discretion that must be allowed physicians in such cases. Anderweg took a calculated risk, exercised discretion, and did what turned out to be best for Nolle. It was not publicized. It was not harmful.

Doran says: When these remarks are applied to the specific case of Patrick's snake venom example, Warren, your view implies that it is permissible for a doctor to administer the venom only if he could keep this course of treatment secret, or take other steps that would prevent harm to the medical profession and to third parties more generally. Is that right?

Warren says: Yes, that's my view. Anderweg might say that he gave the injection of H because it served Nolle's goal of hope and because hope might have a strong placebo effect. It would be much harder to justify snake venom, however. Snake venom may be a reasonable choice in some extreme circumstances, but it may only be administered when, on balance, no harm to others results. In any case, we need to take into account, as your examples show, more harms than just the harm of unfair access to resources.

Here, then, is my revised rule: *Physicians may exercise ample discretion to decide whether or not to use any treatment to which a competent patient gives valid consent, provided that it is in the patient's best interest and harmless to others on balance.* This broader restriction against harm works against unfair practices like lack of equal opportunity and disrepute, as well as other harms. Yet these restrictions still allow the principle to protect our interests. The principle prevents excess conservatism in medicine, thereby allowing progress to be made.

UP FOR DISCUSSION

What kinds of harms are serious enough to serve as harms that we must avoid when exercising the ample discretion principle?

Patrick says: There are many perfectly acceptable treatments that harm others, in some sense, that this principle would seem to rule out. For instance, if there's one kidney available, and two people need it, then there's a clear sense in which the person who doesn't get it is harmed by the first person's getting the kidney. But this kind of harm is allowed, because it's not unfair. So I think you need to add something to the effect that the harms to others that your principle doesn't allow are *unfair* harms.

Warren says: I intended to capture that by "harmless to others on balance," which would rule out a patient's being given a treatment in a way that denied equal opportunity to other patients. There may be a sense in which another patient who is second in line for it is harmed, if someone gets the only kidney, but this is not unwarranted harm or unfair harm of the sort the principle is intended to oppose.

Patrick says: Well, I have another concern. You speak of excess conservatism in medicine that this principle will avoid. Yet a medical establishment that is conservative with regard to the adoption of strange and unproven treatments can still make significant progress. What medical advances are promoted by ample discretion?

Warren says: What if H had cured Nolle? Physicians need some leeway to practise experimental medicine, like the neurosurgeon who recently went against most of his colleagues to induce hypothermia in a comatose patient, for example. The neurosurgeon saved a life and revealed a hypothesis worth researching by using a totally nonstandard treatment. The treatment was untested, but the patient had nothing left to lose. Cutting-edge medicine is, necessarily, not yet accepted by most physicians nor scientifically confirmed.[7]

Patrick says: I don't know, Warren. As I mentioned earlier, I'm not at all against the use of unproven experimental drugs when they are part of legitimate trials and tests, and when the patient has been fully informed of the risks. But this case is different. H is not part of any clinical studies, and Nolle was not informed of the risks involved in taking it. So I believe it was irresponsible for Anderweg, as an MD, to administer H, even if it would not harm Nolle or anyone else.

Doran says: I might be persuaded to agree with you, Patrick, if there was a medically acceptable treatment that could offer meaningful benefit. This may have been the case for Nolle, given what Trad says. But in cases where the patient has no good options, and where the unconventional therapy is in the patient's best interest and harmless on balance to others, I think there may be nothing wrong with the physician honouring the patient's mental well-being— provided, of course, that the patient is informed and counselled about her options.

UP FOR DISCUSSION

If patients who have nothing left to lose are willing to try a new potential cure, what are the limits on administering experimental medications? Would you say that Nolle's situation was one where she had nothing left to lose?

---

[7] According to a CBC television news report in December 2006, Dr. Joseph Varon at St. Luke's hospital in Houston saved Dan O'Reilly from almost certain death after O'Reilly was knocked out by a wave in Ixtapa, Mexico. O'Reilly, who went 45 minutes without oxygen, spent 72 hours in induced hypothermia following coma—a treatment the physician had never tried before. O'Reilly continues to surprise his physiotherapist ("Frozen Man," *The National,* CBC TV, 6 December 2006).

AGAINST THE REVISED AMPLE DISCRETION PRINCIPLE: THE DIVISION OF LABOUR OBJECTION

Patrick says: Well, I suppose that at least part of what's bothering me about H, snake venom, and other untested and unconventional therapies is the following sort of intuition. I take there to be a kind of division of labour in the health services industry. The boundaries aren't sharp, but we have different kinds of health care professionals responsible for different kinds of services.

Medical doctors in our part of the world are trained in the practice of conventional Western medicine, which adheres to pretty rigorous standards regarding testing and administering drugs. When I go to see a medical doctor, I expect to be treated with medicine that has undergone clinical testing, or is currently in an experimental phase (as is the case with many of the drugs used to treat HIV/AIDS, for example), or has been acknowledged by the medical community to have stood the test of time. It seems to me that others assume the same thing when they see their doctors.

Other health professionals are trained in other, less conventional, forms of health care where the standards for testing drugs are slacker or perhaps even non-existent. Consider, for instance, homeopaths and naturopaths. Many of the treatments that homeopaths and naturopaths administer have undergone little, if any, formal clinical testing. When we go to see health care professionals in these fields, the expectation is that we will be treated with non-conventional medicine that may not have been subjected to formal clinical testing.

Given these considerations, I think it is generally irresponsible and reckless, and therefore wrong, for medical doctors to administer untested and unproven alternative therapies such as H, or snake venom, even if a competent patient requests this.

In saying this, I'm not, of course, claiming that it would be wrong for *all* health care professionals to administer strange and unusual therapies. I might not have any objection, for instance, if a shaman administers snake venom therapies. That's the kind of therapy I would expect a practitioner of that sort to administer. Even some naturopaths might do that. So, if Nolle wanted H, Anderweg probably should have referred her to a naturopath or someone who practised alternative medicine.

Doran says: I share your intuition about the division of labour, Patrick. And you might be right that the best thing to do is for Anderweg to refer Nolle to a naturopath, if one is available. But let's suppose

UP FOR DISCUSSION

Do you accept the view that there should be a division of labour among health care professionals? If so, under what conditions are there allowable exceptions?

one is not available, or the one who is available is likely to botch the job, or that access to naturopaths is prohibitively expensive for the patient. Then, all things considered, it may not have been wrong for Anderweg to administer the alternative therapy if Nolle was competent and informed of her options.

I think physicians have a variety of *prima facie* obligations— obligations that both of you have already touched upon. They include duties to promote their patients' health and well-being (physical and psychological); to respect their patients' autonomy; to promote the health of other patients; to safeguard the reputation of their profession; and so forth. In a case such as Nolle's, I'd judge that the duties to promote her autonomy, and her physical and psychological well-being, would win out *if* she was competent and informed. In other cases, though, the circumstances may be different, and my judgment may be different.

Warren says: Well, at least on those conditions we would come up with the same verdict in Nolle's case, but I think Patrick has some further arrows in his quiver for my principle and our conclusion. Before we go on, however, I should say that the division of labour is, in my view, merely an artifact of the ample discretion principle, since it is usually in the best interest of patients if practitioners stay within the scope their practice. Division need not be morally required, however, when it is in the patient's interest that different kinds of practitioners share the labour.

The Psychic Surgery Counterexample

Patrick says: Yes, even if there were no naturopaths available, then it would probably still be wrong for a doctor to administer the venom therapy. You must admit that the venom example gives you pause. Let me try another even more extreme example. Suppose that Nolle was raised in a cult that believed in psychic therapies and psychic phenomena in general. And suppose that Nolle was convinced that her only hope of beating cancer, or at least getting the most out of her remaining time, was to have someone perform **psychic surgery** on her.

Now suppose also that there was no one available to perform this kind of "surgery" except Anderweg. As an MD, Anderweg has a dim view of this sort of thing, of course, but he sees that it would give Nolle hope, just like H, and would not harm her. Finally, suppose that Anderweg could "perform" psychic surgery without any

DEFINITION

Psychic surgery is a magician's trick, although some patients have faith in it and see the magician or trickster who performs it as a saviour. The trickster appears to pull something out of a person's abdomen (often a chicken liver that has been palmed). Then the trickster announces that he or she has removed a tumour, for instance.

harm to the medical profession. Warren's view seems to imply that it is permissible for Anderweg to perform psychic surgery in this situation. I think it would be irresponsible and dishonest, among other things, and therefore wrong . . . very wrong! Physicians have a responsibility, I believe, to uphold certain standards concerning the treatments they provide to their patients.

Warren says: I think the doctor would have to look at all who are affected by this person's treatment, not just the patient. What if other members of the cult who did have better options than the patient might be influenced to try psychic surgery rather than a curative treatment? If, in a vanishingly rare circumstance, only the doctor and the patient would ever learn of it, and it was in the patient's best interest, then the doctor would be morally permitted to perform psychic surgery. As long as only the patient's interests are affected, then the doctor should still have ample discretion to choose treatments that include weird treatments, if those serve the patient's best interest as placebos, for example. We would be bound to choose that if we were in the original position. How else could we protect our interests in the real world? Division of labour for its own sake does not protect them. Those in the original position would look at their chances in the real world and say, "If it can do some good and won't do harm, then go for it." The cases where such tricks as psychic surgery do no harm are, however, so few as to be negligible. Patients are bound to talk about their treatment, and physicians know this. Confidentiality is often breached, and physicians know this. The division of labour will not be total but will remain largely in place for that reason alone.

THEORY

A Kantian who thought that a physician was bound by her oath to uphold certain standards of practice would think that this perfect duty must be done no matter who knew or what were the consequences of doing that duty. In contrast, a utilitarian would permit a physician to use any therapy provided that it had the best consequences, all things considered, for everyone concerned.

Doran says: I do admit the venom example gives me pause. And I agree with Patrick that it would be wrong for Anderweg to perform psychic surgery. I suspect that is because a patient could not be competent and fully informed and still give valid consent to psychic surgery (or snake venom, for that matter). I also think that physicians have a *prima facie* duty to uphold the standards of their profession whether or not anyone finds out about it. Taken together, these constitute powerful conditional reasons against a doctor giving a patient psychic therapy. But the actual case of Nolle is a bit different, given that reasonable people believe in herbal therapies, and given that some herbal therapies almost certainly work.

Warren says: I'll take Doran's help here and say that my view does not license psychic surgery *if* a competent person could not validly consent to psychic surgery.

Patrick says: Given what was argued earlier regarding Nolle's request for H, I'm not sure we need to regard the patient who requests psychic surgery as incompetent or as inadequately informed. If, for example, the person was raised in a culture that practised this sort of thing, and was suspicious of Western medicine, and if she believed that psychic surgery was her best and only hope, then I'm not sure we could regard the patient's request for psychic surgery as invalid. If I'm right, then Warren's principle implies something that seems clearly to be false: that it is permissible for a medical doctor to perform psychic surgery in certain cases.

UP FOR DISCUSSION

Do you agree with Doran that there is only a *prima facie* obligation for doctors to give treatments that are medically approved or undergoing clinical trials? Or, do you agree with Patrick that there should be a more absolute division of labour between physicians and other medical professionals? Is there a third option that you would endorse?

Warren says: Don't forget that the cases in which such things are allowed are vanishingly rare because of third-party harms. When can a physician be sure that the patient will keep such a wild secret as having had psychic surgery?

More Counterexamples to the Ample Discretion Principle: Prayer and Other Unconventional Treatments

Doran says: Here's a different example that may present a problem for your view, Warren. Unlike the psychic surgery case, this example does not raise the question whether the person gives valid consent, nor is the kind of case I have in mind vanishingly rare. Suppose Nolle refuses treatment but just asks Anderweg to pray with her once a week. Is that permissible, or should the doctor refer her to a minister? My initial reaction is that the doctor ought to refer, although I am not sure about this. But what would the ample discretion principle say?

BACKGROUND

A 1996 Time/CNN poll national poll "found that 48% of patients want prayer with their physicians and 64% of Americans think that physicians should join their patients in prayer if the patients ask."

Source: Stephen G. Post, Christina M. Puchalski, and David B. Larson, "Physicians and Patient Spirituality: Professional Boundaries, Competency, and Ethics," *Annals of Internal Medicine* 132, no. 7 (2000): 578–83.

Warren says: Well, I'm an atheist. Still, I have to say that if all the conditions were met, the principle would license the prayer treatment. If there really were no harm to MDs or others, nothing better the physician could do, and it really gave the patient hope, as in Nolle's case, then it would be okay, but only then. Prayer would not be a rational choice for me, but it would for many.

UP FOR DISCUSSION

Is it morally permissible for physicians to pray with their patients if their patients request it? Does it matter if the patient thinks prayer will help cure her, but the physician thinks that prayer has no medical benefit? Does your view change if what the patient wants is not prayer, but psychic surgery?

Patrick says: Good example, Doran. As you two might have guessed, I don't think physicians should be allowed to administer a "prayer treatment." But just to clarify, I'm not claiming that it is always wrong for a doctor to pray with a patient. For instance, suppose a patient has become good friends with his doctor over the years, and the patient and doctor belong to the same church. Then I do not see anything wrong with the doctor praying with his patient. But this must be done as his friend, not as his doctor. Since prayer is not a recognized course of treatment, medical doctors should not be in the business of offering prayer *as a course of treatment,* even if competent patients request it.[8] If a competent patient wants a course of treatment that involves prayer or psychic surgery, her doctor should refer her to a minister or psychic surgeon. Warren, your principle seems much too liberal to me. It would allow doctors to treat people using all kinds of crazy things!

Warren says: Doctors do in fact prescribe *comforts* to patients in palliative care. These comforts may, in rare cases, include some strange and unusual things. These are ways of showing compassion to patients, and they are very much in the interest of those who choose the rules in the original position. The snake venom case is much more troubling, however, because it is harder to reply to the charge that people other than the patient will be harmed. But that is why we had to explicitly bring out the restriction on harming others in the ample discretion principle. Together with the valid consent restriction, these limit the permissible range of weird treatments.

UP FOR DISCUSSION

Do you think that it is permissible for physicians to engage in non-standard treatments that have no therapeutic value but only symbolic value to the patients, or do you think that a physician's role should be limited to more traditional therapies?

FINAL THOUGHTS

Patrick says: Well, there's a lot more to discuss. Unfortunately, however, we're out of time, so why don't we wrap up our debate with some last words for now on the subject.

Doran says: Doctors need to make sure that they are respecting the informed choices of their patients. They do not want to be acting on patient requests when the patients do not adequately understand their

---

[8] The largest clinical study to date on the effectiveness of prayer revealed no clinical benefits from prayer. See "Largest Study of Third-Party Prayer Suggests Such Prayer Not Effective in Reducing Complications Following Heart Surgery," news release from Harvard Medical School, Office of Public Affairs, http://web.med.harvard.edu/sites/RELEASES/html/3_31STEP.html.

predicament or their options. Anderweg, therefore, had a duty to make sure Nolle was relevantly counselled about her illness and options before acting on her request for alternative therapy. I think I agree with the final statement of the ample discretion principle, but I do not think it supports Anderweg's behaviour, given my understanding of the facts about the case. We want health care workers to respond with care and concern for their patients, to look out for their best interests, and to respect their informed choices, while not treating others unfairly and without damaging the medical profession. This is a difficult balancing act. The first steps were to talk with Nolle and to help her see that her situation was different from her husband's, and to explain to her compassionately and patiently why the standard therapies were likely to promise better outcomes in her case than the alternative therapies. If she still insisted on the alternative therapy, then she should have been referred to a competent naturopath. If a competent naturopath was not available, then perhaps Anderweg would have been justified in administering H.

Patrick says: Competent patients have a right to choose whatever course of treatment they would like. And physicians ought, in general, to respect the health care choices of their competent patients. It does not follow from this, however, that medical doctors are always morally permitted to comply with their competent patients' requests, even when those requests are in the patients' best interest and do not unfairly harm others. There are recognized limits to the kinds of tools medical doctors can and should use to treat their patients, and physicians should generally stick within those limits. There are likely exceptions to this, but I don't think Nolle's case is one of those exceptions. Certain herbal therapies may be, or may soon be, within those limits. But snake venom, psychic surgery, prayer, etc., are currently not within those limits, and likely never will be. If Warren's ample discretion permits doctors to administer such things, then I believe that his principle is false.

I am certainly not against progress in medicine. Nor do I oppose physicians' use of new and unconventional drugs and therapies—provided that the drugs and therapies are part of legitimate tests and trials. Nolle, however, asked her physician to inject her with an untested and unproven herbal therapy. I do not think this choice was informed. But even if it was an informed choice, it was reckless and irresponsible, and therefore it was wrong for Anderweg, as an MD, to comply with Nolle's request.

Warren says: The principle does not justify harmful or irrational choices, so it is hard to come up with real cases of things like psychic surgery that this principle would, in fact, justify. In general, we should not unnecessarily tie doctors' hands because of intuitions about division of labour or weirdness of treatments. In reality, division of labour is also often preserved by the conditions on the principle. In extraordinary circumstances, that division may be crossed or weirdness allowed, but only very rarely would venom or psychic surgery plausibly be a treatment to which there is valid consent, and which is in the patient's best interest and not harmful, on balance, to others. Anderweg did no harm and did some good with H, which was a reasonable choice for someone with Nolle's goal of living in hope.

Think like those in the original position. We are all behind a veil of ignorance with respect to the circumstances of our future medical care. If some day you are in a situation where you have only a snowball's chance, wouldn't you want a physician you know and trust to be the one to help you with a long-shot cure? And what about experimental medicine? Many currently accepted treatments were once weird alternatives. Consider the maverick neurosurgeon's successful induced hypothermia cure. We must allow discretionary weirdness as a part of accountable medical practice. That does not mean that anything goes. We must allow ample discretion but not unlimited discretion.

As to informed consent and counselling, Anderweg respected Nolle's adequately informed choice of hope by keeping information from Nolle that would have been worse than useless to her. He knew that Nolle understood that the information she was refusing was only good for the choice of resignation. Anderweg's treatment of Nolle was therefore morally permissible.

UP FOR DISCUSSION

After consideration of the arguments advanced in the debate, do you believe it was permissible for Anderweg to administer H to Nolle? Why or why not?

SUMMARY

Here is a summary of the main questions, concepts, and arguments covered in this chapter:

- The main questions explored are whether it was morally permissible for Anderweg to give an alternative therapy, H, to his patient, Nolle, and whether it is morally permissible, in general, for physicians to administer alternative therapies to their patients who request them.

- Warren argues that it was morally permissible for Anderweg to give H to Nolle, and he believes that it is morally acceptable for physicians, in general, to administer alternative therapies to their patients, provided certain conditions are met.

- Specifically, Warren defends the ample discretion principle: *Physicians may exercise ample discretion to decide whether or not to use any treatment to which a competent patient gives valid consent, provided that it is in the patient's best interest and harmless to others on balance.* Warren thinks this principle is justified because it would be chosen by people in the original position.

- Doran agrees with the ample discretion principle; however, he does not think that Anderweg acted permissibly in Nolle's case. This is because, unlike Warren, Doran does not think that enough was done to ensure that Nolle understood her treatment alternatives so that she could give valid consent.

- Patrick agrees with Doran that Anderweg acted impermissibly in Nolle's case. But Patrick goes further and argues that the ample discretion principle is false because it is vulnerable to counterexamples. Instead, Patrick defends the idea that there should be a division of labour, where physicians administer treatments that are scientifically tested, or are undergoing scientific trials, or are part of accepted medical practice, while practitioners of alternative medicine should treat patients who choose alternative therapies.

Review Questions

1. Why does Warren believe it is permissible for Anderweg to administer H to Nolle?
2. What is the best interest principle? What is the response to Patrick's question about the nature of best interest?
3. Explain Patrick's venom counterexample and what it purports to show. What is Warren's reply?
4. What is the ample discretion principle? What is Warren's argument for this principle?
5. Briefly explain Doran's initial objection to the ample discretion principle and the reply to this objection.
6. Explain Patrick's concern about whether the ample discretion principle protects patient autonomy. Why does Warren think that autonomy is, nonetheless, preserved?
7. What considerations motivate the first revision of the ample discretion principle?
8. What considerations motivate the second revision of the ample discretion principle?
9. Briefly explain Patrick's division of labour objection. How does Doran respond to this objection?
10. Briefly explain Patrick's psychic surgery counterexample and Doran's reply.
11. Describe Doran's prayer counterexample and what it purports to show. How is this example different from the psychic surgery example? Is the reply different as well?

WWW.MCGRAWHILL.CA/OLC/SMOLKIN

GLOSSARY

Abortion: The intentional termination of a pregnancy with the intent and result of killing the prenatal organism.

Absolute moral truth: A moral truth that applies to all persons, at all times in all situations.

Act utilitarianism: The ethical theory that says the right action in a situation is the one that maximizes happiness and minimizes unhappiness, where everyone's happiness and unhappiness is given equal consideration.

Active euthanasia: Directly causing an individual's death—for instance, by administering a lethal injection—for that individual's own health-related good.

Ad hominem: A Latin expression meaning "against the man," a **fallacy** in which one tries to refute an **argument** by attacking the one who offered the argument, rather than the argument itself.

Advance directive: A document in which a person states his or her wishes in the event the person is no longer able to make health care decisions. It comes into effect when the person is no longer **competent.** There are two types: *Instructional directives* (living wills) may give specific instructions or set out general principles to follow. *Proxy directives* (durable powers of attorney for health care) specify who is to make health care decisions for a person who is no longer able to make them. (Adapted from the End of Life Project, Health Law Institute, Dalhousie University. Available online.)

All-things-considered duty: The duty that is most pressing after all *prima facie* duties are weighed in a situation, according to W. D. Ross's **pluralistic deontology.**

Alternative medicine: The kinds of drugs, therapies, practices, etc., that are not a part of conventional Western medicine. Examples of this include acupuncture, homeopathy, naturopathy, and herbal therapy.

Amnesiac: Afflicted by amnesia, the loss of memory of past experiences.

Amnestic anesthetic: A drug that causes temporary amnesia but is designed to temporarily take away sensations.

Amniocentesis: A procedure in which the uterus (the womb) is perforated to obtain amniotic fluid—fluid from the membranes enveloping the **fetus.** The fluid is tested to detect abnormality in fetal development.

Ample discretion principle: Warren's view that physicians may exercise ample discretion to decide whether or not to use any treatment that a competent patient chooses, provided that it is in the patient's best interest and harmless to others on balance.

Anecdotal: Said of evidence that is not the result of research but of stories or anecdotes about the efficacy of certain treatments.

Antirealist: In **metaethics,** those who either deny that moral claims are descriptive at all, or accept this but deny that any of the descriptions are true. So antirealists deny that there are any moral truths or facts.

Appeal to emotion: The **fallacy** of using emotionally charged, biased language in order to persuade someone to accept a **conclusion** without having to think carefully about the issues involved.

Applied ethics *or* practical ethics: A part of **normative ethics** concerned with specific moral issues. E.g.: Is it ever permissible for a woman to have an **abortion?** Is it always wrong for medical professionals to lie to their patients?

Argument: A set of at least two claims one of which is the **conclusion.** Any other claims in the set are **premises.** The conclusion is the claim that one is trying to prove, and the premises are the reasons offered in support of the conclusion.

Asphyxia: A deadly condition caused by oxygen deprivation.

Autonomous: Having **autonomy,** self-determining.

Autonomy: Self-determination.

Begging the question (circular argument): A **fallacy** in which the truth of the **conclusion** is presupposed by one or more **premises.** (All valid **arguments** do this, but circularity is a problem when the conclusion you are arguing for occurs as one of your premises, or is offered as a reason for accepting one of your premises, and you intend to convince someone of the conclusion.)

Blended private/public care: Health care that includes both publicly funded care and care for which people pay privately.

Breech presentation: *Breech* means "buttocks," and breech presentation is the presentation of the buttocks or feet in labour.

Caesarean section *or* **C-section:** The delivery of a **fetus** by surgical incision through the abdominal wall and uterus.

Categorical imperative: A command that states what one ought to do regardless of one's desires or goals. For Kant, these imperatives are the rules of morality. Kant has, however, a particular principle called *the* categorical imperative. It comes in several forms, including the **universal law version** and the **humanity version.**

Chemotherapy (short form, **chemo**): A cancer treatment using chemical means.

Circular argument: See **begging the question.**

Classical act utilitarianism: See **utilitarianism.**

Codifiable: Expressible as a set of rules with priorities for their application.

Cognitivism: In **metaethics,** the view that our moral claims are descriptions of the moral features of actions, persons, etc. As such, moral claims are the kind of thing that are true or false, and that we believe, know, assert, doubt, and deny.

Comforts: Whatever is prescribed for a patient that has no medical use but is merely intended to make the patient more at ease. See also **palliation.**

Competent: Capable of rational self-determination; in this context, capable of rationally choosing one's own medical treatment. Individuals may be competent relative to some tasks, but not others.

Complementary medicine: The use of **alternative medicine** in conjunction with standard Western medicine.

Comprehensive care: In the context of the health care system, care that covers all essential needs of patients.

Conclusion: The claim one is trying to prove through an **argument.**

Conclusion indicator: Verbal clue which signals that a **conclusion** is being offered, e.g., *therefore, thus, hence,* and *so.*

Consequentialism: The view that the right act is entirely determined by its consequences, which are the promotion of the greatest amount of good or the least amount of bad.

Conservatives: In the context of the abortion debate, those who generally oppose abortion—claiming that abortion is wrong in all, or virtually all, cases.

Contractarianism: See **social contract theory.**

Contradiction in conception: A result pertaining to Kant's **universal law version of the categorical imperative.** It occurs when one is not able to will a **maxim** as a **universal law** because the practice would be self-defeating or self-contradictory if it were practised by everyone all the time. It signals the violation of a **perfect duty.**

Contradiction in will: A result pertaining to Kant's **universal law version of the categorical imperative.** Kant admits that one can conceive of a **maxim** as a **universal law,** but still not be able to will it because a contradiction will arise between the universal law and what a person will (later) want. It signals a violation of an **imperfect duty.**

Counterexample: An example that is intended to counter a given claim or **argument.**

CSBC: Caesarean section by choice, Caesarean delivery in the absence of medical indications at the choice of the mother.

CTAS: The Canadian Triage and Acuity Scale (CTAS) introduced during the late 1990s. The CTAS is now being implemented as a national triage standard for Canada's emergency health care system.

Cultural imperialism: A phrase used to object to the imposition of the beliefs of one culture on another.

Cultural relativism: The ethical theory that says there are no objective truths in ethics, and the correct moral rules are determined by each culture.

Deductive argument: An **argument** intended as one in which it is necessary that if the **premises** are true, so is the **conclusion.**

Deontology: A category of ethical theory that sees right action as doing one's duty.

Descriptive ethics: A part of ethics which seeks to describe what is the case rather than what ought to be the case; for instance, it seeks to describe what people actually believe about particular moral issues. Descriptive ethics also is concerned with questions of why people believe what they believe about ethics, and how they come to hold their particular moral beliefs and attitudes.

Difference principle: John Rawls's view that there should be social and economic equality, unless inequality benefits those in the worst-off group.

Diminishing marginal utility: Said of money, it expresses roughly the idea that an extra portion of income is unlikely to benefit a person above a certain level of wealth as much as it would benefit someone below that level of wealth. After you get a certain amount, money is worth less to you (diminishes in utility) as you get more of it.

Dispositional properties: Roughly, properties that objects, persons, etc., have in virtue of their being disposed to behave in a certain way under certain conditions.

Dispositional view of moral properties: The view that moral properties are **dispositional properties.** E.g., an action is morally right in virtue of its tendency to elicit certain responses (e.g., approval).

Doctrine of the mean: Aristotle's doctrine that the **virtues** exist as a mean between two extremes—one of excess and the other of deficiency.

Down syndrome *or* **Down's syndrome:** A condition in which an extra chromosome causes birth defects, notably slow, incomplete physical development and mental retardation.

Duty, all things considered: See **all-things-considered duty.**

Dysphagia: A potentially very dangerous condition causing one to be prone to choke.

Egalitarian: A term with multiple meanings, often said of philosophers who emphasize equality above such values as liberty.

Embryo: A developing organism prior to birth. In humans this stage runs from conception until about the end of the eighth week.

End *or* **end in itself:** In Kant's usage, a **rational being** deserving of respect.

Epistemic problem: A philosophical problem concerning knowledge.

Epistemology: The philosophical study of knowledge.

Equal consideration: The principle that no one's good is to be counted as more important than anyone else's.

Equivocation: The **fallacy** of equivocation occurs when a term slides, without acknowledgement, between two or more different meanings within a single **argument,** so as to make an argument which is not **valid** appear valid.

Ethical objectivism: The view that there are **objective** truths in ethics. By saying that a statement is objectively true, we mean (roughly) that the statement is true independently of whether anyone happens to believe that it is true or desires it to be true.

Ethical relativism: The view that there is no **objective truth** in ethics. Instead, it is suggested that moral truths are simply *relative* to a given individual or group.

Ethics of care: The view that rather than using principles to arrive at the solutions to moral problems, one needs to adopt a perspective of caring. Here the focus is on maintaining and improving one's relationships.

Eudaimonia: A Greek term roughly translated as "flourishing" or "happiness."

Euthanasia: An act or omission, intended by one or more individuals, to bring about the death of another individual for that individual's own (health-related) good.

Excusable: Said of wrong acts for which there is an **excuse.**

Excuse: A reason for wrong action that removes blame by removing the responsibility of the one who did the action.

Extremitarianism: There is no recognized ethical term "extremitarianism." This is a word Warren made up playing on **utilitarianism.** For the extremitarian, the benefits have to be extreme before they can justify exceptions to **worst first** and **first come.**

Fair turn rule: (a proposed **triage** rule) B can go ahead of A in the queue for life-saving treatment if A has had a fair turn at life and B has not.

Fallacy: A mistake in reasoning.

False dilemma: A **fallacy** in which fewer options are presented than are actually available in a way which is misleading.

Feminism: The view that women (and girls) have been, and in various ways continue to be, oppressed; it seeks to understand the nature of the oppression and to determine how best to overcome this oppression.

Fetus: A stage of a developing organism; in humans, from about the end of the eighth week until birth.

First come: (a proposed **triage** rule) Those who arrive first get treated first, other things being equal.

Genetic code: Information encoded in the DNA of an organism that determines what kind of organism it is. Each species has a unique genetic code that distinguishes it from all other species.

Good will: (Kant's conception) If one does an act out of respect for morality—out of respect for a **categorical imperative**—then one is said to have a good will, and so one's act has **moral worth.**

Hard paternalism: The interference with a competent person's liberty for his or her own good.

Health care ethics: An area of inquiry within **normative ethics,** or more narrowly, **applied ethics,** which deals with ethical problems that arise in and around the practice of health.

Hedonism: The view according to which the sole ultimate good is pleasure and the sole ultimate bad is pain.

Hopeless second: (a proposed **triage** rule) Do not treat hopeless cases ahead of those where there is hope.

Humanity: The term that Kant uses to mean the set of **rational beings.**

Humanity version of the categorical imperative test: Kant's principle that one must treat **humanity,** whether in one's own person or that of another, always as an **end** and never merely as a **means.**

Human-sympathy metarule: A part of Warren's favoured ethical approach. It is a rule about making rules in the **original position** that requires the choosers of rules to choose rules that can be followed by those with ordinary human sympathy.

Hypothermia: A low body temperature usually caused by cold weather but sometimes induced as a way to decrease metabolism and use of oxygen by a patient.

Hypothetical imperative: A command that states what one ought to do given the presence of a desire or goal.

Hysterectomy: An operation in which the uterus (the womb) is removed.

Ideal social contract: The ideal set of rules to govern moral relations of people in a community, e.g., rules chosen in the **original position.**

Impartiality rule: (a proposed **triage** rule) Health care professionals should usually be *impartial,* i.e., free from bias, favouritism, or prejudice, in helping patients.

Imperfect duty: According to Kant, a duty that one must sometimes follow, but which need not be followed all the time (e.g., the duty to be charitable).

Incompetent: Not **competent.**

Inconsistent: Rationally incompatible. A set of sentences is inconsistent if and only if not all of them can be true at once. We say a set of desires, preferences, or wishes are inconsistent if and only if a person could not satisfy the whole set. See **rationality.**

Inductive argument: An **argument** intended as one in which it is probable that if the **premises** are true, so is the **conclusion.**

Informed consent: Consent given with a satisfactory understanding of treatment options and the likely effects of treatments if those effects are known.

Inherent value: Value had because of the nature of the thing valued, value not easily lost, for instance because it is **intrinsic value.**

Innocents first rule: (a proposed **triage** rule) Patient A, who is innocent and who cannot wait for care, may be given priority over patient B, who was at fault for the injury and who also cannot wait, other things being equal.

Instrumental value: Value as a means to something else.

Instrumentally good: Good as a means to something else, but not good in itself.

Internalism: The view that reasons or motives are somehow "built into" the fact, or judgment, that an action is morally right (or wrong).

Intrinsic value: The worth that something has in itself, and not because of its utility or usefulness.

Intrinsically good: Good that is valuable for its own sake, and not as a means to something else. See also **intrinsic value.**

Intuitionism *or* **ethical intuitionism:** Within ethics, a term that generally refers to the view that there is a plurality of fundamental moral principles that are known through a special faculty of intuition—i.e., these basic moral principles are self-evident or apprehended directly, rather than through inference or demonstration. In some instances, however, those who accept only one self-evident fundamental principle are called "intuitionists." The term may also be applied to those who think we intuit moral properties.

Invalid argument: An **argument** intended to be deductive but with **premises** that fail to guarantee that the **conclusion** is true. In an invalid argument the conclusion could be false even if all the premises are true.

Involuntary active euthanasia (IAE): Active euthanasia of a **competent** patient without her consent.

Involuntary euthanasia: Euthanasia of a **competent** patient without her consent.

Involuntary passive euthanasia (IPE): Passive euthanasia of a competent patient without her consent.

Jump the queue *or* **queue jumping:** What people are said to do when they unfairly get ahead of others in line for medical care. Also used for getting ahead unfairly in other contexts.

Justice as fairness: The name of John Rawls's **social contract theory** of justice.

Justification: A reason for something that shows that it was permissible. Contrast **excuse** and **mitigation.**

Kantianism: The philosophy of Immanuel Kant.

Libertarian: Said of philosophers who emphasize liberty above such values as equality and beneficence. In political philosophy it is associated with the view that the state may restrict citizens only to protect them against force, theft, or fraud.

Liberty principle: See **principle of maximal equal basic liberties.**

Macroallocation: Large-scale distribution of resources such as those with which public health policies are concerned.

Magnetic resonance imaging (MRI): A technique for scanning for muscle and joint injuries. Both the scans and the machines that scan are referred to as MRIs.

Maxim: As used by Kant, the principle behind one's action.

Maximin: According to Rawls, a strategy that one should adopt in the **original position,** namely choose in such a way so that you will be doing maximally well if you should turn out to be in the minimum (or worst-off) position.

Means only: In Kant's usage, a **thing.**

Means to an end: A way to achieve a goal. When people are used merely as a means to an end they are treated as tools or **things** rather than as **rational beings** who have their own goals and are able to make their own decisions.

Medical benefit: (a proposed **triage** rule) Where the medical interest is great enough, a patient may be given priority over those who came earlier.

Medicalize: To turn a natural process into a medical procedure. This is a term of medical jargon not in common use.

Mesoallocation: Medium-scale allocation of resources, distribution of resources at the level of institutions.

Metaethics: A part of ethics concerning the rational investigation into the nature of morality. Here, the focus is on questions *about* morality, rather than questions *within* morality. E.g.: "Are moral judgments capable of being true or false?" and "What are the meanings of moral terms?"

Metaphysical problem: A philosophical problem concerning reality.

Metaphysics: The philosophical study of reality.

Metarule: A rule that governs the production, use, and interpretation of other, lower-level rules. It is a rule about making rules rather than a rule about what to do.

MI *or* **myocardial infarction:** A heart attack.

Microallocation: Distribution of resources at the level of individuals, selecting which individuals are to receive health care resources.

Minimize YPLL: (a proposed **triage** rule) Minimize years of potential life lost.

Mitigation: A reason for an action that does not excuse or justify a wrong done but lessens blameworthiness.

Moral argument: An **argument** in support of a **substantive moral claim.**

Moral pluralist: One who believes there is no single basic moral principle that explains all of our moral obligations, but instead, that there are many general moral principles.

Morbidity: The lack of health in a population represented as the ratio of diseased or injured persons to healthy persons; hence, maternal morbidity is the rate of ill-health of new mothers. Said of an individual, morbidity means being unhealthy or morbid.

Multiple sclerosis: Scarring of nervous tissue throughout the body, sometimes including the brain, leading to damage to the covering (myelin sheath) of the nerves. It can lead to weakness, loss of coordination, and visual complaints. It may be mild or severe and is usually prolonged with remissions and relapses over many years.

Only in rare cases does it lead to serious loss of intellectual function.

Naturopath: A practitioner of health care based on **alternative medicine** that emphasizes natural healing methods, while avoiding surgery and drugs.

Negative rights: Rights to non-interference, such as the right not to be physically harmed. Negative rights are contrasted with **positive rights.**

Nepotism: Showing favouritism to relatives or close friends when impartial, objective criteria should be used.

Non-consequentialism: The view that the right act is not entirely determined by its consequences.

Non-instrumental value: Value that something has "in itself" or "for its own sake," rather than as a means to some other end or ends. Some hold that pleasure, for instance, has non-instrumental value. See **inherent value, intrinsic value.**

Non-voluntary active euthanasia (NAE): Active euthanasia on individuals who lack the competence to make a decision about **euthanasia.**

Non-voluntary euthanasia: Euthanasia on individuals who lack the competence to make a decision about **euthanasia.**

Non-voluntary passive euthanasia (NPE): Passive euthanasia on individuals who lack the competence to make a decision about **euthanasia.**

Normative: Prescriptive. Normative principles are generally contrasted with descriptive principles.

Normative ethics: A part of ethics concerned, in large part, with general theoretical questions such as what makes acts morally right or wrong; which states of affairs are desirable or undesirable; what constitutes a good life for the person who leads it; which character traits are virtuous and which are vicious; and, most generally, how one ought to live.

Objective truth: There is no single, universally accepted definition of the concept of objective truth. Most would agree, however, that an objective truth is a truth that is independent of whether people happen to think, believe, or feel that it is true. For instance, if it is an objective truth that water is H_2O, then it is true whether or not anyone happens to believe it or desire it to be true. Morality is sometimes said to be objective, meaning that the rightness and wrongness of actions is independent of the thoughts, beliefs, and feelings people happen to have toward those actions. This makes moral claims about right and wrong actions objective truths.

Original position: John Rawls's conception of a hypothetical situation from which people are to choose the principles of justice to regulate the major social institutions. Unlike Rawls, Warren uses the original position to generate all moral rules. In the original position, people are equally powerful, equally intelligent, self-interested, and ignorant of their own advantages and disadvantages in the real world.

Palliation: Easing a patient's pain or the severity of a patient's disease without removing the cause. See also **comforts.**

Passive euthanasia: Allowing an individual to die—e.g., by withholding life-prolonging treatment—for the sake of the individual's (health-related) good.

Paternalism: Interference with a person's liberty for his or her own good. See **hard paternalism, soft paternalism, strong paternalism,** and **weak paternalism.**

Perfect duty: According to Kant, a duty that must always be followed.

Placebo effect: The healing effect of a treatment that works only because the patient believes it will work.

Pluralistic deontology: W. D. Ross's view that morality consists in many conditional duties which will sometimes conflict. In cases of conflict, one must study the situation carefully and try to reach a considered judgment about which duties are most pressing in that situation. Whatever the strongest duties recommend in that situation constitutes the right thing to do in that situation.

Positive rights: Rights whose satisfaction requires the provision of some action, good, or service. Positive rights are contrasted with **negative rights.**

Practical ethics: See **applied ethics.**

Premise: Reasons provided in support of a **conclusion.**

Premise indicator: Verbal clue which signals that a **premise** is being offered. E.g., *because, since, given that, for.*

Prescriptive: Said of language that tells people what they ought to do in contrast to merely describing what people do.

Presumptively, morally permissible: Presumed to be not morally wrong.

***Prima facie* duty:** The usual translation of the Latin phrase *prima facie* is "on the face of it." For W. D. Ross, however, *prima facie* duties should be understood as *conditional* duties. Conditional or *prima facie* duties can then be contrasted with **duties, all things considered.**

Primary social goods: As defined by John Rawls, goods, under the control of society, that everyone, or almost everyone, can be presumed to want, regardless of his or her plans in life. For Rawls, these include rights and liberties, opportunities and powers, income and wealth, and the bases of self-respect.

Principle of charity: Principle according to which an author's claims and **arguments** are to be interpreted in the best possible light. The general aim is to arrive at a fair and sympathetic understanding of the author's position in order to evaluate it critically.

Principle of fair equality of opportunity: A principle of John Rawls's **social contract theory.** It holds that each person should have a meaningful opportunity to attain employment, education, and positions of power.

Principle of maximal equal basic liberties: A principle of John Rawls's **social contract theory.** It holds that each person is to have maximal equal basic liberties such as freedom of expression, thought, assembly, religion, etc.

Prolapse: A falling or sinking down of part of the body. Here it refers to a downward displacement of the uterus.

Psychic surgery: A magician's trick in which the magician appears to remove tissue from a person's body without surgery. Typically this is used to dupe the gullible into thinking they have had a growth removed from inside their bodies.

Public interest: (a proposed **triage** rule) Where the public interest is great enough, a patient may be given priority over those who came earlier.

Quadriplegic: A person who is paralyzed so as to be without the use of all four limbs.

Queue: A line of people waiting for service or admission. This is used metaphorically to refer to the fair ordering of patients awaiting medical care in Canada. See **jump the queue.**

Radiosensitive tumour: A tumour that will respond to **radiotheraphy** (radiation therapy).

Radiotheraphy: The use of ionizing radiation to treat an illness.

Rational being: In Kant's conception, a being that can freely set goals for itself and then determine the various means to accomplish those goals (**hypothetical imperatives**), and can also recognize and choose to follow (or not to follow) moral rules (**categorical imperatives**).

Rational intuition: A faculty or sense that enables one to "see" moral truths directly, without the need for inference, **argument,** etc.

Rational nature: The ability to freely make one's own decisions and to freely set goals for oneself.

Rationality: A perennially contested term referring to the capacity of people to choose actions, beliefs, goals, plans, inferences, and other things on the basis of reasons. It is generally thought to include, but not to be limited to, the capacity to employ rules of reasoning that make up correct logic.

Realist: Said of moral theories that hold that moral claims are (at least partly) descriptive, and that some of these claims are true. So, realists hold that there are moral truths or facts.

Reasonable person test: A test of acceptability. Appeals to what a reasonable person would believe are used by philosophers as a commonsense, intuitive test to clarify concepts, determine right and wrong, etc.

Recuse: Disqualify oneself as a judge; by extension said of other public officials making decisions where they excuse themselves from decision-making on grounds of a conflict of interest.

Redistributive taxation: Taxation which redistributes wealth to modify the ways in which it is distributed in society through the forces of commerce. Usually it is aimed at making citizens' advantages more equal than they would be without the tax.

Reductio ad absurdum: An **argument** to show that a view cannot be correct because it has absurd implications.

Reflective equilibrium: For many, it is the end point of a process of philosophical deliberation. It involves going back and forth between principles and what they imply about specific cases to attain a state of coherence or consistency among the moral principles we accept and our considered moral beliefs.

Remission: A period during (or a stage of) a disease in which the patient does not show any symptoms.

Right to self-determination: Right to **autonomy,** right to self-government.

Robust advantage principle: A part of Warren's ethical approach. It says that we should bias our decisions about allowing social and economic differences so as to provide a robust advantage to the least advantaged. This should be distinguished from John Rawls's **difference principle,** which is much more **egalitarian.**

Rule utilitarianism: The ethical theory that says the right action is the one that is done according to a set of rules that maximizes happiness and minimizes unhappiness if consistently followed.

Sanctity of Life principle: The view that it is wrong to kill human beings because human life is sacred. This principle is subject to various interpretations, e.g., it may protect only *innocent* human life; or it may prohibit only the intentional killing of (innocent) humans. We also consider a Kantian version: the sanctity of *rational* life.

Secondary quality: Roughly, powers of objects to produce certain sensations in us. Colours, tastes, and sounds, e.g., are commonly regarded as secondary qualities. Many philosophers take secondary qualities to be **dispositional properties.**

Situational ethic: The view that whether an act is right or wrong will depend on the particular situation.

Social contract theory: A type of ethical theory that takes a hypothetical agreement among a group of people under special constraints to be the source of the correct moral rules. Social contractarians differ in the details of their theory, but they share the fundamental belief that justified moral rules are the ones that rational individuals would agree to for their own benefit. See **original position** and **veil of ignorance.**

Soft paternalism: The interference with an **incompetent** person's liberty for his or her own good.

Sound argument: A valid **argument** where all of the **premises** are true.

Standard form: The form of an **argument** presented as a numbered list with the **premises** above a horizontal line and the **conclusion** below the horizontal line.

State of nature: A hypothetical time and place where there is no organized society, no recognized social rules, in which everyone is free to do as he or she pleases. This concept is a central part of many **social contract theories.**

Straw man: The **fallacy** of misrepresenting one's opponent's **argument** or view so that it is easily shown to be **unsound** or weak.

Stress incontinence: The inability of the bladder to retain urine under stress, usually because the bladder neck is weakened.

Strong inductive argument: An **inductive argument** where the **premises,** if true, make the **conclusion** probably true. The more support provided by the premises of an inductive argument, the stronger the argument.

Strong paternalism: The interference in a person's liberty for that person's own good, in order to prevent that person from attempting to realize irrational or mistaken goals.

Subjective truth: Truth dependent on whether a person happens to think, believe, or feel it is true. In morality, the view that the rightness or wrongness of actions is dependent on individuals' personal attitudes and feelings toward the actions makes moral truth subjective. This view is given the name *subjectivism.* E.g., a speaker's claim that abortion is wrong is true if and only if the speaker sincerely believes that abortion is wrong (or disapproves of abortion).

Substantial benefit rule: (a proposed **triage** rule) If a patient stands to benefit substantially from being treated first, while the patient ahead in the queue will not benefit substantially from being treated, then the patient who will benefit substantially should be treated first.

Substantive moral claim: A claim made directly about the moral status of acts, policies, persons, etc. Examples of substantive moral claims include "Jones is a bad person" and "**Involuntary euthanasia** is morally wrong."

Surface grammar: Superficial grammatical and idiomatic aspects of language that convey apparent meaning.

Sympathy metarule: See **human-sympathy metarule.**

The categorical imperative: Kant's test for determining whether a particular action is morally permissible or morally wrong. It comes in several forms, including the **universal law version** and the **humanity version.** See also **categorical imperative.**

Thing: in Kant's usage, "not a **rational being.**" Things are not capable of following both **hypothetical imperatives** and **categorical imperatives.**

Third parties: People other than the two main people in a situation. In this context, people other than the patient or the health care provider.

Thought experiment: An example developed to prove or to disprove a particular claim or **argument** or to persuade us of the plausibility of a thesis.

Thromboembolism: The obstruction of a blood vessel with particles carried by the blood from another site.

Triage: Sorting patients by degree of urgency in order to allocate treatment. See **CTAS.**

Trojan Horse: By analogy to the fabled statue of a horse in the siege of Troy, a device used to surreptitiously introduce something.

Two-tier health care: A system in which one tier or level is publicly funded and one tier is privately funded.

Universal care: Care that is provided to every citizen (and lawful resident) regardless of that individual's financial means.

Universal law: A principle that states that everyone follows a particular **maxim** all the time, as if it were a law of nature.

Universal law version of the categorical imperative: Kant's principle "Act only on those **maxims** that you can, at the same time, will as a **universal law.**"

Universalizability: A rule that has this feature can be applied to everyone in similar circumstances.

Unsound argument: An **argument** which either contains a false **premise,** or is logically **invalid,** or both.

Utilitarianism: An ethical theory that takes many forms, but in its classical formulation, as articulated by Jeremy Bentham and John Stuart Mill, is the view that right actions, laws, or policies promote the greatest amount of pleasure, or the least amount of pain, for all concerned.

Valid argument: An **argument** in which it is impossible for all of the **premises** to be true and the **conclusion** false. In other words, *if* all of the premises are true, the conclusion *must be* true.

Valid consent: Acceptable consent. When we speak here of valid consent, it means something different from "valid" as applied to **arguments.** See **valid argument.**

Veil of ignorance: A central feature of the **original position,** a barrier that prevents people from knowing any particular facts about themselves. For instance, they do not know their race, gender, class, natural abilities, religious convictions, specific values, goals in life, and so forth.

Virtue: A character trait needed for being a good person and living well. These traits include the moral virtues: e.g., courage, honesty, industriousness, trustworthiness, compassion, and loyalty. These are deep and stable character traits that dispose those who possess them to take certain actions and to have certain feelings. Honest people, for instance, are disposed to act honestly and to feel disapproval toward persons who are dishonest.

Virtue ethics: Roughly, an approach to ethics that focuses on *moral (virtuous) character,* rather than on principles of right action.

Voluntary active euthanasia (VAE): Active euthanasia on a **competent** person with that person's consent.

Voluntary euthanasia: Euthanasia on a **competent** person with that person's consent.

Voluntary passive euthanasia (VPE): Passive euthanasia on a **competent** person with that person's consent.

Weak inductive argument: An **inductive argument** where the **premises,** if true, provide little support for the **conclusion.**

Weak paternalism: The interference in a person's liberty for that person's own good, in order to prevent that person from behaving in ways that are likely to defeat his or her own goals.

Worst first: (a proposed **triage** rule) Treat the worst cases in the emergency department first.

Xenotransplantation: The transplantation of nonhuman organs into humans.

Zygote: A single diploid cell that results from the merging of a sperm and ovum through a process of fertilization. The developing organism, from the moment of conception until about the end of the eighth week is called an **embryo.** From that point until birth it is called a **fetus.**

INDEX